NUMERICAL METHODS FOR TWO-POINT BOUNDARY-VALUE PROBLEMS

A BLAISDELL BOOK IN NUMERICAL ANALYSIS
AND COMPUTER SCIENCE

CONSULTING EDITOR

Philip J. Davis, Brown University

NUMERICAL METHODS FOR TWO-POINT BOUNDARY-VALUE PROBLEMS

Herbert B. Keller

CALIFORNIA INSTITUTE OF TECHNOLOGY

BLAISDELL PUBLISHING COMPANY

A Division of Ginn and Company

WALTHAM, MASSACHUSETTS · TORONTO · LONDON

To the memory of my parents

LIBRARY OF CONGRESS CATALOG CARD NUMBER: 68-10871
PRINTED IN THE UNITED STATES OF AMERICA.

PREFACE

In this monograph we present a brief, elementary yet rigorous account of practical numerical methods for solving very general two-point boundary-value problems. Three techniques are studied in detail: initial value or "shooting" methods in Chapter 2, finite difference methods in Chapter 3, integral equation methods in Chapter 4. Each method is applied to nonlinear second-order problems, and the first two methods are applied to first-order systems of nonlinear equations. Sturm-Liouville eigenvalue problems are treated with all three techniques in Chapter 5. The application of shooting to generalized or nonlinear eigenvalue problems is also discussed in Chapter 5.

Initial-value methods are seldom advocated in the literature, but we find them extremely practical and theoretically powerful. A modification, called parallel shooting, is introduced to treat those "unstable" cases (with rapidly growing solutions) for which ordinary shooting may be inadequate. High-order accurate methods are stressed, and the well-developed theory of numerical methods for initial-value problems is employed to obtain corresponding results for boundary-value problems. Continuity techniques (related to imbedding) are discussed and illustrated in the examples.

To help maintain an elementary level, we include in Chapter 1 brief accounts of some of the basic prerequisites: existence theorems for initial-value and two-point boundary-value problems, numerical methods for initial-value problems and iterative methods for solving nonlinear systems. In addition, several other areas of numerical analysis enter our study, such as numerical quadrature, eigenvalue-eigenvector calculation, and solution of linear algebraic systems. Since so many diverse numerical procedures play an important role, the subject matter of this monograph is useful in motivating, introducing, and/or reviewing more general studies in numerical analysis. The level of presentation is such that the text could be used by well-prepared undergraduate mathematics students. Advanced calculus, basic numerical analysis, some ordinary differential equations, and a smattering of linear algebra are assumed.

Many of the problems contain extensions of the text material and so should at least be read, if not worked out. More difficult problems are starred.

It is a pleasure to acknowledge the helpful advice received from Professor Eugene Isaacson and Mr. Richard Swenson, both of whom read the entire manuscript. The computations for the examples were accomplished by the superior work of W. H. Mitchell at Caltech and J. Steadman at the Courant Institute, N.Y.U. The typing was done by Miss Connie Engle in her usual flawless manner.

Finally, the support of the U.S. Army Research Office (Durham) and the U.S. Atomic Energy Commission is gratefully acknowledged.

H. B. K.

CONTENTS

CHAPTER 1

INTRODUCTION

1.1 *Initial-Value Problems*

The theory of boundary-value problems for ordinary differential equations relies rather heavily on initial-value problems. Even more significant for the subject of this monograph is the fact that some of the most generally applicable numerical methods for solving boundary-value problems employ initial-value problems. Thus we must assume that the reader is somewhat familiar with the existence and uniqueness theory of, as well as numerical methods for solving, initial-value problems. We shall review here and in Section 1.3 some of the basic results required.

Since every nth-order ordinary differential equation can be replaced by an equivalent system of n first-order equations, we confine our attention to first-order systems of the form

$$\mathbf{u}' = \mathbf{f}(x; \mathbf{u}).$$

Here $\mathbf{u} \equiv (u_1, u_2, \ldots, u_n)^T$ is an n-dimensional column vector with the dependent variables $u_k(x)$ as components; we say that $\mathbf{u}(x)$ is a vector-valued function; $\mathbf{f}(x; \mathbf{u})$ is vector-valued with components $f_k(x, u_1, u_2, \ldots, u_n)$, which are functions of the $n + 1$ variables $(x; \mathbf{u})$. An initial-value problem for the above system is obtained by prescribing at some point, say $x = a$, the value of $\mathbf{u}$, say

$$\mathbf{u}(a) = \boldsymbol{\alpha}.$$

The existence, uniqueness, and continuity properties of the solutions of such problems depend on the continuity or smoothness properties of the function $\mathbf{f}$ in a neighborhood of the initial point $(a; \boldsymbol{\alpha})$. We shall use as a measure of distance between two points in n-space the *maximum norm*

$$|\mathbf{u} - \mathbf{v}| \equiv \max_{1 \le k \le n} |u_k - v_k|.$$

However, all results are equally valid if we employ the *Euclidean norm*

$$|\mathbf{u} - \mathbf{v}|_2 \equiv [(u_1 - v_1)^2 + (u_2 - v_2)^2 + \cdots + (u_n - v_n)^2]^{1/2}.$$

One of the basic results can now be stated as follows.

THEOREM 1.1.1. *Let the function* $\mathbf{f}(x; \mathbf{u})$ *be continuous on the infinite strip*

$$R: a \leq x \leq b, \qquad |\mathbf{u}| < \infty$$

and satisfy there a Lipschitz condition in $\mathbf{u}$ *with constant K, uniformly in x; that is,*

$$|\mathbf{f}(x; \mathbf{u}) - \mathbf{f}(x; \mathbf{v})| \leq K|\mathbf{u} - \mathbf{v}| \qquad \textit{for all} \quad (x; \mathbf{u}) \quad \textit{and} \quad (x; \mathbf{v}) \in R.$$

Then

(a) *the initial-value problem*

$$\mathbf{u}' = \mathbf{f}(x; \mathbf{u}), \qquad \mathbf{u}(a) = \boldsymbol{\alpha} \tag{1.1.1}$$

has a unique solution $\mathbf{u} = \mathbf{u}(x; \boldsymbol{\alpha})$ *defined on the interval*

$$[a, b] \equiv \{x \mid a \leq x \leq b\};$$

(*b*) *this solution is Lipschitz-continuous in* $\boldsymbol{\alpha}$, *uniformly in x; in fact we have*

$$|\mathbf{u}(x; \boldsymbol{\alpha}) - \mathbf{u}(x; \boldsymbol{\beta})| \leq e^{K(x-a)}|\boldsymbol{\alpha} - \boldsymbol{\beta}| \qquad \textit{for all} \quad (x; \boldsymbol{\alpha}) \quad \textit{and} \quad (x; \boldsymbol{\beta}) \in R.$$

Proof. We merely sketch the proof; more details can be found in Ince (1944), pp. 62–72. If a solution exists, we obtain from (1.1.1) by integration

$$\mathbf{u}(x) = \boldsymbol{\alpha} + \int_a^x \mathbf{f}(\xi; \mathbf{u}(\xi))\, d\xi.$$

Conversely, if $\mathbf{u}(x)$ is continuous and satisfies this integral equation, it is differentiable and hence, by differentiation, satisfies (1.1.1). We now construct a solution of this integral equation by means of the *Picard iteration procedure*

$$\mathbf{u}^{(0)}(x) \equiv \boldsymbol{\alpha},$$

$$\mathbf{u}^{(\nu+1)}(x) = \boldsymbol{\alpha} + \int_a^x \mathbf{f}(\xi; \mathbf{u}^{(\nu)}(\xi))\, d\xi, \qquad \nu = 0, 1, \ldots.$$

From the Lipschitz continuity of $\mathbf{f}(x; \mathbf{u})$ we have

$$|\mathbf{u}^{(\nu+1)}(x) - \mathbf{u}^{(\nu)}(x)| \leq \int_a^x K|\mathbf{u}^{(\nu)}(\xi) - \mathbf{u}^{(\nu-1)}(\xi)|\, d\xi, \qquad \nu = 1, 2, \ldots.$$

Then, by induction, with $|f(x; \boldsymbol{\alpha})| \leq M$ on $[a, b]$, it follows that

$$|\mathbf{u}^{(\nu+1)}(x) - \mathbf{u}^{(\nu)}(x)| \leq \frac{M}{K} \frac{(K[x - a])^{\nu+1}}{(\nu + 1)!}.$$

Now the sequence of continuous functions $\{\mathbf{u}^{(\nu)}(x)\}$ can be shown to converge uniformly on $[a, b]$ since

$$\mathbf{u}^{(\nu+1)}(x) = \mathbf{u}^0 + \sum_{\mu=0}^{\nu} [\mathbf{u}^{(\mu+1)}(x) - \mathbf{u}^{(\mu)}(x)].$$

The limiting function clearly satisfies the integral equation and hence (1.1.1); thus, existence is established for any $\boldsymbol{\alpha}$.

The uniqueness of this solution will follow from the continuity of $\mathbf{u}(x, \boldsymbol{\beta})$ by letting $\boldsymbol{\beta} \to \boldsymbol{\alpha}$.

To demonstrate (b) we form

$$[\mathbf{u}(x; \boldsymbol{\alpha}) - \mathbf{u}(x; \boldsymbol{\beta})] = [\boldsymbol{\alpha} - \boldsymbol{\beta}] + \int_a^x [\mathbf{f}(\xi; \mathbf{u}(\xi; \boldsymbol{\alpha})) - \mathbf{f}(\xi; \mathbf{u}(\xi; \boldsymbol{\beta}))]\, d\xi.$$

Then, by the Lipschitz continuity of $\mathbf{f}$, it follows that

$$|\mathbf{u}(x; \boldsymbol{\alpha}) - \mathbf{u}(x; \boldsymbol{\beta})| \leq |\boldsymbol{\alpha} - \boldsymbol{\beta}| + K \int_a^x |\mathbf{u}(\xi; \boldsymbol{\alpha}) - \mathbf{u}(\xi; \boldsymbol{\beta})|\, d\xi.$$

Calling

$$E(x) \equiv \int_a^x |\mathbf{u}(\xi; \boldsymbol{\alpha}) - \mathbf{u}(\xi; \boldsymbol{\beta})|\, d\xi,$$

we may write the above inequality as

$$E'(x) - KE(x) \leq |\boldsymbol{\alpha} - \boldsymbol{\beta}|.$$

This differential inequality may be "solved" by multiplying by the integrating factor $e^{-K(x-a)}$ and integrating over $[a, x]$ to get

$$E(x) \leq \frac{|\boldsymbol{\alpha} - \boldsymbol{\beta}|}{K} [e^{K(x-a)} - 1].$$

The original inequality now yields (b). ▌

In many problems of interest the function $\mathbf{f}(x; \mathbf{u})$ does not have the required continuity properties in the infinite strip R but rather in a finite domain R_B: $a \leq x \leq b$, $|\mathbf{u} - \boldsymbol{\alpha}| \leq B$. In this case a similar theorem holds but the solution may exist only in some smaller interval $a \leq x \leq b_0 \equiv \min(b, B/M)$, *ibid.* (See Problems 1.1.4 and 1.1.5 for other, more powerful, generalizations.)

With little additional effort the result in Theorem 1.1.1 can be strengthened to show that in fact the solution $\mathbf{u}(x; \boldsymbol{\alpha})$ is uniformly differentiable with respect to the initial values α_k, $k = 1, 2, \ldots, n$. However, for some of our applications we require a still stronger result which shows that each derivative $\partial\mathbf{u}(x; \boldsymbol{\alpha})/\partial\alpha_k$ is the solution of a specific initial-value problem for a linear system of ordinary differential equations. This is the content of the following theorem.

THEOREM 1.1.2. *In addition to the hypothesis of Theorem* 1.1.1 *let the Jacobian of* $\mathbf{f}$ *with respect to* $\mathbf{u}$ *have continuous elements on* R; *that is, the nth-order matrix*

$$F(x; \mathbf{u}) \equiv \frac{\partial \mathbf{f}(x; \mathbf{u})}{\partial \mathbf{u}} = \left(\frac{\partial f_i(x; \mathbf{u})}{\partial u_j} \right)$$

is continuous on R. Then for any $\boldsymbol{\alpha}$ *the solution* $\mathbf{u}(x; \boldsymbol{\alpha})$ *of* (1.1.1) *is continuously differentiable with respect to* α_k, $k = 1, 2, \ldots, n$. *In fact, the derivative* $\partial \mathbf{u}(x; \boldsymbol{\alpha})/\partial \alpha_k \equiv \boldsymbol{\xi}^{(k)}(x)$ *is the solution, on* $[a, b]$, *of the linear system*

$$\frac{d}{dx} \boldsymbol{\xi}(x) = F(x; \mathbf{u}(x; \boldsymbol{\alpha}))\boldsymbol{\xi}(x), \tag{1.1.2a}$$

subject to the initial condition

$$\boldsymbol{\xi}(a) = \mathbf{e}^{(k)}. \tag{1.1.2b}$$

(Here $\mathbf{e}^{(k)} \equiv (0, \ldots, 0, 1, 0, \ldots, 0)^T$ is the kth unit vector in n-space.)

Proof. Again we sketch the proof; details can be found in Birkhoff and Rota (1962), pp. 123–124. For arbitrarily small $|h| > 0$ we define the difference quotient

$$\boldsymbol{\eta}(x, h) \equiv \frac{\mathbf{u}(x; \boldsymbol{\alpha} + h\mathbf{e}^{(k)}) - \mathbf{u}(x; \boldsymbol{\alpha})}{h}$$

in terms of the indicated solutions of the initial-value problems (1.1.1) (with initial data $\boldsymbol{\alpha}$ and $\boldsymbol{\alpha} + h\mathbf{e}^{(k)}$). Then it follows that

$$\begin{aligned} \frac{d}{dx} \boldsymbol{\eta}(x, h) &= \frac{1}{h} [\mathbf{f}(x; \mathbf{u} + h\boldsymbol{\eta}) - \mathbf{f}(x; \mathbf{u})] \\ &= F(x; \mathbf{u}(x; \boldsymbol{\alpha}))\boldsymbol{\eta}(x, h) + \boldsymbol{\delta}(x, h)|\boldsymbol{\eta}(x, h)|, \end{aligned}$$

where we have used Taylor's theorem and $|\boldsymbol{\delta}| \to 0$ as $h \to 0$. But by (b) of Theorem 1.1.1, $|\boldsymbol{\eta}|$ must be bounded as $h \to 0$ and so the above equation formally tends to Equation (1.1.2a). We also note that $\boldsymbol{\eta}(a, h) = \mathbf{e}^{(k)}$ for all $|h| \geq 0$. Since the system (1.1.2a) is linear, we can show that the solution $\boldsymbol{\eta}(x, h)$ of the above initial-value problem converges, as $h \to 0$, to the solution of (1.1.2). That the solution $\boldsymbol{\xi}(x) \equiv \boldsymbol{\xi}(x; \boldsymbol{\alpha})$ of (1.1.2) is continuous in $\boldsymbol{\alpha}$ follows easily as in the proof of Theorem 1.1.1. ∎

The system (1.1.2a) is known as the *variational equation* for the system $\mathbf{u}' = \mathbf{f}(x; \mathbf{u})$. We note that it can be obtained formally by assuming $\mathbf{u}$ to depend upon some parameter, say c, differentiating with respect to this parameter and setting $\partial \mathbf{u}/\partial c \equiv \boldsymbol{\xi}$. If this is done to both the system and the initial condition in (1.1.1), using $c = \alpha_k$ as a parameter, we obtain the *variational problem* (1.1.2).

For some of our later studies of eigenvalue problems, we shall require additional results for initial-value problems which contain a parameter in the equations, that is, problems of the form

$$\mathbf{u}' = \mathbf{f}(\lambda, x; \mathbf{u}), \qquad \mathbf{u}(a) = \boldsymbol{\alpha}, \tag{1.1.3}$$

where $\mathbf{f}$ is now a vector-valued function of the $n + 2$ variables $(\lambda, x; \mathbf{u})$. If for all λ in $\lambda_* \leq \lambda \leq \lambda^*$ the hypothesis of Theorem 1.1.1 is satisfied, and in addition $\mathbf{f}(\lambda, x; \mathbf{u})$ depends Lipschitz-continuously on λ, uniformly for $(x; \mathbf{u}) \in R$, then the initial-value problem (1.1.3) has a unique solution, $\mathbf{u}(\lambda, x)$, which is Lipschitz-continuous in λ. Again, this can be strengthened to continuous differentiability of the solution with respect to λ. But if $\mathbf{g}(\lambda, x; \mathbf{u}) \equiv \partial\mathbf{f}(\lambda, x; \mathbf{u})/\partial\lambda$ and $F(\lambda, x; \mathbf{u}) \equiv \partial\mathbf{f}(\lambda, x; \mathbf{u})/\partial\mathbf{u}$ are continuous, we can show that $\boldsymbol{\xi}(x) \equiv \partial\mathbf{u}(\lambda, x)/\partial\lambda$ is a solution of the linear variational problem

$$\frac{d}{dx}\boldsymbol{\xi} = F(\lambda, x; \mathbf{u}(\lambda, x))\boldsymbol{\xi} + \mathbf{g}(\lambda, x; \mathbf{u}(\lambda, x)), \qquad \boldsymbol{\xi}(a) = 0. \tag{1.1.4}$$

Note that this problem is obtained by formal differentiation of the initial-value problem (1.1.3). The initial condition in the variational problem (1.1.4) is homogeneous, while the variational equation is not; this is just the reverse of the situation in the variational problem (1.1.2).

THEOREM 1.1.3. *Let* $\mathbf{f}(\lambda, x; \mathbf{u})$ *satisfy the hypothesis of Theorem* 1.1.1 *for all* λ *in* $\lambda_* \leq \lambda \leq \lambda^*$. *In addition let* $\mathbf{g}(\lambda, x; \mathbf{u}) \equiv \partial\mathbf{f}(\lambda, x; \mathbf{u})/\partial\lambda$ *and the Jacobian matrix*

$$F(\lambda, x; \mathbf{u}) \equiv \frac{\partial\mathbf{f}(\lambda, x; \mathbf{u})}{\partial\mathbf{u}} \equiv \left(\frac{\partial f_i(\lambda, x; \mathbf{u})}{\partial u_j}\right)$$

be continuous. Then for any λ *in* (λ_*, λ^*) *the solution* $\mathbf{u}(\lambda; x)$ *of* (1.1.3) *is continuously differentiable with respect to* λ. *The derivative* $\partial\mathbf{u}(\lambda; \mathbf{x})/\partial\lambda \equiv \boldsymbol{\xi}(\lambda; x)$ *is the solution on* $[a, b]$ *of the variational problem* (1.1.4).

Proof. The proof is almost identical to that of Theorem 1.1.2. [See Coddington and Levinson (1955), pp. 29–31.] ▮

Problems

1.1.1 Show that, in the Euclidean norm, with $b > a$, we have

$$\left\|\int_a^b \mathbf{f}(x)\,dx\right\|_2 \leq \int_a^b \|\mathbf{f}(x)\|_2\,dx.$$

[HINT: Use the triangle inequality, that is, $\|\mathbf{f} + \mathbf{g}\|_2 \leq \|\mathbf{f}\|_2 + \|\mathbf{g}\|_2$ (which follows from the Schwarz inequality $|\mathbf{f}\cdot\mathbf{g}| \leq \|\mathbf{f}\|_2\|\mathbf{g}\|_2$) in the Riemann sums defining the integral.]

Note that in the maximum norm this result follows trivially from its scalar form.

1.1.2 For each $i = 1, 2, \ldots, n$, let the scalar component $f_i(x; \mathbf{u})$ of $\mathbf{f}(x; \mathbf{u})$ satisfy a uniform Lipschitz condition in each component u_j of $\mathbf{u}$ with constant K_{ij}; that is, let

$$|f_i(x; u_1, \ldots, u_j, \ldots, u_n) - f_i(x; u_1, \ldots, v_j, \ldots, u_n)| < K_{ij}|u_j - v_j|.$$

Then show that $\mathbf{f}(x; \mathbf{u})$ is Lipschitz in $\mathbf{u}$ with constant

$$K = \left(\sum_{i=1}^{n} \sum_{j=1}^{n} K_{ij}^2\right)^{1/2}$$

if we use the Euclidean norm. With the maximum norm, show that the Lipschitz constant for $\mathbf{f}$ may be taken as

$$K = n \max_{i,j} K_{ij}.$$

1.1.3 Show that the solution $\mathbf{u}(\lambda, x)$ of (1.1.3) satisfies

$$|\mathbf{u}(\lambda, x) - \mathbf{u}(\mu, x)| \leq K_1(b - a)e^{K_2(b-a)}|\lambda - \mu|, \qquad a \leq x \leq b,$$

where K_1 and K_2 are the Lipschitz constants for $\mathbf{f}(\lambda, x; \mathbf{u})$ in λ and $\mathbf{u}$, respectively.

1.1.4* Prove the following.

THEOREM 1.1.4. *Let an n-vector* $\boldsymbol{\alpha}_0$ *and positive numbers* ρ, K, *and* M *be given such that, with* $R_{\rho,M}(\boldsymbol{\alpha}_0) \equiv \{(x, \mathbf{u}) \mid |\mathbf{u} - \boldsymbol{\alpha}_0| \leq \rho + M(x - a), a \leq x \leq b\}$,

(a) $\mathbf{f}(x, \mathbf{u})$ *is continuous in* $R_{\rho,M}(\boldsymbol{\alpha}_0)$,
(b) $|\mathbf{f}(x, \mathbf{u})| \leq M$ *for all* $(x, \mathbf{u}) \in R_{\rho,M}(\boldsymbol{\alpha}_0)$,
(c) $|\mathbf{f}(x, \mathbf{u}) - f(x, \mathbf{v})| \leq K|\mathbf{u} - \mathbf{v}|$ *for all* $(x, \mathbf{u})$ *and* $(x, \mathbf{v}) \in R_{\rho,M}(\boldsymbol{\alpha}_0)$.

Then the initial-value problem

$$\mathbf{u}' = \mathbf{f}(x, \mathbf{u}), \qquad \mathbf{u}(a) = \boldsymbol{\alpha} \tag{$*$}$$

has a unique solution $\mathbf{u} = \mathbf{u}(\boldsymbol{\alpha}, x)$ *on* $[a, b]$ *for each*

$$\boldsymbol{\alpha} \in N_\rho(\boldsymbol{\alpha}_0) \equiv \{\boldsymbol{\alpha} \mid |\boldsymbol{\alpha} - \boldsymbol{\alpha}_0| \leq \rho\}.$$

The solution is Lipschitz-continuous in $\boldsymbol{\alpha}$; *more precisely*,

$$|u(\boldsymbol{\alpha}, x) - u(\boldsymbol{\beta}, x)| \leq e^{K|x-a|}|\boldsymbol{\alpha} - \boldsymbol{\beta}|$$

for all $x \in [a, b]$ *and all* $\boldsymbol{\alpha}$ *and* $\boldsymbol{\beta} \in N_\rho(\boldsymbol{\alpha}_0)$.

[HINT: Use the Picard method, showing by induction that the iterates $\mathbf{u}_n(x)$ are all such that $(x, \mathbf{u}_n(x)) \in R_{\rho,M}(\boldsymbol{\alpha}_0)$ for $x \in [a, b]$. The proof then follows as in Theorem 1.1.1.]

1.1.5* Replace condition (c) above by the requirement that $\partial\mathbf{f}(x, \mathbf{u})/\partial\mathbf{u}$ be continuous on $R_{\rho,M}(\boldsymbol{\alpha}_0)$ and then show that the solutions $\mathbf{u}(\boldsymbol{\alpha}, x)$ of $(*)$ are continuously differentiable with respect to $\boldsymbol{\alpha}$ in the *open* sphere $|\boldsymbol{\alpha} - \boldsymbol{\alpha}_0| < \rho$; that is, $\partial\mathbf{u}(\boldsymbol{\alpha}, x)/\partial\boldsymbol{\alpha}$ is continuous in $\boldsymbol{\alpha}$ for $\boldsymbol{\alpha}$ in the open sphere and $x \in [a, b]$.

[HINT: The proof of differentiability follows that of Theorems 1.1.2 and 1.1.4. Using the variational problem $V' = [\partial\mathbf{f}(x, \mathbf{u}(\boldsymbol{\alpha}, x))/\partial\mathbf{u}]V$, $V(a) = I$ satisfied by $V(\boldsymbol{\alpha}, x) \equiv \partial\mathbf{u}(\boldsymbol{\alpha}, x)/\partial\boldsymbol{\alpha}$ and the continuity of $\partial\mathbf{f}/\partial\mathbf{u}$, then show that $V(\boldsymbol{\alpha}, x)$ is continuous in $\boldsymbol{\alpha}$.]

1.2 Two-Point Boundary-Value Problems

A boundary-value problem for an ordinary differential equation (or system of equations) is obtained by requiring that the dependent variable (or variables) satisfy subsidiary conditions at two or more distinct points. By means of Theorem 1.1.1 we know that a unique solution of an nth-order equation is determined (for a very large class of equations) by specifying n conditions at one point (that is, for initial-value problems). However, with a total of n boundary conditions imposed at more than one point it is possible that a very smooth nth-order equation has many solutions or even no solution. Thus, as we may expect, the existence and uniqueness theory for boundary-value problems is considerably more complicated and less thoroughly developed than that for initial-value problems. When the boundary conditions are imposed at only two points, which is the usual case in applications, a simple theory can be developed for many special classes of equations and systems of equations. This existence and uniqueness theory plays a role in devising and analyzing numerical methods for solving boundary-value problems, and therefore we study some of its aspects here.

Let us consider first an important class of boundary-value problems in which the solution, $y(x)$, of a second-order equation

$$y'' = f(x, y, y') \tag{1.2.1a}$$

is required to satisfy at two distinct points relations of the form

$$\begin{aligned} a_0 y(a) - a_1 y'(a) &= \alpha, \qquad |a_0| + |a_1| \neq 0; \\ b_0 y(b) + b_1 y'(b) &= \beta, \qquad |b_0| + |b_1| \neq 0. \end{aligned} \tag{1.2.1b}$$

The solution is sought on the interval $[a, b] \equiv \{x \mid a \leq x \leq b\}$.

A formal approach to the exact solution of this problem is obtained by considering a related *initial*-value problem, say

$$u'' = f(x, u, u'), \tag{1.2.2a}$$

$$a_0 u(a) - a_1 u'(a) = \alpha, \qquad c_0 u(a) - c_1 u'(a) = s. \tag{1.2.2b}$$

The second initial condition is to be independent of the first. This is assured if $a_1c_0 - a_0c_1 \neq 0$. Without loss in generality we require that c_0 and c_1 be chosen such that

$$a_1c_0 - a_0c_1 = 1. \tag{1.2.2c}$$

With c_0 and c_1 fixed in this manner, we denote the solution of (1.2.2) by

$$u = u(x; s),$$

to focus attention on its dependence on s. Evaluating the solution at $x = b$, we seek a value of s for which

$$\phi(s) \equiv b_0u(b; s) + b_1u'(b; s) - \beta = 0. \tag{1.2.3}$$

With b and β fixed Equation (1.2.3) is, in general, a transcendental equation in s. If $s = s^*$ is a root of this equation, we then expect the function

$$y(x) \equiv u(x; s^*)$$

to be a solution of the boundary-value problem (1.2.1). This is true in many cases, and in fact all solutions of (1.2.1) can frequently be determined in this way. To be precise, we have the following.

THEOREM 1.2.1. *Let the function* $f(x, u_1, u_2)$ *be continuous on*

$$R\colon a \le x \le b, \qquad u_1^2 + u_2^2 < \infty,$$

and satisfy there a uniform Lipschitz condition in u_1 *and* u_2. *Then the boundary-value problem* (1.2.1) *has as many solutions as there are distinct roots,* $s = s^{(\nu)}$, *of Equation* (1.2.3). *The solutions of* (1.2.1) *are*

$$y(x) = y^{(\nu)}(x) \equiv u(x; s^{(\nu)});$$

that is, the solutions of the initial-value problem (1.2.2) *with initial data* $s = s^{(\nu)}$.

Proof. Introducing the new dependent variables $u_1(x) \equiv u(x)$ and $u_2(x) \equiv u'(x)$, the initial-value problem (1.2.2) can be written as

$$\begin{aligned} u_1' &= u_2, \qquad & u_1(a) &= a_1s - c_1\alpha, \\ u_2' &= f(x, u_1, u_2), \qquad & u_2(a) &= a_0s - c_0\alpha. \end{aligned} \tag{1.2.4}$$

Now with the notation

$$\mathbf{u} \equiv \begin{pmatrix} u_1 \\ u_2 \end{pmatrix}, \qquad \mathbf{f}(x; \mathbf{u}) \equiv \begin{pmatrix} u_2 \\ f(x, u_1, u_2) \end{pmatrix}, \qquad \boldsymbol{\alpha} \equiv \begin{pmatrix} a_1s - c_1\alpha \\ a_0s - c_0\alpha \end{pmatrix},$$

we can apply Theorem 1.1.1, since each component of **f**, and hence **f** itself, is Lipschitz-continuous on R (see Problem 1.1.2). Thus the initial-value problem (1.2.2), has a unique solution, $u_1(x) = u(x; s)$, which exists on $a \le x \le b$.

But clearly, if $\phi(s) = 0$ for some s, then this solution is also a solution of the boundary-value problem (1.2.1). If $s^{(i)}$ and $s^{(j)}$ are distinct roots of Equation (1.2.3), then $u(x; s^{(i)}) \not\equiv u(x; s^{(j)})$, by the uniqueness, so that each distinct root of Equation (1.2.3) yields a distinct solution of (1.2.1).

Now suppose $y(x)$ is a solution of (1.2.1). Then it is also a solution of the initial-value problem (1.2.2) with the parameter value $s = c_0 y(a) - c_1 y'(a)$. But this value of s must satisfy Equation (1.2.3). Thus every solution of the boundary-value problem yields a root of Equation (1.2.3). ∎

By means of this theorem the problem of solving a boundary-value problem is "reduced" to that of finding the root, or roots, of an (in general, transcendental) equation. A very effective class of numerical methods, which we call *initial-value or shooting methods*, is based on this equivalence. As we shall see, more general boundary-value problems than (1.2.1) can be reduced in this way to solving systems of (transcendental) equations.

There is an important class of problems for which we can be assured that Equation (1.2.3) has a unique root. The existence and uniqueness theory for the corresponding boundary-value problems is then settled.

THEOREM 1.2.2. *Let the function $f(x, u_1, u_2)$ in* (1.2.1a) *satisfy the hypothesis of Theorem* 1.2.1 *and have continuous derivatives on R which satisfy, for some positive constant M,*

$$\frac{\partial f}{\partial u_1} > 0, \qquad \left|\frac{\partial f}{\partial u_2}\right| \le M.$$

Let the coefficients in (1.2.1b) *satisfy*

$$a_0 a_1 \ge 0, \qquad b_0 b_1 \ge 0, \qquad |a_0| + |b_0| \ne 0.$$

Then the boundary-value problem (1.2.1) *has a unique solution.*

Proof. Since Theorem 1.2.1 is applicable, we need only show that Equation (1.2.3) has a unique root. By the assumed continuity of the derivatives of f it easily follows, from the formulation (1.2.4), that Theorem 1.1.2 is also applicable. Thus let $u(x; s)$ be the solution of the initial-value problem (1.2.2) and define $\xi(x) \equiv \partial u(x; s)/\partial s$. Then $\xi(x)$ is the solution, on $[a, b]$, of the variational equation

$$\xi'' = p(x)\xi' + q(x)\xi,$$

subject to the initial conditions

$$\xi(a) = a_1, \qquad \xi'(a) = a_0.$$

Here we have introduced

$$q(x) \equiv \frac{\partial f(x, u(x; s), u'(x; s))}{\partial u_1}, \qquad p(x) \equiv \frac{\partial f(x, u(x; s), u'(x; s))}{\partial u_2}.$$

The solution $\xi(x)$ of the above variational problem has a continuous second derivative and is nonzero in some arbitrarily small interval $a < x \leq a + \varepsilon$, by virtue of the initial conditions (we recall that $|a_0| + |a_1| \neq 0$). We shall show that $\xi(x)$ is also nonzero in $a < x \leq b$. With no loss in generality, we may assume that $a_0 \geq 0$ and $a_1 \geq 0$ since $a_0 a_1 \geq 0$ and the variational problem is linear. Then we will show that $\xi(x)$ is positive in $a < x \leq b$. If this is not true, say $\xi(x) \leq 0$ for some x_* in $a < x \leq b$, then $\xi(x)$ must have a positive maximum at some point x_0 in $a \leq x_0 < x_*$. However, the maximum cannot be at $x_0 = a$ if $a_0 \neq 0$, since then $\xi'(a) > 0$. For $a_0 = 0$, the variational equation and $\xi(a) = a_1$ imply $\xi''(a) = q(a)a_1 > 0$ and so the maximum is not at $x_0 = a$ in this case either. Hence we have $a < x_0 < x^*$ and at such an interior maximum by the continuity properties of $\xi(x)$,

$$\xi(x_0) > 0, \qquad \xi'(x_0) = 0, \qquad \xi''(x_0) \leq 0.$$

But the variational equation at this point yields, since $q > 0$,

$$\xi''(x_0) = q(x_0)\xi(x_0) > 0.$$

The contradiction implies that $\xi(x) > 0$ on $a < x \leq b$.

From this result it follows that $q(x)\xi(x) > 0$ on $a < x \leq b$, and the variational equation yields the differential inequality

$$\xi''(x) > p(x)\xi'(x), \qquad a < x \leq b.$$

We may "solve" this inequality by the same procedure used in the proof of Theorem 1.1.1. Thus we multiply through by the integrating factor

$$\exp\left[-\int_a^x p(t)\,dt\right]$$

(which, since $|p| \leq M$, must be positive), to get

$$\left\{\exp\left[-\int_a^x p(t)\,dt\right]\xi'(x)\right\}' > 0.$$

Now integrating the above inequality over $[a, x]$ we get, on recalling that $\xi'(a) = a_0$,

$$\xi'(x) > a_0 \exp\left[\int_a^x p(t)\,dt\right].$$

Another integration and application of $\xi(a) = a_1$ gives

$$\xi(x) > a_1 + a_0 \int_a^x \exp\left[\int_a^t p(t')\,dt'\right] dt, \qquad a < x \leq b.$$

But, since $p \geq -M$, it follows that

$$\exp\left[\int_a^t p(t')\,dt'\right] > e^{-M(t-a)}$$

and, using this, we obtain finally

$$\begin{aligned}\xi'(x) &= \frac{\partial u'(x;s)}{\partial s} > a_0 e^{-M(x-a)} \geq 0, \\ & \qquad\qquad\qquad\qquad\qquad\qquad\qquad\qquad a < x \leq b. \quad (1.2.5) \\ \xi(x) &= \frac{\partial u(x;s)}{\partial s} > a_1 + a_0\left(\frac{1 - e^{-M(x-a)}}{M}\right) > 0,\end{aligned}$$

With no difficulty it can be seen that for the case in which $a_0 \leq 0$ and $a_1 \leq 0$, the inequality signs in Equation (1.2.5) need only be reversed.

In particular, then, setting $x = b$, the function $u(b; s)$ is a monotone function of s with derivative bounded away from zero for any value of a_0. The same is true of $u'(b; s)$ if $a_0 \neq 0$; if $a_0 = 0$, it is not bounded away from zero. But since b_0 and b_1 do not both vanish or have opposite signs, and $b_0 \neq 0$ if $a_0 = 0$, the function $\phi(s)$ in Equation (1.2.3) must have a derivative of one sign which *is* bounded away from zero for all a_0. Such a function takes on each real value once and only once, and hence $\phi(s) = 0$ has a unique root. ▮

We have not sought the weakest possible conditions in the above theorems. It is not difficult to replace $|p| \equiv |\partial f/\partial u_2| \leq M$ by a less-stringent condition requiring only boundedness from above of integrals of p or to relax $q \equiv \partial f/\partial u_1 > 0$ by allowing $q \geq 0$ in some cases (see Problem 1.2.3). The proof can also be extended to apply to more general boundary conditions (see Problems 1.2.5 and 1.2.6). M. Lees (1961) proves existence and uniqueness for the special case of problem (1.2.1) with $a_1 = b_1 = 0$ under much weaker conditions on $f(x, y, y')$.

A very important special case of Theorem 1.2.2 occurs when the function $f(x, u_1, u_2)$ is linear in u_1 and u_2, that is, for linear second-order boundary-value problems. We state this result as follows.

COROLLARY. *Let the functions $p(x)$, $q(x)$, and $r(x)$ be continuous on $[a, b]$ with*

$$q(x) > 0, \qquad a \leq x \leq b.$$

Let the constants a_0, a_1, b_0, and b_1 satisfy

$$\begin{aligned} a_0 a_1 \geq 0, &\qquad |a_0| + |a_1| \neq 0, \\ & \qquad\qquad\qquad\qquad |a_0| + |b_0| \neq 0. \\ b_0 b_1 \geq 0, &\qquad |b_0| + |b_1| \neq 0, \end{aligned}$$

Then the boundary-value problem

$$Ly \equiv -y'' + p(x)y' + q(x)y = r(x), \qquad a < x < b, \qquad (1.2.6a)$$

$$a_0 y(a) - a_1 y'(a) = \alpha, \qquad b_0 y(b) + b_1 y'(b) = \beta \qquad (1.2.6b)$$

has a unique solution for each α, β.

Proof. Writing Equation (1.2.6a) in the form of Equation (1.2.1a) we see that $\partial f/\partial u_1 = q(x)$ and $\partial f/\partial u_2 = p(x)$. Then, since a function continuous on a closed interval is bounded there, $|p(x)| \le M$ for some $M > 0$, and Theorem 1.2.2 applies. ▮

There is a more general result concerning the solution of linear boundary-value problems which we state as follows.

THEOREM 1.2.3. *Let $p(x)$, $q(x)$, and $r(x)$ be continuous on $[a, b]$. Then for any α and β the following mutually-exclusive alternatives hold: either the boundary-value problem*

$$Ly \equiv -y'' + p(x)y' + q(x)y = r(x), \qquad y(a) = \alpha,\ y(b) = \beta, \quad (1.2.7)$$

has a unique solution, or else the corresponding homogeneous boundary-value problem,

$$Ly = 0; \qquad y(a) = y(b) = 0, \quad (1.2.8)$$

has a nontrivial solution [*that is, problem* (1.2.7) *has a unique solution if and only if problem* (1.2.8) *has only the trivial solution, $y \equiv 0$*].

Proof. We define two functions $y^{(1)}(x)$ and $y^{(2)}(x)$ as solutions of the respective initial value problems

$$Ly^{(1)}(x) = r(x), \qquad y^{(1)}(a) = \alpha, \qquad y^{(1)\prime}(a) = 0;$$
$$Ly^{(2)}(x) = 0, \qquad y^{(2)}(a) = 0, \qquad y^{(2)\prime}(a) = 1.$$

From the continuity properties of p, q, and r we are assured by Theorem 1.1.1 that unique solutions of these initial-value problems exist on $[a, b]$. Now form the function

$$u(x; s) \equiv y^{(1)}(x) + sy^{(2)}(x)$$

and seek s such that

$$y(b; s) \equiv y^{(1)}(b) + sy^{(2)}(b) = \beta.$$

This equation, which corresponds to Equation (1.2.3), is linear in s and has a unique solution if and only if $y^{(2)}(b) \neq 0$. But if $y^{(2)}(b) = 0$, then $y^{(2)}(x)$ is a nontrivial solution of the homogeneous problem (1.2.8), and the result follows on applying Theorem 1.2.1. ▮

There is no difficulty in extending the above theorem to include more general boundary conditions of the form of Equation (1.2.6b). We pose this as Problem 1.2.4.

This theorem, or more properly a slight extension of it, is called the *Alternative Theorem.* (The extension gives conditions for the existence of solutions of problem (1.2.7) which are not unique when problem (1.2.8) *does* have nontrivial solutions; a very general treatment can be found in Ince (1944) pp. 204–214.) Clearly the case in which the homogeneous system has a nontrivial solution is important and exceptional. In fact, linear *eigenvalue problems*, which we consider later, are concerned with adjusting a parameter in the coefficients so that this exceptional case occurs (see Chapter 5).

1.2.1 Boundary-Value Problems for General Systems

It is not difficult to extend most of the previous results, valid for single second-order equations, to much more general boundary-value problems. To illustrate the possibilities, we shall consider the general system of n first-order differential equations

$$\mathbf{y}' = \mathbf{f}(x, \mathbf{y}), \qquad a < x < b, \tag{1.2.9a}$$

subject to the most general linear two-point boundary conditions

$$A\mathbf{y}(a) + B\mathbf{y}(b) = \boldsymbol{\alpha}. \tag{1.2.9b}$$

Here $\mathbf{y}(x)$ is an n-dimensional vector with components $y_j(x)$; $\mathbf{f}(x, \mathbf{y})$ is an n-vector with components $f_k(x, \mathbf{y})$ which are functions of the $n + 1$ variables $x, y_j, j = 1, 2, \ldots, n$; A and B are nth-order matrices with constant elements and $\boldsymbol{\alpha}$ is a fixed n-vector. It would seem that most two-point boundary-value problems with linear boundary conditions can be written in the above form. Note that the n conditions in Equation (1.2.9b) are linearly independent if and only if the $n \times 2n$ order matrix $[A, B]$ has rank $= n$.

We may reduce the study of existence and uniqueness of solutions to the boundary-value problem (1.2.9) to the study of the roots of some systems of (transcendental) equations by means of initial-value problems, just as we did for the boundary-value problem (1.2.1). This can be done in many ways, but perhaps the most obvious is as follows. We consider the initial-value problem

$$\text{(a)} \quad \mathbf{u}' = \mathbf{f}(x, \mathbf{u}), \qquad \text{(b)} \quad \mathbf{u}(a) = \mathbf{s}, \tag{1.2.10}$$

where $\mathbf{s}$ is an n-vector to be determined. In terms of the solution $\mathbf{u} = \mathbf{u}(\mathbf{s}; x)$ of the problem (1.2.10) we define the system of n equations

$$\boldsymbol{\phi}(\mathbf{s}) \equiv [A\mathbf{s} + B\mathbf{u}(\mathbf{s}; b)] - \boldsymbol{\alpha} = 0. \tag{1.2.11}$$

Clearly, if $\mathbf{s} = \mathbf{s}^*$ is a root of this equation, we now expect that

$$\mathbf{y}(x) = \mathbf{u}(\mathbf{s}^*; x)$$

is a solution of the boundary-value problem (1.2.9). In fact, just as in Theorem 1.2.1, we now have the following.

THEOREM 1.2.4. *Let* $\mathbf{f}(x, \mathbf{u})$ *be continuous on*

$$R: a \le x \le b, \qquad |\mathbf{u}| < \infty,$$

and satisfy there a uniform Lipschitz condition in $\mathbf{u}$. *Then the boundary-value problem* (1.2.9) *has as many solutions as there are distinct roots* $\mathbf{s} = \mathbf{s}^{(\nu)}$ *of Equation* (1.2.11). *These solutions are*

$$\mathbf{y}(x) = \mathbf{u}(\mathbf{s}^{(\nu)}; x),$$

the solutions of the initial-value problems (1.2.10) *with* $\mathbf{s} = \mathbf{s}^{(\nu)}$.

Proof. The proof is almost identical with that of Theorem 1.2.1 and is left to the reader. ∎

We have thus reduced the problem of solving the boundary-value problem (1.2.9) to that of finding the roots of a system of n transcendental equations. It is generally quite difficult to prove the existence of roots of such systems. Of course if the vector-valued function $\mathbf{f}(x, \mathbf{u})$ is linear in $\mathbf{u}$, then it is easy to show that the system of equations (1.2.11) reduces to a linear algebraic system. In this case existence and uniqueness would follow from the nonsingularity of the appropriate coefficient matrix. The detailed study of a particular class of linear problems is presented in Theorem 1.2.5 below. We present this case in part to develop some results required in our analysis of the more general case of nonlinear boundary-value problems.

THEOREM 1.2.5. *The linear boundary-value problem*

$$\text{(a)}\quad \mathbf{y}' = K(x)\mathbf{y}, \qquad \text{(b)}\quad A\mathbf{y}(a) + B\mathbf{y}(b) = \boldsymbol{\alpha} \tag{1.2.12}$$

has a unique solution for each $\boldsymbol{\alpha}$, *provided that*

$$\begin{aligned} &\text{(a)}\quad K(x) \quad \textit{is continuous on } [a, b]; \\ &\text{(b)}\quad (A + B) \quad \textit{is nonsingular}; \\ &\text{(c)}\dagger \quad \int_a^b \|K(x)\|_\infty\, dx < \ln\left(1 + \frac{1}{m}\right), \end{aligned} \tag{1.2.13}$$

where

$$m \equiv \|(A + B)^{-1}B\|_\infty .$$

Proof. By virtue of condition (1.2.13a) we may apply Theorem 1.2.4 to the linear boundary-value problem (1.2.12). Thus we consider the appropriate initial-value problem

$$\mathbf{u}' = K(x)\mathbf{u}, \qquad \mathbf{u}(a) = \mathbf{s}. \tag{1.2.14a}$$

† For any matrix $\Gamma \equiv (\gamma_{ij})$ the maximum norm is $\|\Gamma\|_\infty = \max_i \sum_j |\gamma_{ij}|$, and is compatible with the maximum vector norm, $|\mathbf{u}|$, in the sense that $|\Gamma\mathbf{u}| \le \|\Gamma\|_\infty \cdot |\mathbf{u}|$.

The unique solution of this linear problem can be represented by means of the matrizant, $\Omega_a^x \{K\}$, as

$$\mathbf{u}(\mathbf{s}, x) = \overset{x}{\underset{a}{\Omega}} \{K\}\mathbf{s}. \tag{1.2.14b}$$

The matrizant is defined [see Ince (1944), pp. 408–411] by the absolutely and uniformly convergent matrix series

$$\overset{x}{\underset{a}{\Omega}} \{K\} \equiv I + \int_a^x K(\xi_1)\, d\xi_1 + \int_a^x \int_a^{\xi_1} K(\xi_1)K(\xi_2)\, d\xi_1\, d\xi_2 + \cdots. \tag{1.2.15}$$

A derivation of this result is indicated in Problem 1.2.7 and we note that it is the fundamental solution of $U' = K(x)U$ which satisfies $U(a) = I$.

The solution (1.2.14b) of the initial-value problem (1.2.14a) will be a solution of the boundary-value problem (1.2.12) *if and only if* **s** satisfies

$$\left[A + B\overset{b}{\underset{a}{\Omega}} \{K\}\right]\mathbf{s} = \boldsymbol{\alpha}. \tag{1.2.16}$$

We note that this is a *linear algebraic system* for the determination of **s**, as anticipated. It is exactly the system of Equations (1.2.11) in a more explicit notation. The coefficient matrix in Equation (1.2.16) can be written, recalling (1.2.13b), as

$$\begin{aligned} A + B\overset{b}{\underset{a}{\Omega}} \{K\} &= (A + B) + B\left(\overset{b}{\underset{a}{\Omega}} \{K\} - I\right) \\ &= (A + B)\left[I + (A + B)^{-1}B\left(\overset{b}{\underset{a}{\Omega}} \{K\} - I\right)\right]. \end{aligned}$$

However, it is known that a matrix of the form $[I + H]$ is nonsingular if $\|H\|_\infty < 1$ [see Isaacson and Keller (1966), Theorem 1.5 in Chapter 1]. But using the fact that for $x \geq a$

$$\left\|\int_a^x K(\xi)\, d\xi\right\|_\infty \leq \int_a^x \|K(\xi)\|_\infty\, d\xi,$$

it follows with little effort (see Problem 1.2.8) that

$$\left\|\overset{b}{\underset{a}{\Omega}} \{K\} - I\right\|_\infty \leq \exp\left(\int_a^b \|K(\xi)\|_\infty\, d\xi\right) - 1. \tag{1.2.17}$$

Thus (1.2.13b) and (1.2.13c) imply that the coefficient matrix in Equation (1.2.16) is nonsingular since

$$\begin{aligned} \left\|(A + B)^{-1}B\left(\overset{b}{\underset{a}{\Omega}} \{K\} - I\right)\right\|_\infty &\leq \|(A + B)^{-1}B\|_\infty \left\|\overset{b}{\underset{a}{\Omega}} \{K\} - I\right\|_\infty \\ &\leq m\left[\exp\left(\int_a^b \|K(\xi)\|_\infty\, d\xi\right) - 1\right] < 1. \quad \blacksquare \end{aligned}$$

The conditions (1.2.13) are only sufficient for the existence of a unique solution to the linear boundary-value problem (1.2.12). Given (1.2.13a), the *necessary and sufficient* conditions are clearly that the coefficient matrix in Equation (1.2.16) be nonsingular. Our condition (1.2.13b) is not necessary for rank $[A,B] = n$, and thus many boundary conditions of interest are not covered by this result. A slight almost trivial weakening of condition (1.2.13c) is indicated in Problem 1.2.10. It should be observed that when conditions (1.2.13a) and (1.2.13b) are satisfied, condition (1.2.13c) is automatically satisfied if the interval $[a, b]$ is sufficiently small. In particular, condition (1.2.13c) is satisfied if the length of the interval is so small that

$$|b - a| < \frac{\ln(1 + 1/m)}{\max\limits_{a \le x \le b} \|K(x)\|_\infty}.$$

We now return to the study of the general nonlinear boundary-value problem (1.2.9). Under appropriate conditions, resembling those in (1.2.13), we shall prove the existence of a unique solution. This will be done by showing that the system of Equations (1.2.11) has a unique root. Since the function $\boldsymbol{\phi}(\mathbf{s})$ is no longer linear in the general case, we can try to employ some type of fixed-point theorems to show that it has a zero. The simplest such result is the Contracting Mapping principle which, when applicable, also yields uniqueness. We shall use this principle, and all the theory required is developed in Section 1.4 (in particular, Theorem 1.4.1). Contracting maps will be employed throughout this work and can be studied independently of the preceding sections. We have delayed their study simply in order to get into the basic subject matter more rapidly.

Our existence and uniqueness theorem for the problem (1.2.9) is as follows.

THEOREM 1.2.6. *Let* $\mathbf{f}(x, \mathbf{u})$ *satisfy on* $R\colon a \le x \le b,\ |\mathbf{u}| < \infty$

$$\text{(a)}\quad \mathbf{f}(x, \mathbf{u}) \text{ continuous};$$

$$\text{(b)}\quad \frac{\partial f_i(x, \mathbf{u})}{\partial u_j} \text{ continuous}, \qquad i, j = 1, 2, \ldots, n; \tag{1.2.18}$$

$$\text{(c)}\quad \left\| \frac{\partial \mathbf{f}(x, \mathbf{u})}{\partial \mathbf{u}} \right\|_\infty \le k(x).$$

Furthermore, let the matrices A *and* B *and the scalar function* $k(x)$ *satisfy*

$$\text{(d)}\quad (A + B) \text{ nonsingular};$$

$$\text{(e)}\quad \int_a^b k(x)\, dx \le \ln\left(1 + \frac{\lambda}{m}\right), \tag{1.2.18}$$

for some λ *in* $0 < \lambda < 1$, *where*

$$m \equiv \|(A + B)^{-1}B\|_\infty .$$

Then the boundary-value problem (1.2.9) *has a unique solution for each* $\boldsymbol{\alpha}$.

Proof. From conditions (1.2.18b, c) it follows that $\mathbf{f}(x, \mathbf{u})$ satisfies a uniform Lipschitz condition in $\mathbf{u}$ (see Problem 1.2.11). But then Theorem 1.2.4 is applicable and implies that the boundary-value problem (1.2.9) has a unique solution if and only if $\boldsymbol{\phi}(\mathbf{s})$ in Equation (1.2.11) has a unique zero.

Let Q be a nonsingular matrix; then it follows that the system

$$\mathbf{s} = \mathbf{g}(\mathbf{s}) \equiv \mathbf{s} - Q\boldsymbol{\phi}(\mathbf{s}) \tag{1.2.19}$$

has roots that are identical with those of Equation (1.2.11). However, if

$$\left\|\frac{\partial \mathbf{g}(\mathbf{s})}{\partial \mathbf{s}}\right\|_\infty \leq \lambda < 1, \tag{1.2.20}$$

we can then apply the Contracting Mapping principle (see Problem 1.2.11 and Theorem 1.4.1) to conclude that Equation (1.2.19) and hence Equation (1.2.11) has a root which is unique. Our proof is thus reduced to verifying the inequality (1.2.20) for some nonsingular matrix Q.

With the definition of the matrix W as

$$\partial \mathbf{u}(\mathbf{s}; x)/\partial \mathbf{s} \equiv W(\mathbf{s}; x),$$

it follows from Equations (1.2.11) and (1.2.19) that

$$\partial \mathbf{g}(\mathbf{s})/\partial \mathbf{s} = I - Q[A + BW(\mathbf{s}; b)]. \tag{1.2.21}$$

An application of Theorem 1.1.2 to the initial-value problem (1.2.10) reveals that $W(\mathbf{s}; x)$, or $W(x)$ for brevity, satisfies the variational system

$$W' = J(\mathbf{s}; x)W, \qquad W(a) = I. \tag{1.2.22}$$

Here we have introduced the Jacobian matrix

$$J(\mathbf{s}; x) \equiv \partial \mathbf{f}(x, \mathbf{u}(\mathbf{s}; x))/\partial \mathbf{u},$$

and by condition (1.2.18c),

$$\|J(\mathbf{s}; x)\|_\infty \leq k(x).$$

The solution of the linear system (1.2.22) is the matrizant of J; that is, recalling the definition (1.2.15),

$$W(x) = \underset{a}{\overset{x}{\Omega}}\{J\}.$$

Now we can write Equation (1.2.21) as

$$\partial \mathbf{g}(\mathbf{s})/\partial \mathbf{s} = I - Q\left[(A + B) + B\left(\mathop{\Omega}_a^b \{J\} - I\right)\right].$$

Since $(A + B)$ is nonsingular by condition (1.2.18d) we take $Q = (A + B)^{-1}$ to get, using the inequalities (1.2.17) and (1.2.18e)

$$\begin{aligned}\left\|\frac{\partial \mathbf{g}(\mathbf{s})}{\partial \mathbf{s}}\right\|_\infty &= \left\|(A + B)^{-1}B\left(\mathop{\Omega}_a^b \{J\} - I\right)\right\|_\infty \\ &\leq m\left(\exp\left(\int_a^b k(x)\,dx\right) - 1\right) \\ &\leq \lambda < 1. \quad \blacksquare\end{aligned}$$

We observe again that Condition (1.2.18e) will certainly be satisfied, given conditions (1.2.18a–d), if $|b - a|$ is sufficiently small. (Of course, one of the objectives in theoretical studies is to prove existence for relatively larger intervals; see Problem 1.2.13.) The relaxation to possibly smaller m as in Problem 1.2.10 is also valid now. If $(A + B)$ is singular, a different choice for Q in (1.2.21) may still result in a contraction. In fact, we shall later advocate the use of Newton's method, which corresponds to the choice $Q = [A + BW(\mathbf{s}, b)]^{-1}$. Existence proofs based on this choice or related choices are indicated in Section 5.5.

These results are far from sufficient to cover most problems that arise in practice. Additional existence proofs (some under much weaker conditions) are contained in Problems 1.2.12, 1.2.13, 1.2.14, and the results of Theorem 4.1.3 covering systems of second-order equations. (See also the discussion in Section 5.5.) However, solutions of boundary-value problems and roots of transcendental systems can exist without formal proofs of these facts. Thus in many of the difficult and important applied problems leading to boundary-value problems we may use the techniques to be developed here without the benefit of existence theorems.

Problems

1.2.1 (a) Determine the solution of the initial-value problem

$$Ly \equiv y'' - k^2 y = 0, \qquad y(a) = \alpha, \qquad y'(a) = s.$$

(b) Use this solution to solve the boundary-value problem

$$Ly = 0, \qquad y(a) = \alpha, \qquad y(b) = \beta.$$

Find conditions on $k(b - a)$ so that a unique solution exists. Does a solution always exist? (Note that Theorem 1.2.2 applies here.)

1.2.2 Repeat Problem 1.2.1 for the equation $Ly \equiv y'' + k^2y = 0$. Under what conditions do nonunique solutions exist?

1.2.3 Prove the analog of Theorem 1.2.2 under the hypothesis

$$\frac{\partial f}{\partial u_1} \geq 0, \qquad \frac{\partial f}{\partial u_2} = 0, \qquad a_0 = b_0 = 1, \qquad a_1 = b_1 = 0,$$

that is, with $f(x, u_1, u_2)$ independent of u_2 and the solution specified at the boundary points [see Henrici (1962), pp. 347–348, for a proof]. Note that the inequalities (1.2.5) give the bounds $\partial u(x; s)/\partial s > (x - a)$ and $\partial u'(x; s)/\partial s > 1$ upon letting $M \to 0$.

1.2.4 Replace the boundary conditions in the boundary-value problems (1.2.7) and (1.2.8) by those in Equations (1.2.1b) and prove the corresponding Alternative Theorem.

1.2.5 Replace the boundary-value problem (1.2.1) by $y'' = f(x, y, y')$ subject to

(a) $a_0y(a) - a_1y'(a) = \alpha, \qquad |a_0| + |a_1| \neq 0,$

(b) $b_0y(b) + b_1y'(b) + b_2y(a) + b_3y'(a) = \beta, \qquad |b_0| + |b_1| \neq 0.$

Show that a unique solution to this problem exists if $f(x, y, y')$ satisfies

$$N > \frac{\partial f}{\partial y} > 0, \qquad \left|\frac{\partial f}{\partial y'}\right| \leq M,$$

and the coefficients a_i, b_i satisfy

$$a_i \geq 0, \qquad b_i \geq 0, \qquad i = 0, 1; \qquad a_0 + b_0 > 0; \qquad a_0b_2 + a_1b_3 \geq 0.$$

1.2.6 Replace the boundary conditions in Problem 1.2.5 by

$$g_1(y(a), -y'(a)) = 0,$$
$$g_2(y(a), y'(a), y(b), y'(b)) = 0.$$

Under the same conditions on f show that a unique solution to the boundary-value problem exists if the partial derivatives of $g_1(x_1, x_2)$ and $g_2(x_1, x_2, x_3, x_4)$ denoted by $g_{ij} \equiv \partial g_i/\partial x_j$ are continuous and satisfy

$$g_{i,j} \geq 0, \qquad i = 1, \qquad j = 1, 2; \qquad i = 2, \qquad j = 3, 4;$$
$$g_{1,1} + g_{1,2} \geq \varepsilon > 0, \qquad g_{2,3} + g_{2,4} \geq \varepsilon > 0;$$
$$g_{1,1} + g_{2,3} > 0, \qquad g_{2,1}g_{1,2} + g_{2,2}g_{1,1} \geq 0.$$

[HINT: Use the result in Problem 1.2.5.]

1.2.7 Use the Picard iteration scheme (see proof of Theorem 1.1.1) to derive formally the representation of the matrizant given in Equation (1.2.15).

1.2.8 Derive the inequality (1.2.17) from the definition (1.2.15).

[HINT: Use the iterated-integral formulas, for scalar functions,

$$\int_a^x \int_a^{\xi_1} k(\xi_1)k(\xi_2)\, d\xi_2\, d\xi_1 = \frac{1}{2!}\left(\int_a^x k(\xi)\, d\xi\right)^2, \ldots .]$$

1.2.9 If the matrix $K(x)$ is self-commuting, that is, if $K(x)K(x') = K(x')K(x)$, show that

$$\underset{a}{\overset{x}{\Omega}} \{K\} = \exp \int_a^x K(\xi)\, d\xi .$$

[HINT: Use induction with the matrix iterated-integral formula to derive the general term of the exponential series.]

1.2.10 Show that Theorems 1.2.5 and 1.2.6 remain valid if we replace the constant m by

$$m = \min\left(\|(A + B)^{-1}B\|_\infty, \|(A + B)^{-1}A\|_\infty\right).$$

[HINT: Use the appropriate initial-value problems with "initial" point $x = b$ in place of $x = a$.]

1.2.11 If the function $\mathbf{g(s)}$ has continuous first derivatives which satisfy, for all $\mathbf{s}$, $\|\partial \mathbf{g(s)}/\partial \mathbf{s}\|_\infty \le \lambda$, then $\mathbf{g(s)}$ satisfies the Lipschitz condition

$$|\mathbf{g(s)} - \mathbf{g(t)}| \le \lambda |\mathbf{s} - \mathbf{t}| .$$

1.2.12 Consider the two-point boundary-value problem

$$\mathbf{y}' = \mathbf{f}(x, \mathbf{y}), \qquad A\mathbf{y}(a) = \boldsymbol{\alpha}, \qquad B\mathbf{y}(b) = \boldsymbol{\beta},$$

where $\mathbf{y}$ and $\mathbf{f}$ are n vectors, A is a $p \times n$ matrix with rank $p > 0$, B is a $q \times n$ matrix with rank $q > 0$, $p + q = n$, $\boldsymbol{\alpha}$ is a p-vector and $\boldsymbol{\beta}$ is a q-vector. Show that with no loss in generality we may take A in the form

$$A \equiv (I_p, A_1),$$

where I_p is the p-order identity matrix and A_1 is some $p \times q$ matrix. Show further that if $\mathbf{f}(x, \mathbf{y})$ satisfies Conditions (1.2.18a–c, e), where

$$m = \|Q^{-1}B\|_\infty \cdot \left\|\binom{-A_q}{I_1}\right\|_\infty \qquad \text{and} \qquad Q \equiv B\binom{-A_1}{I_q}$$

is assumed nonsingular, then the above boundary-value problem has a unique solution for each $\boldsymbol{\alpha}, \boldsymbol{\beta}$.

[HINT: Use the initial-value problem

$$\mathbf{u}' = f(x, \mathbf{u}), \qquad A\mathbf{u}(a) = \mathbf{x}, \qquad C\mathbf{u}(a) = \mathbf{s},$$

where $\mathbf{s}$ is a q-vector and the $q \times n$ matrix $C \equiv (0, I_q)$. The system to be solved is $\boldsymbol{\phi}(\mathbf{s}) \equiv B\mathbf{u}(\mathbf{s}; b) - \boldsymbol{\beta} = 0$, which is of order q. Show that a contracting map is given by $\mathbf{s} = \mathbf{g(s)} \equiv \mathbf{s} - Q^{-1}\boldsymbol{\phi}(\mathbf{s})$.]

1.2.13* Prove the following.

THEOREM 1.2.7 *Let an n-vector* $\mathbf{s}_0$ *and positive constants* ρ, K, *and* M *satisfy, for* $R_{\rho,M}(\mathbf{s}_0) \equiv \{(x, \mathbf{u}) \mid |\mathbf{u} - \mathbf{s}_0| \leq \rho + M(x - a),\quad a \leq x \leq b\}$,

(a) $\mathbf{f}(x, \mathbf{u})$ *continuous on* $R_{\rho,M}(\mathbf{s}_0)$,
(b) $|\mathbf{f}(x, \mathbf{u})| \leq M$ *on* $R_{\rho,M}(\mathbf{s}_0)$,
(c) $|\mathbf{f}(x, \mathbf{u}) - \mathbf{f}(x, \mathbf{v})| \leq K|\mathbf{u} - \mathbf{v}|$ *for all* $(x, \mathbf{u})$, *and* $(x, \mathbf{v}) \in R_{\rho,M}(\mathbf{s}_0)$.

Further, let the matrices A and B and interval length, $|b - a|$, *be such that*

(d) $(A + B)$ *is nonsingular,*
(e) $\|(A + B)^{-1}B\| \cdot M(b - a) + \|(A + B)^{-1}\boldsymbol{\alpha} - \mathbf{s}_0\| \leq \rho$.

Then the boundary-value problem

$$\mathbf{y}' = \mathbf{f}(x, \mathbf{y}), \qquad A\mathbf{y}(a) + B\mathbf{y}(b) = \boldsymbol{\alpha} \tag{1.2.23}$$

has at least one solution with $\mathbf{y}(a) \in N_\rho(\mathbf{s}_0)$.

[HINT: Use the initial-value technique and Theorem 1.1.4 in Problem 1.1.4 to show that the function $\mathbf{g}(\mathbf{s})$, defined in the usual way, is continuous and maps the closed sphere $N_\rho(\mathbf{s}_0)$ into itself. Then by the Brouwer fixed-point theorem $\mathbf{s} = \mathbf{g}(\mathbf{s})$ has at least one root in $N_\rho(\mathbf{s}_0)$. Note that Condition (e) suggests using as the "initial" iterate the value $\mathbf{s}_0 = (A + B)^{-1}\boldsymbol{\alpha}$.]

1.2.14* Demonstrate the following.

COROLLARY. *If in addition to the hypothesis of Theorem* 1.2.7 *we have*

(f) $K|b - a| \leq \log\left(1 + \dfrac{\lambda}{m}\right), \qquad m \equiv \|(A + B)^{-1}B\|$

then the solution of the boundary-value problem (1.2.23) *with* $\mathbf{y}(a) \in N_\rho(\mathbf{s}_0)$ *is unique.*

[HINT: Show that the map $\mathbf{g}(\mathbf{s})$ is now contracting on $N_\rho(\mathbf{s}_0)$.]

1.3 Numerical Methods for Initial-Value Problems

We present here some basic material on numerical methods for solving initial-value problems. The initial-value problems will be assumed of the form

$$\mathscr{L}[\mathbf{u}(x)] \equiv \mathbf{u}' - \mathbf{f}(x, \mathbf{u}) = 0, \qquad a \leq x \leq b \tag{1.3.1a}$$

$$\mathbf{u}(a) = \boldsymbol{\alpha} \tag{1.3.1b}$$

and as indicated the solution is sought on $[a, b]$. The numerical methods for solving the problem (1.3.1), or rather for approximating its solution, all employ some set of discrete points $\{x_j\}$ on $[a, b]$ called a *net* or *lattice*. Although it is not required for all of our procedures, we will take this net to be uniformly spaced, say

$$x_0 = a, \qquad x_j = a + jh; \qquad j = 1, 2, \ldots, J + 1, \qquad h \equiv \frac{b - a}{J + 1}. \quad (1.3.2)$$

The quantity h is called the *mesh size* or *net spacing*. A rule which assigns to each point x_j of the net a corresponding n vector $\mathbf{U}_j$ is called a *net function*, $\{\mathbf{U}_j\}$. Clearly any solution of problem (1.3.1) evaluated on the net determines a net function $\{\mathbf{u}(x_j)\}$. The numerical methods of interest define net functions $\{\mathbf{U}_j\}$ which will be close approximations to $\{\mathbf{u}(x_j)\}$ for sufficiently small net spacing h. The question of close approximations by computed net functions is related to the concepts of consistency, convergence, and stability for which there is a very general and quite complete theory. We shall indicate some of the simpler aspects of this theory to convey its flavor before presenting practical schemes for solving the initial-value problem (1.3.1).

A numerical method assigns to each point x_j of the net an n-vector $\mathbf{U}_j$ by means of some "algebraic" equations involving "neighboring" net points and corresponding values $\mathbf{U}_i$. Specifically, we assume that at most $k + 1$ successive points are involved and write the algebraic system as

$$\mathscr{L}_h[\mathbf{U}_{j+1}, \mathbf{U}_j, \ldots, \mathbf{U}_{j+1-k}] = 0, \qquad j = k - 1, k, \ldots, J, \quad (1.3.3a)$$

$$\mathbf{U}_j = \boldsymbol{\gamma}_j, \qquad j = 0, 1, \ldots, k - 1. \quad (1.3.3b)$$

As this notation implies $\mathbf{U}_{i+1}$ is determined from the quantities $\mathbf{U}_i$, $\mathbf{U}_{i-1}, \ldots,$ $\mathbf{U}_{i-k+1}$. Thus, as indicated in Equation (1.3.3b), the first k values of $\mathbf{U}_i$ must be specified and such a scheme is termed a *k-step method.* To simplify the notation, we shall write

$$\mathscr{L}_h[\mathbf{U}_j] \equiv \mathscr{L}_h[\mathbf{U}_{j+1}, \mathbf{U}_j, \ldots, \mathbf{U}_{j+1-k}].$$

To relate the numerical scheme to the initial-value problem, we define the *local truncation error*, for any sufficiently smooth n-vector $\mathbf{v}(x)$, by†

$$\boldsymbol{\tau}_j[\mathbf{v}] \equiv \mathscr{L}_h[\mathbf{v}(x_j)] - \mathscr{L}[\mathbf{v}(x_j)], \qquad k - 1 \leq j \leq J. \quad (1.3.4)$$

We say that $\mathscr{L}_h[\cdot]$ *is consistent with* $\mathscr{L}[\cdot]$ *if and only if*

$$\lim_{J \to \infty} |\boldsymbol{\tau}_j[\mathbf{v}]| = 0, \qquad k - 1 \leq j \leq J, \quad (1.3.5)$$

for all sufficiently smooth $\mathbf{v}(x)$. (This definition of consistency is frequently weakened to apply only to functions $\mathbf{v}(x)$ which are solutions of $\mathscr{L}[\mathbf{v}] = 0$.)

† In specific cases, the argument of $\mathscr{L}[\cdot]$ may be shifted slightly to obtain a better definition of local truncation error.

A consistent scheme is said to have an *order of accuracy at least p if and only if*†

$$|\boldsymbol{\tau}_j[\mathbf{v}]| = \mathcal{O}(h^p), \qquad k - 1 \leq j \leq J, \tag{1.3.6}$$

for all sufficiently smooth $\mathbf{v}(x)$.

The numerical scheme of Equations (1.3.3) is said to be *convergent* for the initial-value problem (1.3.1) if their solutions satisfy

$$\lim_{J \to \infty} |\mathbf{U}_j - \mathbf{u}(x_j)| = 0, \qquad 0 \leq j \leq J + 1. \tag{1.3.7}$$

A basic notion which relates consistency and convergence is that of *stability*. In contrast to the previous definitions, stability is solely a property of the numerical scheme. We define it as follows: $\mathcal{L}_h[\cdot]$ *is stable* (*or determines a stable scheme*) *if there exists a constant M, independent of the mesh size h, such that for all net functions* $\{\mathbf{V}_j\}$ *and* $\{\mathbf{W}_j\}$,

$$|\mathbf{V}_j - \mathbf{W}_j| \leq M\left\{\max_{i \leq k-1} |\mathbf{V}_i - \mathbf{W}_i| + \max_{i \geq k-1} |\mathcal{L}_h[\mathbf{V}_i] - \mathcal{L}_h[\mathbf{W}_i]|\right\},$$
$$k \leq j \leq J + 1. \tag{1.3.8}$$

The fundamental theorem relating the above concepts is the following.

THEOREM 1.3.1. *Let* $\mathcal{L}_h[\cdot]$ *be stable and consistent with* $\mathcal{L}[\cdot]$. *Then the numerical solution* $\{\mathbf{U}_j\}$ *of the scheme* (1.3.3) *and the exact solution* $\mathbf{u}(x)$ *of the problem* (1.3.1) *satisfy*

$$|\mathbf{U}_j - \mathbf{u}(x_j)| \leq M\left\{\max_{0 \leq i \leq k-1} |\mathbf{u}(x_i) - \boldsymbol{\gamma}_i| + \max_{k-1 \leq i \leq J} |\boldsymbol{\tau}_i[\mathbf{u}]|\right\},$$
$$k \leq j \leq J + 1. \tag{1.3.9}$$

If the initial data in Equation (1.3.3b) *satisfies*

$$\lim_{J \to \infty} |\mathbf{u}(x_i) - \boldsymbol{\gamma}_i| \to 0, \qquad 0 \leq i \leq k - 1, \tag{1.3.10}$$

then the numerical scheme is convergent.

Proof. From Equation (1.3.1a), evaluated at any net point x_j with $k - 1 \leq j \leq J$, we have, using the definition (1.3.4),

$$\begin{aligned} \mathcal{L}_h[\mathbf{u}(x_j)] &= \mathcal{L}_h[\mathbf{u}(x_j)] - \mathcal{L}[\mathbf{u}(x_j)] \\ &= \boldsymbol{\tau}_j[\mathbf{u}(x_j)]. \end{aligned}$$

But then Equation (1.3.3a) and the above yield

$$\mathcal{L}_h[\mathbf{u}(x_j)] - \mathcal{L}_h[\mathbf{U}_j] = \boldsymbol{\tau}_j[\mathbf{u}].$$

† For any two scalar quantities, say $f(h)$ and $g(h)$, depending upon h, the notation $f(h) = \mathcal{O}(g(h))$ means that there exists some positive constant, c, independent of h, such that

$$\lim_{h \to 0} |f(h)/g(h)| \leq c.$$

However, since $\mathscr{L}_h[\cdot]$ is stable, this implies the inequality (1.3.9), on recalling Equations (1.3.1b) and (1.3.3b) and using $\mathbf{V}_j \equiv \mathbf{u}(x_j)$ and $\mathbf{W}_j \equiv \mathbf{U}_j$ in inequality (1.3.8). By consistency $\boldsymbol{\tau}_j[\mathbf{u}] \to 0$ as $J \to \infty$ and so convergence follows from condition (1.3.10). ▮

Bounds on the rate at which the numerical solution converges to the exact solution as $h \to 0$ are easily obtained from the above theorem. We have the obvious

COROLLARY. *In addition to the hypothesis of Theorem* 1.3.1, *let the order of accuracy of* $\mathscr{L}_h[\cdot]$ *as an approximation to* $\mathscr{L}[\cdot]$ *be at least* p. *Let the initial data in Equation* (1.3.3b) *satisfy*

$$|\mathbf{u}(x_i) - \boldsymbol{\gamma}_i| = \mathcal{O}(h^q), \qquad 0 \le i \le k-1. \tag{1.3.11}$$

Then if the solution $\mathbf{u}(x)$ *of the initial-value problem* (1.3.1) *is sufficiently smooth,*

$$|\mathbf{U}_j - \mathbf{u}(x_j)| \le \mathcal{O}(h^q) + \mathcal{O}(h^p). \quad ▮$$

To illustrate the above concepts we examine first the simplest and perhaps best known numerical scheme for solving initial-value problems, namely *Euler's method.* Only the most naive computer user would generally employ this method in practice since, as we shall see, there are much more accurate methods requiring about the same effort.† In the notation of Equations (1.3.3), using the net (1.3.2), Euler's method for approximating the solution of (1.3.1) can be written as

$$\mathscr{L}_h[\mathbf{U}_{j+1}, \mathbf{U}_j] \equiv \frac{1}{h}(\mathbf{U}_{j+1} - \mathbf{U}_j) - \mathbf{f}(x_j, \mathbf{U}_j) = 0, \qquad j = 0, 1, \dots, J; \tag{1.3.12a}$$

$$\mathbf{U}_0 = \boldsymbol{\alpha}^{(h)}. \tag{1.3.12b}$$

The equation for $\mathbf{U}_{j+1}$ only involves $\mathbf{U}_j$ and so this is a one-step method; that is, $k = 1$. The first term on the right-hand side in Equation (1.3.12a) is clearly a difference quotient, intended to approximate $\mathbf{u}'(x_j)$.

To examine consistency for this scheme let $\mathbf{v}(x)$ be any twice continuously differentiable vector function with $|\mathbf{v}''(x)| \le M_2[\mathbf{v}]$ on $[a, b]$. Then from Equations (1.3.4), (1.3.12a), (1.3.1a), and Taylor's theorem,

$$\begin{aligned} |\tau_j[\mathbf{v}]| &= \left|\frac{1}{h}(\mathbf{v}(x_j + h) - \mathbf{v}(x_j)) - \mathbf{v}'(x_j)\right| \\ &\le \frac{h}{2} M_2[\mathbf{v}]. \end{aligned}$$

† On the other hand, *in rare circumstances,* a sophisticated computer user might intentionally use such a low order scheme in the neighborhood of certain types of singularities to reduce the effect of roundoff errors.

From the first line above we see that $\mathscr{L}_h[\cdot]$ is consistent with $\mathscr{L}[\cdot]$ for all functions with one continuous derivative (that is, the solution of (1.3.1) need not have two continuous derivatives). But, from the second line, it follows that Euler's method is consistent and has at least first-order accuracy for twice continuously differentiable functions. If the function $\mathbf{f}(x, \mathbf{u})$ satisfies the conditions of Theorem 1.1.2 and in addition $\mathbf{f}_x$ is continuous on R, then it clearly follows that the problem (1.3.1) has a unique solution with two continuous derivatives, and in fact

$$\mathbf{u}''(x) = \frac{\partial \mathbf{f}(x, \mathbf{u}(x))}{\partial \mathbf{u}} \mathbf{f}(x, \mathbf{u}(x)) + \mathbf{f}_x(x, \mathbf{u}(x)).$$

In this case the constant $M_2[\mathbf{u}]$ can be bounded in terms of bounds for $\|\partial \mathbf{f}/\partial \mathbf{u}\|$, $|\mathbf{f}|$ and $|\mathbf{f}_x|$ on R.

The stability of Euler's method is easily demonstrated provided $\mathbf{f}(x, \mathbf{u})$ satisfies the hypothesis of Theorem 1.1.1. (Since this is our basic existence proof for the initial-value problem, we are not imposing any strong new restrictions.) For any net function $\{\mathbf{V}_j\}$ the definition of $\mathscr{L}_h[\cdot]$ in (1.3.12a) yields the identity

$$\mathbf{V}_{j+1} = \mathbf{V}_j + h\mathbf{f}(x_j, \mathbf{V}_j) + h\mathscr{L}_h[\mathbf{V}_j], \qquad j = 0, 1, \ldots, J.$$

Subtracting the corresponding identity for $\{\mathbf{W}_j\}$ and using the Lipschitz continuity of $\mathbf{f}$, we obtain

$$|\mathbf{V}_{j+1} - \mathbf{W}_{j+1}| \le (1 + hK)|\mathbf{V}_j - \mathbf{W}_j| + h \max_{0 \le i \le J} |\mathscr{L}_h[\mathbf{V}_i] - \mathscr{L}_h[\mathbf{W}_i]|, \qquad j = 0, 1, \ldots, J.$$

Now apply this inequality recursively in j, sum the resulting geometric progression which occurs and reduce the subscript j by unity to get

$$|\mathbf{V}_j - \mathbf{W}_j| \le (1 + hK)^j|\mathbf{V}_0 - \mathbf{W}_0| + \frac{(1 + hK)^j - 1}{K} \max_{0 \le i \le J} |\mathscr{L}_h[\mathbf{V}_i] - \mathscr{L}_h[\mathbf{W}_i]|, \qquad j = 1, 2, \ldots, J + 1.$$

However, with $x_j = a + jh$ and $1 + hK \ge 0$, it is well known (see Problem 1.3.1) that

$$(1 + hK)^j \le \exp[K(x_j - a)].$$

Stability clearly follows with the constant M in the inequality (1.3.8) chosen as, say,

$$M = \exp[K(b - a)] \max(1, K^{-1}).$$

We can now apply Theorem 1.3.1 to deduce convergence for Euler's method, or the Corollary to this Theorem to deduce that

$$\max_j |\mathbf{U}_j - \mathbf{u}(x_j)| \le \mathcal{O}(h),$$

provided $|\boldsymbol{\alpha} - \boldsymbol{\alpha}^{(h)}| = \mathcal{O}(h)$ and $\mathbf{f}$ satisfies the hypothesis of Theorem 1.1.2. A simple modification of this scheme which yields a two-step method with possibly second-order accuracy is presented in Problems 1.3.2 and 1.3.3.

We turn now to more practical or rather higher-order-accurate methods. If we attempt to replace $\mathbf{u}'(x_j)$ by higher-order-accurate approximations than those employed in Euler's method or in the modification of Problem 1.3.2, we are led to schemes which are not stable [see Isaacson and Keller (1966), Section 1.4, Chapter 8]. However, by integrating the system of differential equations (1.3.1a) over the interval $[x_{j-k+1}, x_{j+1}]$, we obtain the system of *integral equations*

$$\mathbf{u}(x_{j+1}) = \mathbf{u}(x_{j-k+1}) + \int_{x_{j-k+1}}^{x_{j+1}} \mathbf{f}(x, \mathbf{u}(x))\, dx, \qquad k - 1 \leq j \leq J. \quad (1.3.13)$$

Now a large class of stable, higher-order-accurate methods can be devised by approximating the integrals in this system.

For $k = 1$ there are no net points interior to the interval of integration. One procedure is to define a set of tentative approximations to $\mathbf{u}(x)$ at a fixed set of points in $[x_j, x_{j+1}]$ and then use them in approximating the integral to define a final approximation to $\mathbf{u}(x_{j+1})$. One of the schemes suggested by this procedure is the well-known *Runge-Kutta method*

$$\mathbf{U}_{j+1} = \mathbf{U}_j + \frac{h}{6}[\mathbf{f}_{j,1} + 2\mathbf{f}_{j,2} + 2\mathbf{f}_{j,3} + \mathbf{f}_{j,4}], \qquad 0 \leq j \leq J, \quad (1.3.14a)$$

where

$$\begin{aligned} \mathbf{f}_{j,1} &\equiv \mathbf{f}(x_j, \mathbf{U}_j), \\ \mathbf{f}_{j,2} &\equiv \mathbf{f}\left(x_j + \frac{h}{2}, \mathbf{U}_j + \frac{h}{2}\mathbf{f}_{j,1}\right), \\ \mathbf{f}_{j,3} &\equiv \mathbf{f}\left(x_j + \frac{h}{2}, \mathbf{U}_j + \frac{h}{2}\mathbf{f}_{j,2}\right), \\ \mathbf{f}_{j,4} &\equiv \mathbf{f}(x_{j+1}, \mathbf{U}_j + h\mathbf{f}_{j,3}). \end{aligned} \qquad (1.3.14b)$$

Under sufficient smoothness conditions on $\mathbf{f}$ (that is, continuous fourth derivatives), a very long calculation [Ince (1944), Appendix B] shows that *the Runge-Kutta method has order of accuracy* 4. Under much weaker conditions (that is, $\mathbf{f}$ Lipschitz-continuous), it can be shown that the *Runge-Kutta method is stable*. This proof is hardly more complicated than that for Euler's method and so we pose it as Problem 1.3.4. In fact, if $\mathbf{f}$ satisfies the hypothesis of Theorem 1.1 and in addition $|\mathbf{f}| \leq B_0$, $|\mathbf{f}_x| \leq B_1$, then it is also quite easy to show that the scheme in Equations (1.3.14) is consistent with the first-order system in Equation (1.3.1a). Further, if we consider only functions $\mathbf{v}(x)$ with Lipschitz-continuous first derivatives (with Lipschitz-constant

K'), then the truncation error of the Runge-Kutta scheme can be bounded by (see Problem 1.3.5)

$$|\boldsymbol{\tau}_j[\mathbf{v}]| \leq \frac{h}{2}(2K' + KB_0 + B_1).$$

Thus we see that under rather mild smoothness conditions the Runge-Kutta method has at least first-order accuracy. In principle it is not difficult to define other one-step methods which have an order of accuracy greater than 4 under appropriate smoothness conditions. However, for most applications the Runge-Kutta scheme is sufficiently accurate.

The *multistep methods* suggested by Equation (1.3.13) with $k \geq 1$ can be written as

$$\mathbf{U}_{j+1} = \mathbf{U}_{j-k+1} + h \sum_{\nu=0}^{k'} c_k \mathbf{f}(x_{j-\nu+1}, \mathbf{U}_{j-\nu+1}),$$
$$\max(k, k') \leq j + 1 \leq J + 1. \quad (1.3.15)$$

Here $k' > 1$ and we use only data at the net points x_i to approximate the integral. It should be noted that if $c_0 \neq 0$, this scheme gives an explicit formula for $\mathbf{U}_{j+1}$ if and only if $\mathbf{f}(x, \mathbf{u})$ is linear in $\mathbf{u}$. Actually, by taking h sufficiently small we could be assured that this system always yields a unique value for $\mathbf{U}_{j+1}$ whenever $\mathbf{f}$ satisfies the hypotheses of Theorem 1.1.1, and that it could be obtained from a convergent iteration scheme (see Section 1.4). However, as a practical procedure we advocate the *predictor–corrector* methods which circumvent the above difficulty. First a tentative value, say $\mathbf{U}^*_{j+1}$, is predicted by a formula of the form (1.3.15) but with $c_0 = 0$, and then this tentative value is used in a different formula with $c_0 \neq 0$.

One of the many schemes which can be obtained in this way is the *modified Adams method* given by

$$\mathbf{U}^*_{j+1} = \mathbf{U}_j + \frac{h}{24}[55\mathbf{f}_j - 59\mathbf{f}_{j-1} + 37\mathbf{f}_{j-2} - 9\mathbf{f}_{j-3}], \quad (1.3.16a)$$

$$\mathbf{U}_{j+1} = \mathbf{U}_j + \frac{h}{24}[9\mathbf{f}(x_{j+1}, \mathbf{U}^*_{j+1}) + 19\mathbf{f}_j - 5\mathbf{f}_{j-1} + \mathbf{f}_{j-2}], \quad (1.3.16b)$$

$$\textit{where} \quad \mathbf{f}_\nu \equiv \mathbf{f}(x_\nu, \mathbf{U}_\nu), \quad j = 3, 4, \ldots, J.$$

Here we have used Equation (1.3.15) with $k = 1$, $k' = 4$ for Equation (1.3.16a) and $k' = 3$ for Equation (1.3.16b). We call Equation (1.3.16a) the *predictor* and Equation (1.3.16b) the *corrector*. [Such a scheme can be viewed as the first step in an attempt to solve Equation (1.3.16b), with $\mathbf{U}^*_{j+1}$ replaced by $\mathbf{U}_{j+1}$, by iterations. But we do not continue the process.] To start the calculations in Equations (1.3.16), values of

$$\mathbf{U}_0, \mathbf{U}_1, \mathbf{U}_2, \mathbf{U}_3$$

must be determined. This can be done using the Runge-Kutta method (1.3.14), with $\mathbf{U}_0 = \mathbf{u}(x_0)$, and then

$$|\mathbf{U}_j - \mathbf{u}(x_j)| = \mathcal{O}(h^4), \qquad j = 0, 1, 2, 3, \tag{1.3.17}$$

if $\mathbf{f}$ is sufficiently smooth. Alternatively Taylor's expansion could be employed using

$$u' = \mathbf{f}(x, \mathbf{u}), \qquad u'' = \mathbf{f}_x(x, \mathbf{u}) + \frac{\partial \mathbf{f}(x, \mathbf{u})}{\partial \mathbf{u}} \mathbf{u}', \qquad \ldots$$

to evaluate the higher derivatives.

The truncation error $\boldsymbol{\tau}_j[\mathbf{u}]$ in the scheme (1.3.16) can be estimated in terms of the errors $h\boldsymbol{\sigma}_j^*[\mathbf{u}]$ and $h\boldsymbol{\sigma}_j[\mathbf{u}]$ by which the exact solution fails to satisfy Equations (1.3.16a) and (1.3.16b), respectively [with $\mathbf{U}_\nu$ replaced by $\mathbf{u}(x_\nu)$ and $\mathbf{U}_{j+1}^*$ by $\mathbf{u}(x_{j+1})$]. It is well known that

$$|\boldsymbol{\sigma}_j^*[\mathbf{u}]| \le \tfrac{251}{720} M_5[\mathbf{u}]h^4, \qquad |\boldsymbol{\sigma}_j[\mathbf{u}]| \le \tfrac{19}{720} M_5[\mathbf{u}]h^4$$

[see Isaacson and Keller (1966), Table 1.1, Section 2, Chapter 8], provided $\mathbf{u}$ has a continuous fifth derivative. Then, recalling that Equations (1.3.16) define $h\mathscr{L}_h[\mathbf{U}_j]$ in the notation of Equation (1.3.3a), it follows that

$$\begin{aligned} |\boldsymbol{\tau}_j[\mathbf{u}]| &\le \frac{9h}{24} \left| \frac{\partial \mathbf{f}}{\partial \mathbf{u}} \boldsymbol{\sigma}_j^*[\mathbf{u}] \right| + |\boldsymbol{\sigma}_j[\mathbf{u}]| \\ &\le \tfrac{3}{8} \cdot \tfrac{251}{720} M M_5[\mathbf{u}]h^5 + \tfrac{19}{720} M_5[\mathbf{u}]h^4 = \mathcal{O}(h^4), \end{aligned}$$

where M is a bound on the maximum absolute row sum of $\partial \mathbf{f}/\partial \mathbf{u}$. Thus, for sufficiently smooth functions, *the modified Adams method has order of accuracy* 4.

It is not difficult to show that this scheme is also stable, under the mild condition that $\mathbf{f}(x, \mathbf{u})$ be Lipschitz-continuous in $\mathbf{u}$. Thus if conditions (1.3.17) are satisfied by the initial data we can apply the Corollary of Theorem 1.3.1 to the modified Adams method to see that $\mathcal{O}(h^4)$ accuracy can be obtained. Of course we can easily define other stable multistep methods (that is, $k' > 1$) that have accuracy greater than four, but the scheme in (1.3.16) is adequate for many applications.

Comparing the Runge-Kutta scheme (1.3.14) with the scheme (1.3.16), it should be noted that the former requires four evaluations of $\mathbf{f}(x, \mathbf{u})$ at each step while the latter requires only two (since some evaluations can be retained in going from j to $j + 1$). As this is generally the major source of computations it would seem more efficient to use the modified Adams method. However, as indicated, some separate starting procedure is then required to evaluate $\mathbf{U}_\nu$ for $\nu = 1, 2, 3$, and Runge-Kutta is frequently used for this purpose. This implies that both procedures must be included in an appropriate digital computer code, and as a result one is tempted to use only the one-step method. But this choice, dictated by efforts to simplify the computer code, is frequently a false economy unless only a very few initial-value problems are to be solved.

Problems

1.3.1 Show that for all real numbers z,

$$1 + z \leq e^z,$$

and equality holds only if $z = 0$. If $1 + z \geq 0$, show that for all integers $j \geq 0$,

$$(1 + z)^j \leq e^{jz}.$$

1.3.2 The *midpoint rule* for solving the initial-value problem (1.3.1) is defined by

$$\text{(a)}\quad \mathscr{L}_h[\mathbf{U}_j] \equiv \frac{1}{2h}(\mathbf{U}_{j+1} - \mathbf{U}_{j-1}) - \mathbf{f}(x_j, \mathbf{U}_j) = 0, \qquad j = 1, 2, \ldots, J;$$

$$\text{(b)}\quad \mathbf{U}_0 = \boldsymbol{\gamma}_0, \qquad \mathbf{U}_1 = \boldsymbol{\gamma}_1.$$

Show that $\mathscr{L}_h[\cdot]$ is consistent with $\mathscr{L}[\cdot]$ for continuously differentiable functions, is at least first-order accurate for twice continuously differentiable functions and at least second-order accurate for three times continuously differentiable functions.

1.3.3 Show that $\mathscr{L}_h[\cdot]$, defined in Problem 1.3.2, is stable if $\mathbf{f}(x, \mathbf{u})$ satisfies the hypothesis of Theorem 1.1.1 (note that $k = 2$ in this scheme). The constant in the stability inequality can be taken as

$$M = \exp\,[2K(b - a)]\max\left(1, \frac{1}{2K}\right),$$

where K is the Lipschitz constant for $\mathbf{f}$.

1.3.4 The operator notation for the Runge-Kutta method is

$$h\mathscr{L}_h[\mathbf{U}_j] \equiv \mathbf{U}_{j+1} - \mathbf{U}_j - \frac{h}{6}[\mathbf{f}_{j,1} + 2\mathbf{f}_{j,2} + 2\mathbf{f}_{j,3} + \mathbf{f}_{j,4}], \qquad 0 \leq j \leq J,$$

where the $\mathbf{f}_{j,\nu}$ are as defined in Equations (1.3.14b). If $\mathbf{f}(x, \mathbf{y})$ is Lipschitz-continuous in $\mathbf{y}$ with constant K, show that for any net functions $\{\mathbf{U}_j\}$ and $\{\mathbf{V}_j\}$

$$|\mathbf{U}_{j+1} - \mathbf{V}_{j+1}| \leq K'|\mathbf{U}_j - \mathbf{V}_j| + h|\mathscr{L}_h[\mathbf{U}_j] - \mathscr{L}_h[\mathbf{V}_j]|, \qquad 0 \leq j \leq J,$$

where

$$K' = 1 + hK + \frac{1}{2!}h^2K^2 + \frac{1}{3!}h^3K^3 + \frac{1}{4!}h^4K^4.$$

Complete the stability proof for the Runge-Kutta method.

1.3.5 Show that the Runge-Kutta method is *consistent* for all $\mathbf{v}(x)$ with continuous $\mathbf{v}'(x)$ if $\mathbf{f}$ satisfies the hypothesis of Theorem 1.1.1 and if in addition $|f| \le B_0$, $|\mathbf{f}_x| \le B_1$. If $\mathbf{v}'(x)$ is Lipschitz-continuous with constant K', show that

$$|\boldsymbol{\tau}_j[\mathbf{v}]| = |\mathscr{L}_h[\mathbf{v}(x_j)] - \mathscr{L}[\mathbf{v}(x_j)]| \le \frac{h}{2}(2K' + KB_0 + B_1).$$

1.3.6 Prove the stability of the modified Adams method (1.3.16) when $\mathbf{f}(x, \mathbf{u})$ is Lipschitz-continuous in $\mathbf{u}$.

1.4 Iterative Solution of Nonlinear Systems; Contracting Maps

All of the numerical methods that we study for solving nonlinear boundary-value problems lead to the problem of solving a nonlinear system of equations (either algebraic or transcendental). In some cases (see for example Section 2.2) the system is only a single equation while in other cases (see Section 3.2) the system may contain hundreds of equations. The procedures used to solve these systems are all iterative so we examine the basic theory of some of these procedures.

The nonlinear system will be assumed of the form

$$\boldsymbol{\phi}(\mathbf{s}) = 0, \tag{1.4.1}$$

or else of the form

$$\mathbf{s} = \mathbf{g}(\mathbf{s}). \tag{1.4.2}$$

Here $\mathbf{s}$ is an n-vector and $\boldsymbol{\phi}$ and $\mathbf{g}$ are vector-valued functions. It is a simple matter to convert one of these forms into the other without gaining or losing roots. For instance, if $A(\mathbf{s})$ is any nth-order matrix which is bounded and nonsingular for all $\mathbf{s}$, then the system of the form (1.4.2) with

$$\mathbf{g}(\mathbf{s}) \equiv \mathbf{s} - A(\mathbf{s})\boldsymbol{\phi}(\mathbf{s}), \tag{1.4.3}$$

is equivalent to the system (1.4.1) (that is, they have identical roots).

The simplest scheme for approximating a root of Equation (1.4.2) is known as *functional iteration*. It proceeds from some initial guess at the root, say $\mathbf{s} = \mathbf{s}^{(0)}$, and then generates the sequence of iterates $\{\mathbf{s}^{(\nu)}\}$ by

$$\mathbf{s}^{(\nu+1)} = \mathbf{g}(\mathbf{s}^{(\nu)}), \qquad \nu = 0, 1, \ldots. \tag{1.4.4}$$

This scheme is occasionally quite practical and can even be used to prove existence of a solution. We have the so-called *Contracting Mapping* theorem, which follows.

THEOREM 1.4.1. *Let* $\mathbf{g}(\mathbf{s})$ *satisfy the Lipschitz condition*

$$|\mathbf{g}(\mathbf{s}) - \mathbf{g}(\mathbf{t})| \le \lambda|\mathbf{s} - \mathbf{t}|, \qquad \lambda < 1$$

for all $\mathbf{s} \in N_\rho(\mathbf{s}^{(0)})$ *and* $\mathbf{t} \in N_\rho(\mathbf{s}^{(0)})$, *where*

$$N_\rho(\mathbf{s}^{(0)}) \equiv \{\mathbf{s} \mid |\mathbf{s} - \mathbf{s}^{(0)}| \leq \rho\}.$$

Let $\mathbf{s}^{(0)}$ *be such that*

$$|\mathbf{s}^{(0)} - \mathbf{g}(\mathbf{s}^{(0)})| \leq (1 - \lambda)\rho.$$

Then the sequence in (1.4.4) *with initial iterate* $\mathbf{s}^{(0)}$ *satisfies*

(a) $\mathbf{s}^{(\nu)} \in N_\rho(\mathbf{s}^{(0)}), \qquad \nu = 0, 1, \ldots;$

(b) $\lim_{\nu \to \infty} \mathbf{s}^{(\nu)} = \mathbf{s}^*;$

(c) $\mathbf{s}^* = \mathbf{g}(\mathbf{s}^*)$ *and is the unique root in* $N_\rho(\mathbf{s}^{(0)})$;

(d) $|\mathbf{s}^{(\nu)} - \mathbf{s}^*| \leq \lambda^\nu \dfrac{|\mathbf{s}^{(1)} - \mathbf{s}^{(0)}|}{1 - \lambda}.$

Proof. By the hypothesis $\mathbf{s}^{(1)} = \mathbf{g}(\mathbf{s}^{(0)}) \in N_\rho(\mathbf{s}^{(0)})$ and we prove (a) by induction. Thus, if $\mathbf{s}^{(1)}, \ldots, \mathbf{s}^{(\nu)} \in N_\rho(\mathbf{s}^{(0)})$, we have

$$|\mathbf{s}^{(\nu+1)} - \mathbf{s}^{(\nu)}| = |\mathbf{g}(\mathbf{s}^{(\nu)}) - \mathbf{g}(\mathbf{s}^{(\nu-1)})| \leq \lambda|\mathbf{s}^{(\nu)} - \mathbf{s}^{(\nu-1)}|.$$

Applying this recursively in ν we get, since $|\mathbf{s}^{(1)} - \mathbf{s}^{(0)}| \leq (1 - \lambda)\rho$,

$$|\mathbf{s}^{(\nu+1)} - \mathbf{s}^{(\nu)}| \leq \lambda^\nu(1 - \lambda)\rho.$$

But then, using $0 \leq \lambda < 1$,

$$\begin{aligned}|\mathbf{s}^{(\nu+1)} - \mathbf{s}^{(0)}| &\leq |\mathbf{s}^{(\nu+1)} - \mathbf{s}^{(\nu)}| + |\mathbf{s}^{(\nu)} - \mathbf{s}^{(\nu-1)}| + \cdots + |\mathbf{s}^{(1)} - \mathbf{s}^{(0)}| \\ &\leq (\lambda^\nu + \lambda^{\nu-1} + \cdots + 1)(1 - \lambda)\rho \leq \rho,\end{aligned}$$

so $\mathbf{s}^{(\nu+1)} \in N_\rho(\mathbf{s}^{(0)})$.

To prove (b) we show that $\{\mathbf{s}^{(\nu)}\}$ is a Cauchy sequence. In fact, just as above, we get for any integers ν and μ

$$|\mathbf{s}^{(\nu+\mu)} - \mathbf{s}^{(\nu)}| \leq \lambda^\nu\rho,$$

and since $|\lambda| < 1$ the Cauchy criterion is satisfied. We call the limit vector $\mathbf{s}^*$. Since $\mathbf{g}(\mathbf{s})$ is continuous, by taking the limit $\nu \to \infty$ of Equations (1.4.4) it follows that $\mathbf{s}^*$ is a root of Equation (1.4.2). If there were two roots in $N_\rho(\mathbf{s}^{(0)})$, say $\mathbf{s}^*$ and $\mathbf{t}^*$, then

$$|\mathbf{s}^* - \mathbf{t}^*| = |\mathbf{g}(\mathbf{s}^*) - \mathbf{g}(\mathbf{t}^*)| \leq \lambda|\mathbf{s}^* - \mathbf{t}^*|,$$

and since $|\lambda| < 1$ we must have $\mathbf{s}^* = \mathbf{t}^*$. Finally, letting $\mu \to \infty$ in an inequality above, we get $|\mathbf{s}^{(\nu)} - \mathbf{s}^*| \leq \lambda^\nu\rho$. However, if, in the recursions leading to this result, we do not use $|\mathbf{s}^{(1)} - \mathbf{s}^{(0)}| < (1 - \lambda)\rho$ but retain the left-hand factor, we obtain (d). ∎

It should be observed that if $\rho = \infty$ in this theorem, then the iterations (1.4.4) converge for any initial estimate $\mathbf{s}^{(0)}$.

As we shall see in many practical applications of contracting maps, the function $\mathbf{g}(\mathbf{s})$ cannot be evaluated exactly. Thus, in place of Equations (1.4.4), the iterates which are actually generated satisfy, say,

$$\mathbf{s}^{(\nu+1)} = \mathbf{g}(\mathbf{s}^{(\nu)}) + \boldsymbol{\delta}^{(\nu)}, \qquad \nu = 0, 1, \ldots, \tag{1.4.5}$$

where the vectors $\boldsymbol{\delta}^{(\nu)}$ represent the errors in evaluating $\mathbf{g}(\mathbf{s}^{(\nu)})$. We cannot expect convergence to a root in this situation, but under proper conditions close approximations can still be obtained. This can be stated as follows.

THEOREM 1.4.2. *Let* $\mathbf{s} = \mathbf{s}^*$ *be a root of Equation* (1.4.2) *where* $\mathbf{g}(\mathbf{s})$ *satisfies the Lipschitz condition*

$$|\mathbf{g}(\mathbf{s}) - \mathbf{g}(\mathbf{t})| \le \lambda|\mathbf{s} - \mathbf{t}|, \qquad \lambda < 1,$$

for all $\mathbf{s} \in N_\rho(\mathbf{s}^*)$ *and* $\mathbf{t} \in N_\rho(\mathbf{s}^*)$. *Let the errors* $\boldsymbol{\delta}^{(\nu)}$ *occurring in Equations* (1.4.5) *be bounded by*

$$|\boldsymbol{\delta}^{(\nu)}| < \delta, \qquad \nu = 0, 1, \ldots.$$

If the initial iterate $\mathbf{s}^{(0)}$ *satisfies* $\mathbf{s}^{(0)} \in N_{\rho_0}(\mathbf{s}^*)$, *where*

$$0 < \rho_0 \le \rho - \frac{\delta}{1 - \lambda},$$

then the iterates $\{\mathbf{s}^{(\nu)}\}$ *generated in Equations* (1.4.5) *satisfy*

(a) $\mathbf{s}^{(\nu)} \in N_\rho(\mathbf{s}^*)$,

(b) $|\mathbf{s}^* - \mathbf{s}^{(\nu)}| \le \lambda^\nu \rho_0 + \dfrac{\delta}{1 - \lambda}, \qquad \nu = 0, 1, \ldots.$

Proof. Since $\mathbf{s}^{(0)} \in N_{\rho_0}(\mathbf{s}^*)$ and $\rho \ge \rho_0$ it is clear that $\mathbf{s}^{(0)} \in N_\rho(\mathbf{s}^*)$. To prove (a) by induction, assume it valid for $\mathbf{s}^{(1)}, \ldots, \mathbf{s}^{(\nu-1)}$ and then, by Equations (1.4.5) and the hypothesis,

$$\begin{aligned} |\mathbf{s}^* - \mathbf{s}^{(\nu)}| &= |\mathbf{g}(\mathbf{s}^*) - \mathbf{g}(\mathbf{s}^{(\nu-1)}) - \boldsymbol{\delta}^{(\nu-1)}| \\ &\le \lambda|\mathbf{s}^* - \mathbf{s}^{(\nu-1)}| + \delta \\ &\le \lambda^2|\mathbf{s}^* - \mathbf{s}^{(\nu-2)}| + \lambda\delta + \delta \\ &\;\;\vdots \\ &\le \lambda^\nu|\mathbf{s}^* - \mathbf{s}^{(0)}| + \frac{1 - \lambda^\nu}{1 - \lambda}\,\delta. \end{aligned}$$

But $|\mathbf{s}^* - \mathbf{s}^{(0)}| \le \rho_0$ and $0 \le \lambda < 1$ so that $|\mathbf{s}^* - \mathbf{s}^{(\nu)}| \le \rho_0 + (\delta/1 - \lambda)$ from which (a) follows. Then (b) is obvious from the final inequality above. ∎

It is clear from (b) that the error bound on the computed root can be made arbitrarily close to $\delta/(1 - \lambda)$, but perhaps no smaller.

To "solve" equations of the form (1.4.1) we need only determine a matrix $A(\mathbf{s})$ such that $\mathbf{g}(\mathbf{s})$ as defined in Equation (1.4.3) satisfies the hypothesis of Theorem 1.4.1 (or Theorem 1.4.2 if errors are permitted). A particularly effective procedure of this form is *Newton's method*, in which we take $A(\mathbf{s}) \equiv J^{-1}(\mathbf{s})$, where

$$J(\mathbf{s}) \equiv \frac{\partial \boldsymbol{\phi}(\mathbf{s})}{\partial \mathbf{s}} \equiv \left(\frac{\partial \phi_i(\mathbf{s})}{\partial s_j}\right)$$

is the Jacobian matrix of $\boldsymbol{\phi}$ with respect to $\mathbf{s}$. The corresponding iteration scheme is

$$\mathbf{s}^{(\nu+1)} = \mathbf{s}^{(\nu)} - J^{-1}(\mathbf{s}^{(\nu)})\boldsymbol{\phi}(\mathbf{s}^{(\nu)}), \qquad \nu = 0, 1, \ldots. \tag{1.4.6}$$

Of course the computations should not be carried out in this form, employing the inverse of $J(\mathbf{s}^{(\nu)})$, but rather by solving the linear systems in

$$J(\mathbf{s}^{(\nu)})\,\Delta\mathbf{s}^{(\nu)} = -\boldsymbol{\phi}(s^{(\nu)}), \qquad \mathbf{s}^{(\nu+1)} = \mathbf{s}^{(\nu)} + \Delta\mathbf{s}^{(\nu)}, \qquad \nu = 0, 1, \ldots. \tag{1.4.7}$$

The convergence of Newton's method is frequently quite rapid, even better in fact than the geometric type of convergence illustrated in Theorems 1.4.1 and 1.4.2. We do not present the best possible results here but shall be content to show that in a sense the previous type of error analysis applies with *arbitrarily small* values of λ. Thus we state the following.

THEOREM 1.4.3. *Let the function* $\boldsymbol{\phi}(\mathbf{s})$ *have a zero at* $\mathbf{s} = \mathbf{s}^*$, *continuous first derivatives in some neighborhood* $N_\rho(\mathbf{s}^*)$ *of* $\mathbf{s}^*$ *and nonsingular Jacobian at* $\mathbf{s}^*$, *that is,* $\det J(\mathbf{s}^*) \neq 0$. *Then for each* λ *in* $0 < \lambda < 1$ *there exists a positive number* ρ_λ *such that for any* $\mathbf{s}^{(0)} \in N_{\rho_\lambda}(\mathbf{s}^*)$ *the Newton iterates* (1.4.6) *converge to* $\mathbf{s}^*$ *with*

$$|\mathbf{s}^* - \mathbf{s}^{(\nu)}| \leq \lambda^\nu |\mathbf{s}^* - \mathbf{s}^{(0)}|.$$

Proof. As the terms in the function $\det J(\mathbf{s})$ are products of combinations of the derivatives $\partial\phi_i(\mathbf{s})/\partial s_j$, this function must be continuous on $N_\rho(\mathbf{s}^*)$. But since $\det J(\mathbf{s}^*) \neq 0$, it follows by the continuity that $\det J(\mathbf{s}) \neq 0$ on $N_{\rho'}(\mathbf{s}^*)$ for some positive $\rho' \leq \rho$. Now consider the matrix

$$B(\mathbf{s}, \mathbf{h}) \equiv I - J^{-1}(\mathbf{s})J(\mathbf{s} + \mathbf{h}),$$

which for each $\mathbf{s} \in N_{\rho'}(\mathbf{s}^*)$ is a continuous function of $\mathbf{h}$ for $\mathbf{s} + \mathbf{h} \in N_\rho(\mathbf{s}^*)$. If the elements of the inverse of the Jacobian are denoted by $J^{-1}(\mathbf{s}) \equiv (a_{ij}(\mathbf{s}))$ then we may write the *maximum absolute row sum* of $B(\mathbf{s}, \mathbf{h})$ as

$$\delta(\mathbf{s}, \mathbf{h}) \equiv \max_{1 \leq i \leq n} \left\{ \left| 1 - \sum_{k=1}^{n} a_{ik}(\mathbf{s}) \frac{\partial \phi_k(\mathbf{s} + \mathbf{h})}{\partial s_i} \right| + \sum_{j \neq i} \left| \sum_{k=1}^{n} a_{ik}(\mathbf{s}) \frac{\partial \phi_k(\mathbf{s} + \mathbf{h})}{\partial s_j} \right| \right\}.$$

It is clear that $\delta(\mathbf{s}, \mathbf{0}) = 0$ for each $\mathbf{s} \in N_{\rho'}(\mathbf{s}^*)$ since $B(\mathbf{s}, \mathbf{0}) = 0$ and $\delta(\mathbf{s}, \mathbf{h})$ is a continuous function of $\mathbf{h}$ whenever $B(\mathbf{s}, \mathbf{h})$ is. Thus, for any positive $\lambda < 1$, we can be assured that $\delta(\mathbf{s}, \mathbf{h}) \leq \lambda < 1$, provided $\mathbf{s}$ is sufficiently close to $\mathbf{s}^*$ and $\mathbf{h}$ is sufficiently small.

The details that we actually use in the proof are slightly more complicated than the above, but the idea is the same. In place of $\delta(\mathbf{s}, \mathbf{h})$ we must introduce a function of the three vectors $\mathbf{s}$, $\mathbf{h}$ and $\boldsymbol{\theta} = (\theta_1, \ldots, \theta_n)$ with $0 < \theta_i < 1$:

$$\delta(\mathbf{s}, \mathbf{h}, \boldsymbol{\theta}) \equiv \max_{1 \leq i \leq n} \left\{ \left| 1 - \sum_{k=1}^{n} a_{ik}(\mathbf{s}) \frac{\partial \phi_k(\mathbf{s} + \theta_k \mathbf{h})}{\partial s_i} \right| + \sum_{j \neq 1} \left| \sum_{k=1}^{n} a_{ik}(\mathbf{s}) \frac{\partial \phi_k(\mathbf{s} + \theta_k \mathbf{h})}{\partial s_j} \right| \right\}.$$

Again $\delta(\mathbf{s}, \mathbf{0}, \boldsymbol{\theta}) = 0$ for $\mathbf{s} \in N_{\rho'}(\mathbf{s}^*)$ and $\delta(\mathbf{s}, \mathbf{h}, \boldsymbol{\theta})$ is continuous in $\mathbf{h}$ and $\boldsymbol{\theta}$ whenever $B(\mathbf{s}, \mathbf{h})$ is continuous in $\mathbf{h}$. Thus for any positive $\lambda < 1$ we can find a $\rho_\lambda > 0$ such that

$$\delta(\mathbf{s}, \mathbf{h}, \boldsymbol{\theta}) \leq \lambda < 1, \tag{1.4.8a}$$

provided that

$$\mathbf{s} \in N_{\rho_\lambda}(\mathbf{s}^*), \qquad |\mathbf{h}| \leq \rho_\lambda, \qquad \text{and} \quad 0 < \theta_i < 1, \qquad i = 1, 2, \ldots, n. \tag{1.4.8b}$$

(In general we may expect that $\rho_\lambda \leq \rho'/2$.)

Now we shall show that the iterates in Equations (1.4.6) satisfy the basic inequality

$$|\mathbf{s}^* - \mathbf{s}^{(\nu+1)}| \leq \lambda |\mathbf{s}^* - \mathbf{s}^{(\nu)}|, \qquad \nu = 0, 1, \ldots, \tag{1.4.9}$$

provided that $\mathbf{s}^{(0)} \in N_{\rho_\lambda}(\mathbf{s}^*)$. For an induction, assume it true for $\mathbf{s}^{(1)}, \ldots, \mathbf{s}^{(\nu)}$ and then from Equations (1.4.6) and $\boldsymbol{\phi}(\mathbf{s}^*) = 0$,

$$\begin{aligned} \mathbf{s}^* - \mathbf{s}^{(\nu+1)} &= \mathbf{s}^* - \mathbf{s}^{(\nu)} + J^{-1}(\mathbf{s}^{(\nu)}) \boldsymbol{\phi}(\mathbf{s}^{(\nu)}) \\ &= [\mathbf{s}^* - \mathbf{s}^{(\nu)}] - J^{-1}(\mathbf{s}^{(\nu)})[\boldsymbol{\phi}(\mathbf{s}^*) - \boldsymbol{\phi}(\mathbf{s}^{(\nu)})]. \end{aligned}$$

But by Taylor's theorem we have, with $\mathbf{h}^{(\nu)} \equiv \mathbf{s}^* - \mathbf{s}^{(\nu)}$,

$$\phi_i(\mathbf{s}^*) = \phi_i(\mathbf{s}^{(\nu)} + \mathbf{h}^{(\nu)}) = \phi_i(\mathbf{s}^{(\nu)}) + \sum_{j=1}^{n} \frac{\partial \phi_i(\mathbf{s}^{(\nu)} + \theta_i \mathbf{h}^{(\nu)})}{\partial s_j} h_j^{(\nu)}, \qquad 0 < \theta_i < 1, \qquad i = 1, 2, \ldots, n.$$

Using this in the previous equation yields, componentwise,

$$\begin{aligned} s_i^* - s_i^{(\nu+1)} = {} & \left[1 - \sum_{k=1}^{n} a_{ik}(\mathbf{s}^{(\nu)}) \frac{\partial \phi_k(\mathbf{s}^{(\nu)} + \theta_k \mathbf{h}^{(\nu)})}{\partial s_i} \right] (s_i^* - s_i^{(\nu)}) \\ & + \sum_{j \neq i} \left[\sum_{k=1}^{n} a_{ik}(\mathbf{s}^{(\nu)}) \frac{\partial \phi_k(\mathbf{s}^{(\nu)} + \theta_k \mathbf{h}^{(\nu)})}{\partial s_j} \right] (s_j^* - s_j^{(\nu)}), \qquad 1 \leq i \leq n. \end{aligned}$$

Taking absolute values, we easily obtain

$$|\mathbf{s}^* - \mathbf{s}^{(\nu+1)}| \leq \delta(\mathbf{s}^{(\nu)}, \mathbf{s}^* - \mathbf{s}^{(\nu)}, \boldsymbol{\theta})|\mathbf{s}^* - \mathbf{s}^{(\nu)}|.$$

But obviously this result applies for $\nu = 0$ and so the induction is concluded. The theorem now follows, as in the proof of Theorem 1.4.1, from the recursive application of the basic inequality (1.4.9). ∎

If $\boldsymbol{\phi}(\mathbf{s})$ has continuous second derivatives then it can be shown that Newton's method is frequently second-order (see Problem 1.4.4), that is, that

$$|\mathbf{s}^* - \mathbf{s}^{(\nu+1)}| \leq M|\mathbf{s}^* - \mathbf{s}^{(\nu)}|^2, \qquad \nu = 0, 1, \ldots.$$

In fact this can easily be seen from the above proof since $\delta(\mathbf{s}, \mathbf{h}, \boldsymbol{\theta}) = \delta(\mathbf{s}, \mathbf{0}, \boldsymbol{\theta}) + \mathcal{O}(\mathbf{h}) = \mathcal{O}(\mathbf{h})$, using the expansion to next order in h. Further results on Newton's method are contained in Problems 1.4.6 and 1.4.7.

In the case of *scalar equations* there are numerous procedures that may yield convergent second-order or even higher-order iterations. A particularly effective such scheme for solving $s = g(s)$ is *Aitken's* δ^2*-method*, defined as

$$s_{\nu+1} = s_\nu - \frac{\delta_\nu^2}{\delta'_{\nu+1} - \delta_\nu}, \qquad \nu = 0, 1, \ldots, \tag{1.4.10a}$$

where

$$\begin{aligned} s'_{\nu+1} &= g(s_\nu), & s''_{\nu+1} &= g(s'_{\nu+1}); \\ \delta_\nu &= s'_{\nu+1} - s_\nu, & \delta'_{\nu+1} &= s''_{\nu+1} - s'_\nu. \end{aligned} \tag{1.4.10b}$$

The convergence properties of this scheme are thoroughly discussed in Isaacson and Keller (1966), pp. 103–108.

Problems

1.4.1 If $\mathbf{g}(\mathbf{s})$ has continuous first derivatives for all $\mathbf{s} \in N_\rho(\mathbf{s}^{(0)})$ and

$$\mu \equiv \max_{1 \leq i \leq n,\, \mathbf{s} \in N_\rho(\mathbf{s}^{(0)})} \sum_{j=1}^{n} |\partial g_i(\mathbf{s})/\partial s_j| < 1, \qquad |\mathbf{s}^{(0)} - \mathbf{g}(\mathbf{s}^{(0)})| \leq (1 - \mu)\rho,$$

show that the *conclusions* of Theorem 1.4.1 hold for the sequence $\mathbf{s}^{(\nu+1)} = \mathbf{g}(\mathbf{s}^{(\nu)})$.

1.4.2 If $\mathbf{g}(\mathbf{s}^*) = \mathbf{s}^*$ and $|\mathbf{g}(\mathbf{s}^*) - \mathbf{g}(\mathbf{s})| \leq \lambda|\mathbf{s}^* - \mathbf{s}|$, $\lambda < 1$ for all $\mathbf{s} \in N_\rho(\mathbf{s}^*)$, then $\mathbf{s}^{(\nu+1)} = \mathbf{g}(\mathbf{s}^{(\nu)}) \rightarrow \mathbf{s}^*$ for any $\mathbf{s}^{(0)} \in N_\rho(\mathbf{s}^*)$. [Note that this is weaker than the Lipschitz continuity of $\mathbf{g}(\mathbf{s})$.]

1.4.3 Let the scalar function $\phi(s)$ have a continuous first derivative which satisfies $0 < \gamma \leq \phi'(s) \leq \Gamma$ for all s. Show that the iterations

$$s_{\nu+1} = s_\nu - m\phi(s_\nu), \qquad \nu = 0, 1, \ldots,$$

converge to the root of $\phi(s) = 0$ for any s_0 and fixed m in

$$0 < m < \frac{2}{\Gamma}.$$

Show that the "best" choice for the parameter is

$$m = \frac{2}{\Gamma + \gamma},$$

in which case

$$\lambda = \frac{\Gamma - \gamma}{\Gamma + \gamma}$$

is a bound on the geometric convergence factor.

1.4.4 Show that Newton's method with initial guess $\mathbf{s}^{(0)}$ is actually second-order, provided that $\boldsymbol{\phi}(\mathbf{s})$ has continuous second derivatives which satisfy

$$\sum_{i,j,k} \left| \frac{\partial^2 \phi_k(\mathbf{s})}{\partial s_i \, \partial s_j} \right| \le \frac{\delta_0^2}{M} < 1,$$

where $\boldsymbol{\phi}(\mathbf{s}^*) = 0$, $\|J^{-1}(\mathbf{s})\| \le M$ for all $\mathbf{s} \in N_\rho(\mathbf{s}^*)$ and

$$\delta_0 = |\mathbf{s}^* - \mathbf{s}^{(0)}| < \rho.$$

1.4.5* Prove the following.

THEOREM 1.4.4. *Let $\boldsymbol{\phi}(\mathbf{s})$ have Lipschitz-continuous first derivatives on $N_\rho(\mathbf{s}^{(0)})$ and satisfy*

(a) $J(\mathbf{s}^{(0)}) \equiv \dfrac{\partial \boldsymbol{\phi}(\mathbf{s}^{(0)})}{\partial \mathbf{s}}$ *is nonsingular,* $\|J^{-1}(\mathbf{s}^{(0)})\| \le K_0$;

(b) $\|J(\mathbf{s}) - J(\mathbf{t})\| \le K_1 |\mathbf{s} - \mathbf{t}|$ *for all* $\mathbf{s}$ *and* $\mathbf{t} \in N_\rho(\mathbf{s}^{(0)})$;

(c) $|J^{-1}(\mathbf{s}^{(0)}) \boldsymbol{\phi}(\mathbf{s}^{(0)})| \le \eta$.

Further, let

(d) $K_0 K_1 \rho < 1, \qquad \eta \le (1 - K_0 K_1 \rho)\rho.$

Then $\boldsymbol{\phi}(\mathbf{s}) = 0$ has a unique root in $N_\rho(\mathbf{s}^{(0)})$. This root is the limit of the sequence $\{\mathbf{s}^{(\nu)}\}$ defined by

$$\mathbf{s}^{(0)} = \mathbf{s}^{(0)},$$
$$\mathbf{s}^{(\nu+1)} = \mathbf{s}^{(\nu)} - J^{-1}(\mathbf{s}^{(0)}) \boldsymbol{\phi}(\mathbf{s}^{(\nu)}), \qquad \nu = 0, 1, 2, \ldots.$$

[HINT: Show that the mapping $\mathbf{s} = \mathbf{g}(\mathbf{s})$ with $\mathbf{g}(\mathbf{s}) \equiv \mathbf{s} - J^{-1}(\mathbf{s}^{(0)}) \boldsymbol{\phi}(\mathbf{s})$ satisfies the hypothesis of Theorem 1.4.1.]

1.4.6 With $J(\mathbf{s}) \equiv \partial \boldsymbol{\phi}(\mathbf{s})/\partial \mathbf{s}$ continuous on a convex domain D, define $J(\mathbf{s}, \mathbf{t}) \equiv \int_0^1 J(\mathbf{s} + \theta[\mathbf{t} - \mathbf{s}]) \, d\theta$. For all $\mathbf{s}$ and $\mathbf{t} \in D$ show that $J(\mathbf{s}, \mathbf{t}) = J(\mathbf{t}, \mathbf{s})$ and $\phi(\mathbf{s}) - \phi(\mathbf{t}) = J(\mathbf{s}, \mathbf{t})(\mathbf{s} - \mathbf{t})$.

If $\|J(\mathbf{s}) - J(\mathbf{t})\| \le K|\mathbf{s} - \mathbf{t}|$ for all $\mathbf{s}$ and $\mathbf{t} \in D$, show that

$$\|J(\mathbf{s}) - J(\mathbf{s}, \mathbf{t})\| \le \frac{K}{2} |\mathbf{s} - \mathbf{t}|.$$

1.4.7* Prove the following.

THEOREM 1.4.5. *Let the hypothesis of Theorem* 1.4.4 *be satisfied and in addition*

(d)′ $K_0 K_1 \rho < \frac{2}{3}, \qquad \eta \le (1 - \frac{3}{2} K_0 K_1 \rho)\rho.$

Then Newton's method,

$$\mathbf{s}^{(\nu+1)} = \mathbf{s}^{(\nu)} - J^{-1}(\mathbf{s}^{(\nu)})\boldsymbol{\phi}(\mathbf{s}^{(\nu)}), \qquad \nu = 0, 1, 2, \ldots,$$

with initial guess $\mathbf{s}^{(0)}$, *converges to the unique root of* $\boldsymbol{\phi}(\mathbf{s}) = 0$ *in* $N_\rho(\mathbf{s}^{(0)})$. [HINT: First show that $J(\mathbf{s})$ is nonsingular for all $\mathbf{s} \in N_\rho(\mathbf{s}^{(0)})$. Then show by induction, using Problem 1.4.6, that all $\mathbf{s}^{(\nu)} \in N_\rho(\mathbf{s}^{(0)})$. Use the unique root $\mathbf{s}^*$, established in Problem 1.4.5, and deduce, again using Problem 1.4.6, that

$$|\mathbf{s}^{(\nu+1)} - \mathbf{s}^*| \le \frac{K_0 K_1 \rho}{2(1 - K_0 K_1 \rho)} |\mathbf{s}^{(\nu)} - \mathbf{s}^*|, \qquad \nu = 1, 2, \ldots.].$$

1.4.8* (Continuation of Problem 1.4.7.) Show that the errors in Newton's method under the conditions of Theorem 1.4.5 actually satisfy

$$|\mathbf{s}^{(\nu+1)} - \mathbf{s}^*| \le \left(\frac{\lambda}{3}\right)^{2^\nu} \frac{\rho}{\lambda}, \qquad \nu = 1, 2, \ldots,$$

where $\lambda = K_0 K_1 \rho / 2(1 - K_0 K_1 \rho)$.

SUPPLEMENTARY REFERENCES AND NOTES

Section 1.1 The theory of existence, uniqueness, and dependence of solutions on parameters for initial-value problems is quite well-developed. Accounts of this theory, in order of increasing sophistication, are to be found in Birkhoff and Rota (1962), Ince (1944), Coddington and Levinson (1955), and Hartman (1964).

Section 1.2 The theory of linear two-point boundary-value problems is treated in Coddington and Levinson (1955), pp. 284–312; Ince (1944), pp. 204–222, and Hartman (1964), pp. 407–412. The important special case of second-order equations receives a thorough treatment in all of these texts. Existence theory for general nonlinear problems is not fully developed. The case of periodic solutions is treated in Hartman (1964), pp. 413–435, and these methods can also be applied to more general boundary-value problems. Many other results are contained in journals; a few references related to the present study are R. Conti (1961), H. Keller (1966), M. Lees (1966), A. Lasota and Z. Opial (1966).

Section 1.3 The theory of Dahlquist (1956), (1959) is basic for a thorough understanding of numerical methods for initial-value problems. This theory is presented in great detail and extended in Henrici (1962), the standard reference in this field. Briefer accounts are contained in Isaacson and Keller (1966), Antosiewicz and Gautschi (1962), and their references.

Section 1.4 More general discussions of iterative methods for solving nonlinear systems are contained in the texts: Ostrowski (1960), Traub (1964), Isaacson and Keller (1966). A thorough study of the convergence of Newton's method is contained in Kantorovich and Akilov (1964) and the effect of roundoff or inaccurate evaluation of the functions and derivatives is given by Lancaster (1966). Roundoff effects in contracting maps are studied in detail by Urabe (1956). Additional iterative methods of interest are studied in Ortega and Rockoff (1966).

CHAPTER 2

INITIAL-VALUE METHODS (SHOOTING)

2.1 *Linear Second-Order Equations and Systems*

We consider first the single linear second-order equation

$$Ly \equiv -y'' + p(x)y' + q(x)y = r(x), \qquad a \le x \le b, \tag{2.1.1a}$$

subject to the general two-point boundary conditions

$$a_0 y(a) - a_1 y'(a) = \alpha, \quad b_0 y(b) + b_1 y'(b) = \beta, \quad |a_0| + |b_0| \ne 0. \tag{2.1.1b}$$

We assume the functions $p(x)$, $q(x)$, and $r(x)$ to be continuous on $[a, b]$ and require that *the homogeneous problem*

$$Lz = 0; \qquad a_0 z(a) - a_1 z'(a) = 0, \qquad b_0 z(b) + b_1 z'(b) = 0 \tag{2.1.2}$$

have only the trivial solution, $z(x) \equiv 0$. Then by the Alternative Theorem (see Problem 1.2.5) the boundary-value problem (2.1.1) has a solution which is unique. Of course we could have required (2.1.1) to have a unique solution, and then it would follow that (2.1.2) has only the trivial solution. We shall describe and analyze the initial-value or shooting method for computing accurate approximations to the solution of the linear boundary-value problem (2.1.1).

Two functions $y^{(1)}(x)$ and $y^{(2)}(x)$ are uniquely defined on $[a, b]$ as solutions of the respective initial-value problems

$$Ly^{(1)} = r(x); \qquad y^{(1)}(a) = -\alpha c_1, \qquad y^{(1)\prime}(a) = -\alpha c_0; \tag{2.1.3a}$$

and

$$Ly^{(2)} = 0; \qquad y^{(2)}(a) = a_1, \qquad y^{(2)\prime}(a) = a_0. \tag{2.1.3b}$$

Here c_0 and c_1 are any constants such that

$$a_1c_0 - a_0c_1 = 1. \tag{2.1.3c}$$

The fact that these problems have unique solutions on $[a, b]$ is an obvious consequence of Theorem 1.1.1. The function $y(x)$ defined by

$$y(x) = y(x; s) \equiv y^{(1)}(x) + sy^{(2)}(x), \qquad a \leq x \leq b, \tag{2.1.4a}$$

satisfies $a_0y(a) - a_1y'(a) = \alpha(a_1c_0 - a_0c_1) = \alpha$ and so will be a solution of problem (2.1.1) if s is chosen such that

$$\phi(s) \equiv b_0y(b; s) + b_1y'(b; s) - \beta = 0.$$

This equation is linear in s and has the single root

$$s = \frac{\beta - [b_0y^{(1)}(b) + b_1y^{(1)'}(b)]}{[b_0y^{(2)}(b) + b_1y^{(2)'}(b)]}, \tag{2.1.4b}$$

provided that $[b_0y^{(2)}(b) + b_1y^{(2)'}(b)] \neq 0$. However, if this quantity does vanish, then $z(x) \equiv y^{(2)}(x)$ would be a *nontrivial* solution of the homogeneous problem (2.1.2). Since this has been excluded, we see that the above construction of a solution of (2.1.1) is valid.

The initial-value or shooting method consists in simply carrying out the above procedure numerically; that is, we compute approximations to $y^{(1)}(x)$, $y^{(1)'}(x)$, $y^{(2)}(x)$, and $y^{(2)'}(x)$ and use them in Equations (2.1.4). To solve the initial-value problems (2.1.3) and (2.1.4) numerically, we first write them as equivalent first-order systems, say

$$\begin{pmatrix} y^{(1)} \\ v^{(1)} \end{pmatrix}' = \begin{pmatrix} v^{(1)} \\ pv^{(1)} + qy^{(1)} - r \end{pmatrix}, \quad y^{(1)}(a) = -\alpha c_1, \quad v^{(1)}(a) = -\alpha c_0; \tag{2.1.5a}$$

and

$$\begin{pmatrix} y^{(2)} \\ v^{(2)} \end{pmatrix}' = \begin{pmatrix} v^{(2)} \\ pv^{(2)} + qy^{(2)} \end{pmatrix}, \quad y^{(2)}(a) = a_1, \quad v^{(2)}(a) = a_0. \tag{2.1.5b}$$

Now any of the numerical methods discussed in Section 1.3 can be employed. Of course, the same method should be used to solve both systems (2.1.5a–b), and for convenience we will require that this be done on the net

$$x_j = a + jh, \qquad j = 0, 1, \ldots, J, \qquad h = \frac{b - a}{J}; \tag{2.1.6}$$

so that $x_J = b$.

Let the numerical solutions of (2.1.5) obtained on the net (2.1.6) be denoted, in obvious notation, by the net functions

$$\{Y_j^{(1)}\}, \quad \{V_j^{(1)}\}, \quad \{Y_j^{(2)}\}, \quad \{V_j^{(2)}\}.$$

We assume that the scheme employed has an order of accuracy at least p and is stable. Then if the solutions of problems (2.1.5a–b) are sufficiently smooth, we are assured that for $0 \leq j \leq J$,

$$|y^{(\nu)}(x_j) - Y_j^{(\nu)}| = \mathcal{O}(h^p), \quad |v^{(\nu)}(x_j) - V_j^{(\nu)}| = \mathcal{O}(h^p), \quad \nu = 1, 2, \tag{2.1.7}$$

provided the initial data used in the calculations also satisfy these relations. At the point $x_0 = a$ the exact data can be used so that

$$Y_0^{(1)} = -\alpha c_1, \quad v_0^{(1)} = -\alpha c_0\,; \quad Y_0^{(2)} = a_1, \quad V_0^{(2)} = a_0. \tag{2.1.8}$$

To approximate the solution, $y(x)$, of the boundary-value problem (2.1.1) we now form, by analogy with Equations (2.1.4),

$$Y_j = Y_j^{(1)} + s_h Y_j^{(2)}, \quad j = 0, 1, \ldots, J, \tag{2.1.9a}$$

where

$$s_h = \frac{\beta - [b_0 Y_J^{(1)} + b_1 V_J^{(1)}]}{[b_0 Y_J^{(2)} + b_1 V_J^{(2)}]}. \tag{2.1.9b}$$

We may expect, in light of the estimates (2.1.7), that $|Y_j - y(x_j)| = \mathcal{O}(h^p)$. This is indeed true but, as we shall also show, there may be practical difficulties in actually computing an accurate approximation to $y(x)$ for a fixed small $h > 0$.

Let us define the errors in the numerical solutions by

$$e_j \equiv Y_j - y(x_j), \quad e_j^{(\nu)} \equiv Y_j^{(\nu)} - y^{(\nu)}(x_j), \quad \varepsilon_j^{(\nu)} \equiv V_j^{(\nu)} - v^{(\nu)}(x_j),$$
$$\nu = 1, 2; \quad 0 \leq j \leq J.$$

Evaluate Equation (2.1.4a) at $x = x_j$ and subtract the result from Equation (2.1.9a) to get, with the above notation,

$$\begin{aligned} e_j &= e_j^{(1)} + s_h Y_j^{(2)} - s y^{(2)}(x_j) \\ &= [e_j^{(1)} + s e_j^{(2)}] + (s_h - s) Y_j^{(2)}, \quad 0 \leq j \leq J. \end{aligned} \tag{2.1.10a}$$

However, a small calculation, using Equations (2.1.4b) and (2.1.9b), reveals that

$$s_h - s = -\frac{[b_0 e_J^{(1)} + b_1 \varepsilon_J^{(1)}] + s[b_0 e_J^{(2)} + b_1 \varepsilon_J^{(2)}]}{(b_0 Y_J^{(2)} + b_1 V_J^{(2)})}. \tag{2.1.10b}$$

Recalling the estimates (2.1.7), we have

$$b_0 Y_J^{(2)} + b_1 V_J^{(2)} = (b_0 y^{(2)}(b) + b_1 y^{(2)\prime}(b)) + \mathcal{O}(h^p),$$

and so for sufficiently small h the denominator in Equation (2.1.10b) cannot vanish. From Equations (2.1.10) we now conclude that

$$|Y_j - y(x_j)| = \mathcal{O}(h^p), \quad 0 \leq j \leq J.$$

It is no more difficult to demonstrate that

$$V_j \equiv V_j^{(1)} + s_h V_j^{(2)} = y'(x_j) + \mathcal{O}(h^p), \qquad 0 \leq j \leq J,$$

so we also have accurate approximations to the derivative of the solution, for sufficiently small h.

The above result can now be summarized as follows.

THEOREM 2.1.1. *Let the boundary-value problem* (2.1.1) *have a unique solution, $y(x)$. Let the numerical solutions of the initial-value problems* (2.1.5a–b), *using a stable method with order of accuracy p on the net* (2.1.6), *be denoted by* $\{Y_j^{(\nu)}\}$, $\{V_j^{(\nu)}\}$, $\nu = 1, 2$. *Then the net functions*

$$Y_j = Y_j^{(1)} + s_h Y_j^{(2)}, \qquad V_j = V_j^{(1)} + s_h V_j^{(2)}, \qquad 0 \leq j \leq J,$$

with s_h as given by Equation (2.1.9b) *and h sufficiently small, satisfy*

$$|y(x_j) - Y_j| = \mathcal{O}(h^p), \qquad |y'(x_j) - V_j| = \mathcal{O}(h^p), \qquad 0 \leq j \leq J,$$

provided the initial-value problems (2.1.5a–b) *have sufficiently smooth solutions.* ∎

A particularly important case of the general boundary-value problem (2.1.1) occurs when $a_0 = b_0 = 1$ and $a_1 = b_1 = 0$ in the boundary conditions (that is, y specified at both ends). The error expressions (2.1.10) yield in this special case

$$e_j = [e_j^{(1)} + se_j^{(2)}] - [e_J^{(1)} + se_J^{(2)}]\frac{Y_j^{(2)}}{Y_J^{(2)}}, \qquad 0 \leq j \leq J.$$

However, the initial condition imposed on $Y_j^{(2)}$ is now, from Equations (2.1.8) with $a_1 = 0$, just $Y_0^{(2)} = 0$. Thus we have $e_0 = e_J = 0$ and our approximate solution must be very accurate near both endpoints. Of course if the ratio $Y_j^{(2)}/Y_J^{(2)}$ becomes large in the interior, $a < x_j < b$, this accuracy may be greatly diminished. In particular, if the fixed number $y^{(2)}(b)$ is small, then $Y_J^{(2)} = y^{(2)}(b) + \mathcal{O}(h^p)$, which depends upon h, may be very close to zero for some particular mesh spacing.

Returning to the general problem, we see that a similar loss in accuracy or error magnification may occur whenever

$$Y_j^{(2)}/(b_0 Y_J^{(2)} + b_1 V_J^{(2)})$$

becomes very large. Of course since this ratio involves computed quantities, a practical assessment of this difficulty is possible.

Another very important source of difficulty can be loss of significant digits in forming the expressions in Equations (2.1.9a). Thus if $Y_j^{(1)}$ and $s_h Y_j^{(2)}$ are nearly equal and of opposite sign for some range of j values, we get cancellation of the leading digits. Unfortunately this situation can easily arise. For instance suppose that the solution of the initial-value problem (2.1.3a) grows in magnitude as $x \to b$ and that the boundary condition at $x = b$ has $b_1 = 0$ (that is, $y(b) = \beta$ is specified). Then if $|\beta| \ll |b_0 Y_J^{(1)}|$ we have, from Equation (2.1.9b), approximately

$$s_h \doteq -(Y_J^{(1)}/Y_J^{(2)}),$$

and so Equation (2.1.9a) becomes

$$Y_j \doteq Y_j^{(1)} - \left(\frac{Y_J^{(1)}}{Y_J^{(2)}}\right) Y_j^{(2)}.$$

Clearly the cancellation problem occurs here for x_j near b. Note that the solution $y^{(1)}(x)$ need not grow very fast, and in fact for $\beta = 0$, corresponding to the commonly-occurring boundary condition $y(b) = 0$, the difficulty is always potentially present. If either of the solutions, $y^{(1)}(x)$ or $y^{(2)}(x)$, changes rapidly near $x = b$, then these errors will not propagate very far from the endpoint.

The loss of significant digits can also occur with $b_1 \neq 0$ but is always easily observed. However, when employing an automatic digital computer *one must remember to test for this effect* as there may be no sign of it in a list of the leading digits of $\{Y_j\}$. If the loss of significance cannot be easily overcome by carrying additional figures, that is, by using double-precision arithmetic, then the parallel-shooting techniques of Section 2.4 can be employed.

There is no difficulty in extending the results of this section to the case in which $a_0 = 0$ but $a_1 \neq 0$ in the boundary conditions (2.1.1b). We pose this as Problem 2.1.1.

The initial-value method can easily be applied to problems which are much more general than problem (2.1.1). To illustrate such applications we shall consider a two-point boundary-value problem for a system of n coupled linear second-order differential equations. As we shall see, such problems can be solved in terms of the solution of $n + 1$ initial-value problems for the system. More general linear (and nonlinear) systems are treated in Section 2.3.

We write the system as

$$L\mathbf{y} \equiv -\mathbf{y}'' + P(x)\mathbf{y}' + Q(x)\mathbf{y} = \mathbf{r}(x), \qquad a \leq x \leq b, \qquad (2.1.11a)$$

where $\mathbf{y}(x)$ and $\mathbf{r}(x)$ are n-vectors and $P(x)$ and $Q(x)$ are nth-order matrices whose elements are continuous functions of x. The two-point boundary conditions are

$$\begin{aligned} A_0\mathbf{y}(a) - A_1\mathbf{y}'(a) &= \boldsymbol{\alpha}, \qquad \det A_0 \neq 0, \\ B_0\mathbf{y}(b) + B_1\mathbf{y}'(b) &= \boldsymbol{\beta}. \end{aligned} \qquad (2.1.11b)$$

Here A_0, A_1, B_0, and B_1 are nth-order constant matrices, $\boldsymbol{\alpha}$ and $\boldsymbol{\beta}$ are constant n-vectors and again we assume that the homogeneous problem, that is, $\boldsymbol{\alpha} \equiv \boldsymbol{\beta} \equiv \mathbf{r}(x) \equiv 0$ in (2.1.11), has only the trivial solution, $\mathbf{y}(x) \equiv 0$. An alternative theorem holds for such systems and so we know that a unique solution exists.

We now introduce $n + 1$ vector-valued functions $\mathbf{y}^{(\nu)}(x)$, $\nu = 0, 1, \ldots, n$, as the solutions of the corresponding initial-value problems

$$L\mathbf{y}^{(0)} = \mathbf{r}(x), \qquad A_0\mathbf{y}^{(0)}(a) - A_1\mathbf{y}^{(0)\prime}(a) = \boldsymbol{\alpha}, \qquad \mathbf{y}^{(0)\prime}(a) = \mathbf{0}; \tag{2.1.12a}$$

$$L\mathbf{y}^{(\nu)} = \mathbf{0}, \qquad A_0\mathbf{y}^{(\nu)}(a) - A_1\mathbf{y}^{(\nu)\prime}(a) = \mathbf{0}, \qquad \mathbf{y}^{(\nu)\prime}(a) = \mathbf{I}^{(\nu)}, \qquad \nu = 1, 2, \ldots, n. \tag{2.1.12b$^\nu$}$$

The vector $\mathbf{I}^{(\nu)}$ is the νth-unit vector, that is, the νth column of the nth-order identity matrix I. By Theorem 1.1.1 it follows that each initial-value problem in (2.1.12) has a unique solution on $[a, b]$. The solutions of problems (2.1.12b$^\nu$) form an nth-order matrix which we denote by

$$Y(x) \equiv (\mathbf{y}^{(1)}(x), \mathbf{y}^{(2)}(x), \ldots, \mathbf{y}^{(n)}(x)).$$

Then with an arbitrary n-vector, $\mathbf{s} = (s_1, s_2, \ldots, s_n)^T$, define the vector

$$\begin{aligned} \mathbf{y}(x; \mathbf{s}) &\equiv \mathbf{y}^{(0)}(x) + Y(x)\mathbf{s} \\ &\equiv \mathbf{y}^{(0)}(x) + \sum_{\nu=1}^{n} s_\nu \mathbf{y}^{(\nu)}(x). \end{aligned} \tag{2.1.13}$$

Now if $\mathbf{s}$ is a root of

$$\boldsymbol{\phi}(\mathbf{s}) \equiv B_0\mathbf{y}(b; \mathbf{s}) + B_1\mathbf{y}'(b; \mathbf{s}) - \boldsymbol{\beta} = 0, \tag{2.1.14}$$

then the function $\mathbf{y}(x) = \mathbf{y}(x; \mathbf{s})$ is the solution of the boundary-value problem (2.1.11).

Proceeding formally, with Equation (2.1.13) in Equation (2.1.14), we see that $\boldsymbol{\phi}(\mathbf{s})$ is linear in $\mathbf{s}$ and the system (2.1.14) has the unique solution

$$\mathbf{s} = [B_0 Y(b) + B_1 Y'(b)]^{-1}(\boldsymbol{\beta} - [B_0\mathbf{y}^{(0)}(b) + B_1\mathbf{y}^{(0)\prime}(b)]), \tag{2.1.15}$$

provided the indicated inverse exists. However, if the matrix

$$[B_0 Y(b) + B_1 Y'(b)] \tag{2.1.16}$$

is singular, then its columns must be linearly dependent. That is, since the columns are $B_0\mathbf{y}^{(\nu)}(b) + B_1\mathbf{y}^{(\nu)\prime}(b)$, $\nu = 1, 2, \ldots, n$, there must exist scalars a_ν, $\nu = 1, 2, \ldots, n$, not all vanishing, such that

$$\sum_{\nu=1}^{n} a_\nu[B_0\mathbf{y}^{(\nu)}(b) + B_1\mathbf{y}^{(\nu)\prime}(b)] = 0.$$

But then the function

$$\mathbf{z}(x) \equiv \sum_{\nu=1}^{n} a_\nu \mathbf{y}^{(\nu)}(x)$$

satisfies $B_0\mathbf{z}(b) + B_1\mathbf{z}'(b) = 0$ and so is a solution of the homogeneous boundary-value problem corresponding to (2.1.11). It has been assumed that this problem has only the trivial solution, $\mathbf{z}(x) \equiv 0$, and since

$$\mathbf{z}(0) = \sum_{\nu=1}^{n} a_\nu \mathbf{I}^{(\nu)}$$

it follows that $a_\nu = 0$, $\nu = 1, 2, \ldots, n$. From this contradiction we conclude that Equation (2.1.14) indeed has the unique solution shown in Equation (2.1.15).

Numerical solutions of (2.1.11) are obtained by solving each of the $n + 1$ initial-value problems in (2.1.12) and forming, at the net points, the quantities corresponding to (2.1.13) and (2.1.15). The linear system (2.1.14) which must be solved is usually of relatively small order and so is not, in principle, a difficult numerical problem.

To estimate the accuracy of the initial-value method applied to the problem (2.1.11) we proceed as in the previous case (where $n = 1$). Thus we need not write the obvious first-order systems which are solved in place of (2.1.12). Rather we denote by $\mathbf{Y}_j$, $\mathbf{Y}_j^{(\nu)}$, $\mathbf{V}_j^{(\nu)}$, and $\mathbf{s}^{(h)}$ the numerical approximations to $\mathbf{y}(x_j)$, $\mathbf{y}^{(\nu)}(x_j)$, $\mathbf{y}^{(\nu)\prime}(x_j)$, and $\mathbf{s}$, respectively. If a stable method with order of accuracy at least p is employed to solve the initial value problems then we may assume that

$$|\mathbf{e}_j^{(\nu)}| \equiv |\mathbf{Y}_j^{(\nu)} - \mathbf{y}^{(\nu)}(x_j)| = \mathcal{O}(h^p), \qquad |\boldsymbol{\epsilon}_j^{(\nu)}| \equiv |\mathbf{V}_j^{(\nu)} - \mathbf{y}^{(\nu)\prime}(x_j)| = \mathcal{O}(h^p),$$
$$\nu = 0, 1, \ldots, n; \qquad 0 \le j \le J.$$

Now subtracting Equation (2.1.13) with $x = x_j$ from its numerical counterpart we get

$$\mathbf{e}_j \equiv \mathbf{Y}_j - \mathbf{y}(x_j) = \mathbf{e}_j^{(0)} + \sum_{\nu=1}^{n} s_\nu \mathbf{e}_j^{(\nu)} + \sum_{\nu=1}^{n} (s_\nu^{(h)} - s_\nu)\mathbf{Y}_j^{(\nu)}, \qquad 0 \le j \le J. \tag{2.1.17}$$

Similarly from Equation (2.1.14) and its numerical equivalent we find that

$$H(\mathbf{s}^{(h)} - \mathbf{s}) = -(B_0\mathbf{e}_J^{(0)} + B_1\boldsymbol{\epsilon}_J^{(0)}) + [B_0E + B_1\varepsilon]\mathbf{s}, \tag{2.1.18a}$$

where the matrix H is

$$H \equiv [B_0 Y(b) + B_1 Y'(b)] + [B_0E + B_1\varepsilon]. \tag{2.1.18b}$$

Here E is the matrix with columns $\mathbf{e}_J^{(\nu)}$, $\nu = 1, 2, \ldots, n$, and ε has the columns $\boldsymbol{\epsilon}_J^{(\nu)}$, $\nu = 1, 2, \ldots, n$. Thus for sufficiently small h the matrix H is nonsingular, since the matrix (2.1.16) is nonsingular (see Problem 2.1.3), and we conclude that

$$|\mathbf{Y}_j - \mathbf{y}(x_j)| = \mathcal{O}(h^p), \qquad 0 \le j \le J,$$

just as in the case with $n = 1$. A similar estimate applies for the first derivatives.

Combining these observations we may easily construct a proof of the following.

THEOREM 2.1.2. *Let the boundary-value problem* (2.1.11) *have a unique solution,* $\mathbf{y}(x)$. *Let the numerical solutions of problems* (2.1.12a, b^ν), *using a stable method with order of accuracy p on the net* (2.1.6), *be denoted by* $\{\mathbf{Y}_j^{(\nu)}\}$, $\{\mathbf{V}_j^{(\nu)}\}$, $\nu = 0, 1, \ldots, n$. *Define the net functions*

$$\mathbf{Y}_j(\mathbf{s}) = \mathbf{Y}_j^{(0)} + \sum_{\nu=1}^{n} s_\nu \mathbf{Y}_j^{(\nu)}, \qquad \mathbf{V}_j(\mathbf{s}) = \mathbf{V}_j^0 + \sum_{\nu=1}^{n} s_\nu \mathbf{V}_j^{(\nu)}, \qquad 0 \le j \le J.$$

For sufficiently small h a unique vector $\mathbf{s}^{(h)} \equiv (s_1^{(h)}, s_2^{(h)}, \ldots, s_n^{(h)})$ *is defined as the solution of the linear system*

$$\boldsymbol{\phi}(\mathbf{s}) \equiv B_0 \mathbf{Y}_J(\mathbf{s}) + B_1 \mathbf{V}_J(\mathbf{s}) - \boldsymbol{\beta} = 0. \tag{2.1.19}$$

With this root the net functions $\{\mathbf{Y}_j(\mathbf{s}^{(h)})\}$ *and* $\{\mathbf{V}_j(\mathbf{s}^{(h)})\}$ *satisfy*

$$|\mathbf{y}(x_j) - \mathbf{Y}_j(\mathbf{s}^{(h)})| = \mathcal{O}(h^p), \qquad |\mathbf{y}'(s_j) - \mathbf{V}_j(s^{(h)})| = \mathcal{O}(h^p), \qquad 0 \le j \le J,$$

provided that the initial-value problems (2.1.12) *have sufficiently smooth solutions.* ∎

Although this theorem is similar to Theorem 2.1.1 and the error estimates, valid as $h \to 0$, are gratifying, it should not be inferred that the practical difficulties are as simple as they were in the case $n = 1$. Combining Equations (2.1.17) and (2.1.18), we see that if H is ill-conditioned for finite values of h we may lose accuracy. The cancellation difficulty in forming (2.1.13) is now even more important. It can occur, for instance, if any fixed corresponding components of $s_{\nu_1}\mathbf{y}^{(\nu_1)}(x)$ and $s_{\nu_2}\mathbf{y}^{(\nu_2)}(x)$ for fixed $\nu_1 \ne \nu_2$ are nearly equal, of opposite sign, and in magnitude larger than the other corresponding components for $\nu \ne \nu_1, \nu_2$. But again some of the sources of error may be eliminated by using the parallel-shooting methods of Section 2.4.

Problems

2.1.1 Replace the condition $\det A_0 \ne 0$ in Equations (2.1.11b) by the condition rank $[A_0, A_1] = n$ and show how to solve the resulting boundary-value problem (2.1.11).

2.1.2 Prove the Alternative Theorem for the linear second-order system (2.1.11). [HINT: Use the reduction to an initial-value problem for one system which has a unique solution.]

2.1.3* Show that $A + B$ is nonsingular if A is nonsingular and the elements of B are sufficiently small [see Isaacson and Keller (1966), Theorem 1.5, Chapter 1].

2.1.4 Use the above result to show that Equation (2.1.19) has a unique solution $\mathbf{s}^{(h)}$ for sufficiently small h. [HINT: Relate the coefficient matrix to H in Equation (2.1.18b).]

2.1.5 Use the initial-value method to solve the boundary-value problem

$$y'' = -100y, \qquad y(0) = 1, \qquad y(2\pi + \varepsilon) = 1.$$

If the linearly-independent solutions

$$y^{(1)}(x) = \cos 10x, \qquad y^{(2)}(x) \equiv 10^{-1} \sin 10x$$

are employed, show that, for small $|\varepsilon|$,

$$s = 5\varepsilon + \mathcal{O}(\varepsilon^3).$$

Discuss the possible computational difficulties caused by small $|\varepsilon|$.

2.1.6 Use the initial-value method to solve the boundary-value problem:

$$y'' = 100y, \qquad y(0) = 1, \qquad y(3) = \varepsilon + \cosh 30.$$

If the linearly-independent solutions

$$y^{(1)}(x) = \cosh 10x, \qquad y^{(2)}(x) = 10^{-1} \sinh 10x$$

are employed, show that

$$s = 10\varepsilon/\sinh 30.$$

Explain the difficulty in carrying out the numerical solution for small $|\varepsilon|$.

2.2 *Nonlinear Second-Order Equations*

We now consider second-order equations, which may be nonlinear, of the form

$$y'' = f(x, y, y'), \qquad a \le x \le b, \tag{2.2.1a}$$

subject to the general two-point boundary conditions

$$\begin{aligned} a_0 y(a) - a_1 y'(a) &= \alpha, \qquad a_i \ge 0, \\ b_0 y(b) + b_1 y'(b) &= \beta, \qquad b_i \ge 0; \qquad a_0 + b_0 > 0. \end{aligned} \tag{2.2.1b}$$

The function $f(x, y, z)$ in Equation (2.2.1a) will be assumed to satisfy the hypothesis of Theorem 1.2.2. This assures us that the boundary-value problem (2.2.1) has a solution which is unique.

The related initial-value problem that we consider is

$$u'' = f(x, u, u'), \qquad a \le x \le b, \tag{2.2.2a}$$

$$u(a) = a_1 s - c_1 \alpha, \qquad u'(a) = a_0 s - c_0 \alpha, \tag{2.2.2b}$$

where c_0 and c_1 are any constants such that

$$a_1 c_0 - a_0 c_1 = 1. \tag{2.2.2c}$$

The solution of this problem, which we denote by $u = u(x; s)$, will be a solution of the boundary-value problem (2.2.1) if and only if s is a root of

$$\phi(s) \equiv b_0 u(b; s) + b_1 u'(b; s) - \beta = 0. \tag{2.2.3}$$

Under the previously-stated conditions on f, it is shown in the proof of Theorem 1.2.2 that *the function $\phi(s)$ has a positive derivative which is bounded away from zero for all s*, and so Equation (2.2.3) has a unique root for any value of β.

The initial-value or shooting methods we now study essentially consist of iterative schemes for approximating the root of Equation (2.2.3). In particular we shall employ schemes of the type indicated in Section 1.4. These all require evaluations of the function $\phi(s)$ for a sequence of values of s. This is done by means of numerical solutions of a sequence of initial-value problems of the form (2.2.2). [Of course if $f(x, y, z)$ is linear in y and z, then $\phi(s)$ is linear in s and the root of $\phi(s) = 0$ could be determined by only two evaluations of $\phi(s)$. This is what was done in Section 2.1. However, a linear equation can also be solved by iteration and so the present procedures also apply to linear boundary-value problems.] Obviously we should try to employ very rapidly converging iteration schemes as this would reduce the number of initial-value problems that must be solved. We shall discuss the use of several different schemes, one of which is Newton's method and is particularly well-suited for the current class of problems. First we must consider some effects of using numerical approximations to $u(b; s)$ and $u'(b; s)$ in attempting to evaluate $\phi(s)$.

To solve the initial-value problem (2.2.2) numerically, we write it as a first-order system, with $v \equiv u'$;

$$\begin{aligned} u' &= v, & u(a) &= a_1 s - c_1 \alpha; \\ v' &= f(x, u, v), & v(a) &= a_0 s - c_0 \alpha. \end{aligned} \tag{2.2.4}$$

If we write the solution of this system as

$$u = u(x; s), \qquad v = v(x; s),$$

the function $\phi(s)$ as defined in (2.2.3) becomes

$$\phi(s) \equiv b_0 u(b; s) + b_1 v(b; s) - \beta. \tag{2.2.5}$$

Again, any of the methods in Section 1.3 can be used to solve the initial-value problem (2.2.4) numerically. We use the net in (2.1.6) and denote the numerical solution, for each value of s, by

$$U_j(s), \qquad V_j(s), \qquad 0 \le j \le J. \tag{2.2.6a}$$

If the numerical method has order of accuracy p and is stable, and if the solutions of (2.2.4) are sufficiently smooth, then

$$|U_j(s) - u(x_j; s)| = \mathcal{O}(h^p), \qquad |V_j(s) - v(x_j; s)| = \mathcal{O}(h^p), \qquad 0 \le j \le J. \tag{2.2.6b}$$

In terms of the numerical solution we define the function

$$\Phi(s) \equiv b_0 U_J(s) + b_1 V_J(s) - \beta, \tag{2.2.7}$$

and from Equations (2.2.6) and (2.2.5) it follows that

$$|\Phi(s) - \phi(s)| = \mathcal{O}(h^p). \tag{2.2.8}$$

Thus in general we cannot hope to evaluate $\phi(s)$ exactly but rather we get an $\mathcal{O}(h^p)$ approximation to it.

It is clear, from the above error bounds, that the solution of the boundary-value problem (2.2.1) can be approximated to an accuracy at least $\mathcal{O}(h^p)$ if the root $s = s^*$ of Equation (2.2.3) is known. However we can *at best* hope to approximate s^* to an accuracy of $\mathcal{O}(h^p)$, by virtue of the estimate (2.2.8). But then the solution of the boundary-value problem will also be approximated to this same accuracy by means of the following.

LEMMA 2.2.1. *Let $u(x; s)$ and $v(x; s)$ denote the solution of the initial-value problem* (2.2.4) *with* $\mathbf{f} \equiv (1, f(x, u, v))^T$ *satisfying the hypothesis of Theorem* 1.1.1. *Let* $\{U_j(s)\}$, $\{V_j(s)\}$ *denote the numerical solution of* (2.2.4) *on the net in* (2.1.6) *using a stable,* pth-*order-accurate scheme. Then if the solutions of* (2.2.4) *are sufficiently smooth, we have for any values s and t*

$$\left.\begin{aligned} |U_j(t) - u(x_j; s)| &\le \mathcal{O}(h^p) + \mathcal{O}(|s - t|), \\ |V_j(t) - v(x_j; s)| &\le \mathcal{O}(h^p) + \mathcal{O}(|s - t|), \end{aligned}\right\} \quad 0 \le j \le J. \tag{2.2.9}$$

Proof. From the hypothesis it follows by Theorem 1.1.1 that u and v are Lipschitz-continuous in s. But then

$$\begin{aligned} |U_j(t) - u(x_j; s)| &\le |U_j(t) - u(x_j; t)| + |u(x_j; t) - u(x_j; s)| \\ &\le \mathcal{O}(h^p) + K'|s - t|, \end{aligned}$$

where we have used the estimate (2.2.6b), which is valid, and K' is the Lipschitz constant for u. A similar result holds for v. ∎

If in (2.2.9) we set $s = s^*$ and $|s^* - t| = \mathcal{O}(h^p)$ we see that both the solution of the boundary-value problem (2.2.1) and its first derivative can be computed to within $\mathcal{O}(h^p)$ if s^* can be approximated to this accuracy.

To approximate the root of Equation (2.2.3) we write the equation in the form

$$s = g(s) \equiv s - m\phi(s), \qquad m \neq 0, \tag{2.2.10a}$$

and consider the functional iteration scheme: s_0 = arbitrary,

$$s_{\nu+1} = g(s_\nu), \qquad \nu = 0, 1, 2, \ldots. \tag{2.2.10b}$$

The fact that the sequence $\{s_\nu\}$ converges to the root under quite general circumstances is the content of the following.

THEOREM 2.2.1. *Let $f(x, y, y')$ in Equation* (2.2.1a) *satisfy the hypothesis of Theorem* 1.2.2, *and in addition for some positive constant N,*

$$\frac{\partial f}{\partial y} \leq N.$$

Then the function $\phi(s)$ in Equation (2.2.3) *has a continuous derivative, $\dot{\phi}(s)$, which satisfies*

$$0 < \gamma \leq \dot{\phi}(s) \leq \Gamma, \tag{2.2.11a}$$

where

$$\gamma \equiv b_0\left[a_1 + a_0\left(\frac{1 - e^{-2\mu L}}{2\mu}\right)\right] + b_1 a_0 e^{-2\mu L};$$

$$\Gamma \equiv \frac{e^{\mu L}}{2\sigma}\{[(\sigma - \mu)a_1 + a_0][(\sigma + \mu)b_1 + b_0]e^{\sigma L} - [(\sigma + \mu)a_1 - a_0][(\sigma - \mu)b_1 - b_0]e^{-\sigma L}\}; \tag{2.2.11b}$$

$$\mu \equiv \frac{M}{2}, \qquad \sigma \equiv \sqrt{\mu^2 + N}, \qquad L \equiv b - a.$$

For any s_0 and fixed m in

$$0 < m < 2/\Gamma \tag{2.2.11c}$$

the iterates in Equations (2.2.10b) *converge to the root s^* of Equation* (2.2.3). *In particular, with the choice $m = 2/(\Gamma + \gamma)$, the iterates satisfy*

$$|s_\nu - s^*| \leq \left[\frac{1 - (\gamma/\Gamma)}{1 + (\gamma/\Gamma)}\right]^\nu \frac{|\phi(s_0)|}{\gamma}; \qquad \nu = 1, 2, \ldots. \tag{2.2.12}$$

Proof. We first note that Theorem 1.1.2 is applicable to the system (2.2.4). Thus the functions $\xi(x) \equiv \partial u(x; s)/\partial s$ and $\xi'(x) \equiv \partial u'(x; s)/\partial s$, where $u(x; s)$ is the solution of (2.2.2), are continuous functions of s for all $x \in [a, b]$. But then

$$\dot{\phi}(s) = b_0\xi(b) + b_1\xi'(b)$$

is also continuous in s.

As in the proof of Theorem 1.2.2 we have the variational problem for $\xi(x)$,

$$\xi'' = p(x)\xi' + q(x)\xi, \qquad \xi(a) = a_1, \qquad \xi'(a) = a_0, \qquad a \leq x \leq b,$$

where now

$$|p(x)| \leq M, \qquad 0 < q(x) \leq N.$$

It has already been shown [see the inequalities (1.2.5)] that since $a_0 \geq 0$ and $a_1 \geq 0$,

$$\xi'(x) > a_0 e^{-2\mu(x-a)} > 0, \qquad \xi(x) > a_1 + a_0\left(\frac{1 - e^{-2\mu(x-a)}}{2\mu}\right) > 0,$$

and so clearly, with the notation in (2.2.11), $\dot{\phi}(s) \geq \gamma$. To obtain an upper bound we observe that now

$$\xi'' \leq M\xi' + N\xi.$$

It easily follows (see Problem 2.2.1) that $\xi(x) \leq \eta(x)$ and $\xi'(x) \leq \eta'(x)$, where $\eta(x)$ is the solution of

$$\eta'' = M\eta' + N\eta, \qquad \eta(a) = \xi(a), \qquad \eta'(a) = \xi'(a).$$

But this linear problem with constant coefficients has the solution

$$\eta(x) = \frac{e^{\mu(x-a)}}{2\sigma}\{[(\sigma - \mu)a_1 + a_0]e^{\sigma(x-a)} + [(\sigma + \mu)a_1 - a_0]e^{-\sigma(x-a)}\},$$

and so $\dot{\phi}(s) \leq \Gamma$ follows, establishing (2.2.11a).

We now use the mean-value theorem to deduce that

$$g(s) - g(t) = (s - t) - m[\phi(s) - \phi(t)] = [1 - m\dot{\phi}(t + \theta(s - t))](s - t), \qquad 0 < \theta < 1.$$

Thus $g(s)$ in Equations (2.2.10) satisfies a Lipschitz condition with constant λ given by

$$\lambda = \max(|1 - m\gamma|, |1 - m\Gamma|).$$

For any m in $0 < m < 2/\Gamma$, it follows that $\lambda < 1$, and thus Theorem 1.4.1 is applicable (with $\rho = \infty$) to the scheme (2.2.10b). With $m = 2/(\Gamma + \gamma)$ we obtain

$$\lambda = \frac{\Gamma - \gamma}{\Gamma + \gamma},$$

and part (d) of Theorem 1.4.1 yields (2.2.12). ∎

One of the nice features of this result is that it determines a specific value for m, in terms of known data and the two bounds M and N, which insures convergence. However, if we consider for the moment the case with $a_1 = b_1 = 0$, $a_0 = b_0 = 1$ (that is, function specified at both endpoints), then Equation (2.2.11b) yields

$$\frac{\gamma}{\Gamma} = \left(1 + 4\frac{N}{M^2}\right)^{1/2} e^{-M(b-a)} \frac{\sinh\,[M(b-a)/2]}{\sinh\,[(1 + (4N/M^2))^{1/2}M(b-a)/2]}.$$

From this we see that the convergence factor, $(\Gamma - \gamma)/(\Gamma + \gamma)$, in (2.2.12) may be very close to unity if the interval $(b - a)$ is "long" or the constants M or N are "large." In such cases many iterations may be required to obtain an accurate approximation to the root. However, we shall consider more rapidly convergent schemes shortly.

Let us now consider the effects on the above procedure which result from the fact that $\phi(s)$ cannot be evaluated exactly. That is, we employ the iteration scheme in Equations (2.2.10), using the numerical solutions (2.2.6) of (2.2.2) to evaluate the function $\phi(s)$. Recalling Equation (2.2.7), the actual iteration scheme is then: $s_0 =$ arbitrary,

$$s_{\nu+1} = s_\nu - m\Phi(s_\nu), \qquad \nu = 0, 1, 2, \ldots. \tag{2.2.13}$$

The basic result can be stated as follows.

THEOREM 2.2.2. *Let $f(x, y, y')$ in Equation* (2.2.1*a*) *satisfy the hypothesis of Theorem* 2.2.1. *Let numerical solutions* (2.2.6) *of the initial-value problem* (2.2.4) *be computed as in Lemma* 2.2.1. *Let the sequence $\{s_\nu\}$ be defined by Equations* (2.2.13), *with $\Phi(s)$ as defined in Equation* (2.2.7). *Then for any m in $0 < m < 2/\Gamma$ we have, with $y(x)$, the solution of the boundary-value problem* (2.2.1), *for some positive $\lambda = \lambda(m) < 1$,*

$$|U_j(s_\nu) - y(x_j)| \le \mathcal{O}(h^p) + \mathcal{O}(\lambda^\nu), \qquad |V_j(s_\nu) - y'(x_j)| \le \mathcal{O}(h^p) + \mathcal{O}(\lambda^\nu),$$
$$0 \le j \le J, \qquad \nu = 0, 1, \ldots.$$

Proof. We may apply Lemma 2.2.1 with $t = s_\nu$ and $s = s^*$, the root of Equation (2.2.3), in which case $u(x; s^*) = y(x)$. The proof is then reduced to estimating $|s^* - s_\nu|$. But from the estimate (2.2.8), which is valid by hypothesis, we can write Equations (2.2.13) as

$$s_{\nu+1} = s_\nu - m\phi(s_\nu) + \mathcal{O}(h^p), \qquad \nu = 0, 1, \ldots.$$

It has been shown in Theorem 2.2.1 that $g(s) \equiv s - m\phi(s)$ is Lipschitz-continuous with constant $\lambda < 1$ for m in $0 < m \le 2/\Gamma$. Now Theorem 1.4.2 can be applied, with $\delta \equiv \mathcal{O}(h^p)$, to deduce that

$$|s^* - s_\nu| \le \lambda^\nu|s^* - s_0| + \mathcal{O}(h^p). \quad \blacksquare$$

It should be noted that the convergence factor λ, in the above theorem, is independent of the net spacing h. Thus for each h one can find an integer $\nu = \nu(h, p, \lambda)$ such that

$$\lambda^{\nu} \leq h^{p},$$

and so, in principle, the total error can be made $\mathcal{O}(h^p)$.

The virtue of rapidly converging iteration schemes for solving Equation (2.2.3) is quite clear and we recall, from Theorem 1.4.3, that Newton's method may have arbitrarily small convergence factors, λ. Thus we indicate the proper way in which to employ this method in the present problem. The iterations $\{s_\nu\}$ are now defined by: s_0 = arbitrary,

$$s_{\nu+1} = s_\nu - \frac{\phi(s_\nu)}{\dot{\phi}(s_\nu)}, \qquad \nu = 0, 1, \ldots. \tag{2.2.14}$$

We have previously indicated how $\phi(s)$ in Equation (2.2.5) is to be evaluated, or rather approximated, by $\Phi(s)$, in terms of a numerical solution of the initial-value problem (2.2.4). We shall evaluate $\dot{\phi}(s)$ by means of a numerical solution of the variational problem corresponding to (2.2.4). This variational problem, or one equivalent to it, has already been employed in Theorem 2.2.1 to study the properties of $\dot{\phi}(s)$. If we introduce

$$\xi(x) \equiv \frac{\partial u(x; s)}{\partial s}, \qquad \eta(x) \equiv \frac{\partial v(x; s)}{\partial s},$$

where u and $v = u'$ are the solution of (2.2.4), then formal differentiation in this initial-value problem yields

$$\begin{aligned} \xi' &= \eta, & \xi(a) &= a_1; \\ \eta' &= p(x; s)\eta + q(x; s)\xi, & \eta(a) &= a_0, \end{aligned} \tag{2.2.15a}$$

where

$$p(x; s) \equiv \frac{\partial f(x, u(x; s), v(x; s))}{\partial v}, \qquad q(x; s) \equiv \frac{\partial f(x, u(x; s), v(x; s))}{\partial u}. \tag{2.2.15b}$$

Thus we have, from Equation (2.2.5),

$$\dot{\phi}(s) \equiv b_0\xi(b; s) + b_1\eta(b; s). \tag{2.2.16}$$

The numerical solution of the initial-value problem (2.2.15) should be evaluated on the net (2.1.6), along with the numerical solution of the initial-value problem (2.2.4) and by the same method. Then in many cases the coefficients $p(x)$ and $q(x)$ can be evaluated with little additional computation over that required to evaluate $f(x, u, v)$. Thus one iteration in Newton's method (2.2.14) requires the solution of two initial-value problems, but the amount of computation may frequently be less than that required for two iterations in the scheme (2.2.10).

Finally, we point out the obvious but frequently forgotten fact that "shooting" can be applied in either direction. This applies to linear problems as well. If the solutions of the initial-value problem grow from $x = a$ to $x = b$, then it is likely that the shooting method will be most effective in reverse; that is, using $x = b$ as the initial point. We call this procedure *reverse shooting.*

Problems

2.2.1 Let $\xi(x)$ and $\eta(x)$ satisfy on $[a, b]$:

$$\xi'' \le M\xi' + N\xi,$$
$$\eta'' = M\eta' + N\eta; \quad \xi(a) = \eta(a) \ge 0, \quad \xi'(a) = \eta'(a) \ge 0.$$

If the constants M and N satisfy $M \ge 0$ and $N \ge 0$, show that $\xi(x) \le \eta(x)$ and $\xi'(x) \le \eta'(x)$ on $[a, b]$. [HINT: "Solve" the differential inequality satisfied by $\zeta(x) \equiv \eta(x) - \xi(x)$. First derive the result that $[\zeta' + B\zeta] \ge 0$, where $B = (-M \pm \sqrt{M^2 + 4N})/2$. Then it follows that $\zeta(x) \ge 0$ on $[a, b]$ and so $[\zeta'' + M\zeta'] \ge 0$ which implies $\zeta'(x) \ge 0$.]

2.2.2* If $f(x, u, v)$ is as in Theorem 2.2.1 and in addition $\partial f(x, u, v)/\partial u$ and $\partial f(x, u, v)/\partial v$ are Lipschitz-continuous functions of u and v, show that $\dot{\phi}(s)$ as defined in Equation (2.2.16) is a Lipschitz-continuous function of s.

2.2.3 Use Theorem 2.2.1, Problem 2.2.2, and Problem 1.4.7 to show that Newton's method in (2.2.14) converges if $|b - a|$ is sufficiently small and some later iterate in (2.2.10) is used as initial guess.

2.2.4 Show that the choice $m = 2/(\Gamma + \gamma)$ in Theorem 2.2.1 is in general the best possible in light of the inequalities (2.2.11a).

2.2.5 Compute the solution of

$$y'' = \tanh y + \cos y'; \quad y(0) - y'(0) = 1, \quad y(1) + y'(1) = 0,$$

by shooting. Try using several different uniformly-spaced nets (that is, different values of h), contracting maps, and Newton's method.

2.2.6 Verify the applicability of the theoretical results to the problem formulated in Problem 2.2.5.

2.3 *Linear and Nonlinear Systems*

The application of initial-value techniques to rather general nonlinear boundary-value problems is immediate. First of all, the particular equation or set of equations can be replaced by an equivalent system of say n first-order equations of the form

$$\mathbf{y}' = \mathbf{f}(x, \mathbf{y}), \quad a < x < b. \tag{2.3.1a}$$

The components, $y_j(x)$, of the n-vector $\mathbf{y}$ are either the original dependent variables or some derivatives of them or linear combinations of these functions. Assuming the original two-point boundary conditions to be linear, we can now write them in the form

$$A\mathbf{y}(a) + B\mathbf{y}(b) = \boldsymbol{\alpha}. \tag{2.3.1b}$$

Here A and B are constant square matrices of order n and $\boldsymbol{\alpha}$ is a specified n-vector. In the indicated reduction to (2.3.1) we have assumed that the highest-order derivatives of each dependent variable which occurred in the original system of differential equations did not occur in the boundary conditions. The n boundary conditions in Equation (2.3.1b) will be independent if the matrix (A, B), which is $n \times 2n$, has rank n. It should be noted that periodic boundary conditions are included as a special case in (2.3.1b).

For purposes of our general discussion we associate with the boundary-value problem (2.3.1) the initial-value problem

$$\text{(a)}\quad \mathbf{u}' = \mathbf{f}(x, \mathbf{u}), \qquad \text{(b)}\quad \mathbf{u}(a) = \mathbf{s}. \tag{2.3.2}$$

Under appropriate smoothness conditions on $\mathbf{f}(x, \mathbf{u})$ we are assured, as in Theorems 1.1.1 and 1.1.2, that a unique solution of (2.3.2) exists on $a \leq x \leq b$, say

$$\mathbf{u} = \mathbf{u}(\mathbf{s}; x),$$

and it depends Lipschitz-continuously or even differentiably on the components of $\mathbf{s}$. We now seek $\mathbf{s}$ such that $\mathbf{u}(\mathbf{s}; x)$ is a solution of the boundary-value problem (2.3.1). This occurs if and only if $\mathbf{s}$ is a root of the system of n equations

$$\boldsymbol{\phi}(\mathbf{s}) \equiv A\mathbf{s} + B\mathbf{u}(\mathbf{s}; b) - \boldsymbol{\alpha} = 0 \tag{2.3.3}$$

(see Theorem 1.2.4). In particular cases the initial values in Equation (2.3.2b) may be chosen quite conveniently, for instance so that say p of the conditions in (2.3.1b) are automatically satisfied. Then only $q = n - p$ undetermined components s_j would occur in the chosen replacement of (2.3.2b). These components must then be determined in order to satisfy the q conditions in (2.3.3) that are not identically satisfied. This procedure can be applied whenever p independent conditions in Equation (2.3.1b) involve only p components of $\mathbf{y}(a)$ [see Problem 1.2.12].

Under the hypothesis of Theorem 1.2.6, which we assume to hold, we are assured that Equation (2.3.3) has a unique root, or equivalently that the boundary-value problem (2.3.1) has a unique solution. Furthermore the root of Equation (2.3.3) is also the fixed point of a contracting map which we write as

$$\mathbf{s} = \mathbf{g}(\mathbf{s}) \equiv \mathbf{s} - Q[A\mathbf{s} + B\mathbf{u}(\mathbf{s}; b) - \boldsymbol{\alpha}]. \tag{2.3.4}$$

Here, since $(A + B)$ is assumed nonsingular, we take

$$Q \equiv (A + B)^{-1}.$$

(We recall that the most general boundary conditions (2.3.1b) do not necessarily satisfy this condition and the computations in such cases may converge with a different choice for Q.) Our formal procedure is now clear. To show that the solution of the boundary-value problem (2.3.1) can be computed to any desired accuracy, we approximate the root of Equation (2.3.4) by iterations and use a sufficiently accurate such approximation to "solve" the initial-value problem (2.3.2) numerically. Of course, in carrying out the implied iterations, a sequence of numerical solutions of (2.3.2) is required. We indicate below more details in this convergence proof which is quite similar to that in Section 2.2, and then we discuss the practical aspects of actually computing an accurate approximation. Newton's method is again advocated and we show that it is applicable in the present case.

Let one of the numerical methods of Section 1.3 be used to obtain a numerical solution of the initial-value problem (2.3.2) on the net (2.1.6). We denote the numerical solution at each net point x_j, for each value of $\mathbf{s}$, by the n-vectors

$$\mathbf{U}_j(\mathbf{s}), \qquad j = 0, 1, \ldots, J.$$

If the numerical method is stable and has order of accuracy p, and the solutions of the initial-value problem (2.3.2) are, as we assume, sufficiently smooth, then

$$|\mathbf{U}_j(\mathbf{s}) - \mathbf{u}(\mathbf{s}; x_j)| \leq \mathcal{O}(h^p), \qquad j = 0, 1, \ldots, J. \tag{2.3.5}$$

Now, just as in Lemma 2.2.1, it follows that for any two sets of initial data $\mathbf{s}$ and $\mathbf{t}$

$$|\mathbf{U}_j(\mathbf{t}) - \mathbf{u}(\mathbf{s}; x_j)| \leq \mathcal{O}(h^p) + \mathcal{O}(|\mathbf{s} - \mathbf{t}|), \qquad j = 0, 1, \ldots, J. \tag{2.3.6}$$

If $\mathbf{s}$ is a root of Equation (2.3.3) all we need do, by the estimate (2.3.6), is to find a $\mathbf{t}$ such that $|\mathbf{s} - \mathbf{t}| = \mathcal{O}(h^p)$, and then $\mathbf{U}_j(\mathbf{t})$ is accurate of order p.

From the proof of Theorem 1.2.6 we know that $\mathbf{g}(\mathbf{s})$ in (2.3.4) satisfies

$$\left\| \frac{\partial \mathbf{g}(\mathbf{s})}{\partial \mathbf{s}} \right\|_\infty \leq \lambda < 1. \tag{2.3.7}$$

Thus, as previously stated, $\mathbf{g}(\mathbf{s})$ is contracting [by Problem 1.2.11]. However, in terms of the numerical solution, we approximate $\mathbf{g}(\mathbf{s})$ by

$$\mathbf{G}(\mathbf{s}) \equiv \mathbf{s} - Q[A\mathbf{s} + B\mathbf{U}_J(\mathbf{s}) - \boldsymbol{\alpha}], \tag{2.3.8a}$$

and the iterations employed to obtain the root of Equation (2.3.4) are $\mathbf{s}^{(0)} =$ arbitrary,

$$\mathbf{s}^{(\nu+1)} = \mathbf{G}(\mathbf{s}^{(\nu)}), \qquad \nu = 0, 1, 2, \ldots. \tag{2.3.8b}$$

However, by (2.3.5), (2.3.4), and (2.3.8a), we have

$$|\mathbf{G}(\mathbf{s}) - \mathbf{g}(\mathbf{s})| = |QB(\mathbf{U}_J(s) - \mathbf{u}(\mathbf{s}; b))| \le \mathcal{O}(h^p).$$

Thus the iterates (2.3.8b) actually satisfy

$$\mathbf{s}^{(\nu+1)} = \mathbf{g}(\mathbf{s}^{\nu}) + \mathcal{O}(h^p).$$

But since $\mathbf{g}(\mathbf{s})$ is contracting, it follows that Theorem 1.4.2 is applicable. Then if $\mathbf{s}^*$ is the root of Equation (2.3.4), the iterates in (2.3.8) must satisfy

$$|\mathbf{s}^* - \mathbf{s}^{(\nu)}| \le \lambda^{\nu}|\mathbf{s}^* - \mathbf{s}^{(0)}| + \mathcal{O}(h^p).$$

Using this result with $\mathbf{t} = \mathbf{s}^{(\nu)}$ and $\mathbf{s} = \mathbf{s}^*$ in (2.3.6), we obtain what may be summarized as follows.

THEOREM 2.3.1. *Let* $\mathbf{f}(x, \mathbf{y})$, *A and B satisfy the hypothesis of Theorem* 1.2.6. *Further, let* $\mathbf{f}(x, \mathbf{y})$ *be so smooth that the numerical solutions* $\mathbf{U}_j(\mathbf{s})$ *of the initial-value problem* (2.3.2) *computed by a stable* p*th-order method on the net* (2.1.6) *satisfy* (2.3.5). *Then the sequence* $\mathbf{s}^{(\nu)}$ *defined in* (2.3.8) *is such that*

$$|\mathbf{U}_j(\mathbf{s}^{(\nu)}) - \mathbf{y}(x_j)| \le \mathcal{O}(h^p) + \lambda^{\nu}|\mathbf{s}^* - \mathbf{s}^{(0)}|, \quad j = 0, 1, \ldots, J, \quad \nu = 0, 1, \ldots;$$

where $\mathbf{y}(x) \equiv \mathbf{u}(\mathbf{s}^*; x)$ *is the unique solution of the boundary-value problem* (2.3.1) *and* $\lambda < 1$ *satisfies the inequality* (1.2.18e). ▮

Of course the iteration scheme (2.3.8) is frequently not of practical value (when, for example, $1 - \lambda$ is too small), and we would generally prefer a higher-order method for greater efficiency. For this purpose we recall Newton's method for approximating a root of Equation (2.3.3) as follows: $\mathbf{s}^{(0)} =$ arbitrary,

$$\mathbf{s}^{(\nu+1)} = \mathbf{s}^{(\nu)} + \Delta\mathbf{s}^{(\nu)}, \qquad \nu = 0, 1, \ldots, \tag{2.3.9a}$$

where $\Delta\mathbf{s}^{(\nu)}$ is the solution of the nth-order linear algebraic system

$$\frac{\partial\boldsymbol{\phi}(\mathbf{s}^{(\nu)})}{\partial\mathbf{s}}\Delta\mathbf{s}^{(\nu)} = -\boldsymbol{\phi}(\mathbf{s}^{(\nu)}), \qquad \nu = 0, 1, \ldots. \tag{2.3.9b}$$

These iterates are well defined when the coefficient matrix, or Jacobian matrix, $\partial\boldsymbol{\phi}/\partial\mathbf{s}$ is nonsingular for each $\mathbf{s}^{(\nu)}$. If this can be established, then the question of convergence is relevant. However, in the present case, Theorem 1.4.3 becomes applicable when the Jacobian is nonsingular. Thus to justify Newton's method applied to Equation (2.3.3) we need only show that $\partial\boldsymbol{\phi}(\mathbf{s})/\partial\mathbf{s}$ is nonsingular.

Differentiating in Equation (2.3.3), we obtain the representation

$$\frac{\partial\boldsymbol{\phi}(\mathbf{s})}{\partial\mathbf{s}} = A + BW(\mathbf{s}; b). \tag{2.3.10}$$

Here the nth-order matrix $W(\mathbf{s}; x) \equiv \partial\mathbf{u}(\mathbf{s}; x)/\partial\mathbf{s}$ is the solution of the variational system, obtained by differentiating in (2.3.2),

$$\text{(a)} \quad W' = \frac{\partial\mathbf{f}(x, \mathbf{u}(\mathbf{s}; x))}{\partial\mathbf{u}} W, \qquad \text{(b)} \quad W(0) = I. \tag{2.3.11}$$

We may write Equation (2.3.10), recalling the assumption that $(A + B)$ is nonsingular, as

$$\frac{\partial\boldsymbol{\phi}(\mathbf{s})}{\partial\mathbf{s}} = (A + B)[I + (A + B)^{-1}B(W(\mathbf{s}; b) - I)].$$

But it is shown in the proof of Theorem 1.2.6 that

$$\|(A + B)^{-1}B(W(\mathbf{s}; b) - I)\|_\infty < 1,$$

and so we can conclude that the Jacobian matrix is nonsingular (see Isaacson and Keller (1966), p. 16) for all $\mathbf{s}$. Of course, the matrix (2.3.10) may very well be nonsingular even though $(A + B)$ is singular. Thus, Newton's method is frequently applicable when our present proof of the fact is not.

The calculational procedure for employing Newton's method consists in solving $n + 1$ initial-value problems for nth-order systems at each iteration. The single nonlinear system (2.3.2) is integrated numerically with $\mathbf{s} = \mathbf{s}^{(\nu)}$, say, and at the same time and on the same net the n linear systems in (2.3.11) are integrated using the currently-computed values of $\mathbf{U}_j(\mathbf{s}^{(\nu)})$ in place of $\mathbf{u}(\mathbf{s}^{(\nu)}; x_j)$ to evaluate the elements in $\partial\mathbf{f}(x, \mathbf{u})/\partial\mathbf{u}$. Then $\mathbf{s}^{(\nu+1)}$ is computed from (2.3.9) where, however, $\boldsymbol{\phi}(\mathbf{s})$ in Equation (2.3.3) and $\partial\boldsymbol{\phi}(\mathbf{s})/\partial\mathbf{s}$ in Equation (2.3.10) are approximated using the appropriate numerical solutions for $\mathbf{u}$ and W at $x_J = b$.

There may be great practical merit in applying Newton's method to linear systems of differential equations. Sometimes the iteration schemes are less sensitive to cancellation errors that can disturb and even invalidate direct applications of shooting, as pointed out in Section 2.1. More important, however, is the fact that the matrix $W(x)$, the solution of (2.3.11), is independent of $\mathbf{s}$ for linear problems. That is, if $\mathbf{f}(x, \mathbf{u})$ has the form

$$\mathbf{f}(x, \mathbf{u}) = K(x)\mathbf{u} + \mathbf{f}_0(x), \tag{2.3.12}$$

where $K(x)$ is an nth-order matrix, then clearly

$$\frac{\partial\mathbf{f}(x, \mathbf{u})}{\partial\mathbf{u}} = K(x)$$

and the variational problem (2.3.11) reduces to

$$\text{(a)} \quad W' = K(x)W, \qquad \text{(b)} \quad W(0) = I. \tag{2.3.13}$$

Recalling Equation (2.3.10), we then see that $\partial\boldsymbol{\phi}(\mathbf{s})/\partial\mathbf{s}$ is independent of $\mathbf{s}$ and hence the system of Equations (2.3.3) for the determination of $\mathbf{s}$ is *a linear system.* (This was shown before more directly, in Section 1.2.1.) Since $W(x) \equiv \partial\mathbf{u}(\mathbf{s}; x)/\partial\mathbf{s}$, and we have just shown that $\boldsymbol{\phi}(\mathbf{s})$ is linear, so that $\boldsymbol{\phi}(\mathbf{s}) = [\partial\boldsymbol{\phi}(\mathbf{s})/\partial\mathbf{s}]\mathbf{s} + \boldsymbol{\phi}(\mathbf{0})$, it follows that Equation (2.3.3) can be written as

$$[A + BW(b)]\mathbf{s} = \boldsymbol{\alpha} - B\mathbf{u}(\mathbf{0}; b). \tag{2.3.14}$$

Thus by solving the n systems (2.3.13) the coefficient matrix is determined, and by solving the single system (2.3.2) with $\mathbf{s} = \mathbf{0}$ and $\mathbf{f}$ as given by Equation (2.3.12), the inhomogeneous data are determined.

Now to solve a *sequence* of linear boundary-value problems, given by (2.3.1) and (2.3.12), in which the boundary conditions change, we need only use the new data A, B, and $\boldsymbol{\alpha}$ in Equation (2.3.14), solve the resulting linear algebraic system for $\mathbf{s}$ and then solve the initial-value problem (2.3.2) using this value of $\mathbf{s}$. If in addition the inhomogeneous term in the differential equation is to be changed [this is the term $\mathbf{f}_0(x)$ in Equation (2.3.12)], we need one additional integration of (2.3.2) with $\mathbf{s} = \mathbf{0}$, as above, to compute $\mathbf{u}(\mathbf{0}; b)$. In many linear problems of interest it is only the inhomogeneous data that are to be altered and in such cases the above-indicated procedures are very efficient. It may frequently be worthwhile, in such cases, to compute $W(x)$ with extra accuracy (that is, multiple precision).

Of course in most nonlinear problems of practical interest the hypothesis of Theorem 1.2.6 will not be satisfied. We have already seen, for instance, that the condition, $(A + B)$ nonsingular, is rather special. Nevertheless, the initial-value method we have indicated is very frequently applicable though the proofs are not. The practical problem is to determine some matrix Q, now $\neq (A + B)^{-1}$, so that (2.3.4) is contracting; see for example Problems 2.3.4 and 2.3.5. Much more general results are indicated in Section 5.5 and, for instance, in Conti (1958) or Losota and Opial (1966). Of course if the initial unknown vector $\mathbf{s}$ can be reduced to a $q = n - p$-dimensional vector, as previously discussed, this should be done. Then the system of Equations (2.3.3) reduces to q equations, the corresponding Jacobian matrix in Equation (2.3.10) is of order q and the matrix W is $n \times q$. Now only $q + 1$ systems of order n need be integrated for each iteration [see Problem 1.2.12]. Needless to say this reduction should be done for linear problems when applicable.

It may be a formidable task to apply any iteration scheme successfully when one does not have some reasonable estimate of the location of a zero of $\boldsymbol{\phi}(\mathbf{s})$. Unfortunately there are no universal procedures for obtaining such estimates. But patience in searching for an acceptable first estimate is frequently rewarded. It is not unusual in practice to devote ninety percent or more of the computing effort to locating a neighborhood of a root. In many problems of scientific interest, as opposed to textbook problems, there are parameters in the equations or boundary conditions, and solutions are required over an entire domain of these parameters. But then when a solution has been obtained for one set of parameter values we can frequently make small changes in the values of the parameters and obtain neighboring solutions with ease.

This device of altering a parameter can be so effective that several techniques for solving nonlinear problems are based on *introducing* such a parameter. For instance we may introduce a single parameter t in such a way that for $t = 1$ the problem is the one whose solution is desired and for $t = 0$ it is some problem that is easily solved. Now if the solution depends continuously on t we may be able to proceed in small steps Δt, starting from $t = 0$ as indicated above, to compute finally the solution for $t = 1$. The study of these methods is briefly considered in Section 5.5.1. Let it suffice to say here that two very powerful techniques for proving existence theorems—the continuity and Poincaré continuation methods—are based on this idea [see Bers, John, and Schechter (1964), pp. 238–240, 285, Lasota and Opial (1966) and Section 5.5].

Problems

2.3.1 Show that the necessary and sufficient condition for the n linear boundary conditions in (2.3.1b) to be linearly independent is that rank $(A, B) = n$ [here A and B are nth-order matrices while (A, B) is a matrix with n rows and $2n$ columns].

2.3.2 Show that a necessary and sufficient condition for rank $(A, B) = n$ is that there be two nth-order matrices, say P_1 and P_2, such that the nth-order matrix $AP_1 + BP_2$ is nonsingular.

2.3.3 Use the results stated in Problems 2.3.1 and 2.3.2 to deduce that a *necessary* condition for the applicability of Newton's method in solving (2.3.1), that is, in finding a root of Equation (2.3.3), is that the boundary conditions (2.3.1b) be linearly independent.

2.3.4* If $\partial \mathbf{f}(x, \mathbf{u})/\partial \mathbf{u}$ is Lipschitz-continuous in $\mathbf{u}$, the matrix

$$[A + BW(\mathbf{s}^{(0)}; b)]$$

in Equation (2.3.10) is nonsingular and $|\boldsymbol{\phi}(\mathbf{s}^{(0)})|$ is sufficiently small, then Equation (2.3.3) has a root if $|b - a|$ is sufficiently small. Use the result in Problem 1.4.5 of Chapter 1 to indicate a proof of the above and estimate the magnitudes of $|\boldsymbol{\phi}(\mathbf{s}^{(0)})|$ and $|b - a|$ in terms of the magnitudes of $|\mathbf{f}|$, $\|\partial \mathbf{f}/\partial \mathbf{u}\|$ and the Lipschitz constant.

2.3.5 Formulate the boundary-value problem

$$y'' + y = 0, \qquad y(0) = 0, \qquad y'(L) = \cos L$$

in terms of a first-order system. Show that the conditions of Theorems 1.2.5 and 1.2.6 are satisfied if $L < \log 2$. For $L > \log 2$, show that a contraction is obtained by using, in place of $Q = (A + B)^{-1} = I$, the matrix

$$Q = \begin{pmatrix} 1 & 0 \\ 0 & q \end{pmatrix},$$

with any q satisfying

$$0 < q \cos L < 2.$$

What happens when $\cos L = 0$? Try actual computations in the above with varying values of L.

2.4 *Variants of Shooting; Parallel Shooting*

In the previous sections we have discussed some of the difficulties which arise in the shooting method. Of those discussed the best known, perhaps because it is the most common, is that caused by the growth of solutions of the initial-value problems which must be solved. We recall that this causes a loss in accuracy in attempts to solve the corresponding algebraic or transcendental system. [Technically we may say that the problem of finding a root of $\boldsymbol{\phi}(\mathbf{s}) = 0$ is "ill-conditioned" or "not properly posed" in the sense of Section 3, Chapter 1, in Isaacson and Keller (1966).] As has been pointed out, greater accuracy in the computations may sometimes overcome this difficulty. This is not always practicable or desirable and so we shall describe variations of the shooting method that can frequently eliminate this difficulty. The finite-difference or integral-equation methods of Chapters 3 and 4 do not suffer from this particular growth problem, in principle.

There is another more striking phenomenon that can hamper the initial-value method when it is applied to nonlinear problems. We have already pointed out that many, if not most, boundary-value problems of interest do not satisfy the nice conditions imposed in results like our Theorems 2.2.2 and 2.3.1 which insure the applicability of shooting. In particular the functions $f(x, y, y')$ or $\mathbf{f}(x, \mathbf{y})$ may be unbounded in the x, $\mathbf{y}$-domain of interest. Then solutions of the corresponding initial-value problems may become singular in $[a, b]$ for some values of the initial data. If this occurs we cannot even carry out the integration from a to b in order to improve the initial data. Furthermore, the location of the singularity is frequently a very sensitive function of the initial data and thus great accuracy in the initial estimate of $s^{(0)}$ or $\mathbf{s}^{(0)}$ may be required in order to start an iterative scheme; see Problem 2.4.1. When this difficulty with singularities occurs it is quite apparent in the computations. The parallel shooting schemes presented below can frequently circumvent the trouble, or else a finite difference procedure can be employed.

As we shall see, parallel shooting is actually a combination of difference methods and initial-value methods.

The variant known as multiple or parallel shooting is designed to reduce the growth of the solutions of the initial-value problems which must be solved. This is done by dividing the interval $[a, b]$ into a number of subintervals, integrating appropriate initial-value problems over each subinterval, and then *simultaneously* adjusting all of the "initial" data in order to satisfy the boundary conditions and appropriate continuity conditions at the subdivision points. The variety of procedures afforded by this technique is limitless, and we consider only two rather obvious forms of it here. Of course the motivation in selecting subintervals and directions of integration is, as indicated above, to reduce the magnification of errors caused by growing solutions.

To illustrate we shall consider the boundary-value problem, on an interval $a \leq x \leq b$, for a system of n first-order equations:

$$\text{(a)}\quad \mathbf{y}' = \mathbf{f}(x, \mathbf{y}), \qquad \text{(b)}\quad A\mathbf{y}(a) + B\mathbf{y}(b) = \boldsymbol{\alpha}. \tag{2.4.1}$$

We divide this interval into J subintervals with the points x_j, say

$$a \equiv x_0 < x_1 < x_2 < \cdots < x_{J-1} < x_J \equiv b. \tag{2.4.2a}$$

We refer to the interval $x_{j-1} \leq x \leq x_j$ as the jth subinterval and denote its length by

$$\Delta_j \equiv x_j - x_{j-1}. \tag{2.4.2b}$$

Now on each subinterval we introduce the new independent variable t, the new dependent variable $\mathbf{y}_j(t)$, and the new n-vector functions $\mathbf{f}_j(t, \mathbf{z})$ by

$$\begin{aligned} t &\equiv \frac{x - x_{j-1}}{\Delta_j}, \qquad \mathbf{y}_j(t) \equiv \mathbf{y}(x) = \mathbf{y}(x_{j-1} + t\Delta_j), \\ \mathbf{f}_j(t, \mathbf{z}) &\equiv \Delta_j \mathbf{f}(x_{j-1} + t\Delta_j, \mathbf{z}), \\ &\quad \text{for} \quad x_{j-1} < x < x_j, \qquad j = 1, 2, \ldots, J. \end{aligned} \tag{2.4.3}$$

With these changes of variables the system (2.4.1a) becomes, on the jth subinterval,

$$\frac{d\mathbf{y}_j}{dt} = \mathbf{f}_j(t, \mathbf{y}_j(t)), \qquad 0 < t < 1; \qquad j = 1, 2, \ldots, J. \tag{2.4.4a}$$

The boundary conditions (2.4.1b) are now

$$A\mathbf{y}_1(0) + B\mathbf{y}_J(1) = \boldsymbol{\alpha}. \tag{2.4.4b}$$

Continuity of the solution of (2.4.1) at each interior point x_j is expressed by the conditions

$$\mathbf{y}_{j+1}(0) - \mathbf{y}_j(1) = 0, \qquad j = 1, 2, \ldots, J - 1. \tag{2.4.4c}$$

The J systems of n first-order equations (2.4.4a) can be written in the vector form

$$\frac{d}{dt}\mathbf{Y} = \mathbf{F}(t, \mathbf{Y}), \qquad 0 < t < 1, \tag{2.4.5a}$$

and the J sets of conditions (2.4.4b, c) can be written in the matrix-vector form

$$P\mathbf{Y}(0) + Q\mathbf{Y}(1) = \boldsymbol{\gamma}. \tag{2.4.5b}$$

Here we have introduced the nJ-dimensional vectors

$$\mathbf{Y}(t) \equiv \begin{pmatrix} \mathbf{y}_1(t) \\ \mathbf{y}_2(t) \\ \vdots \\ \mathbf{y}_J(t) \end{pmatrix}, \qquad \mathbf{F}(t, \mathbf{Y}) \equiv \begin{pmatrix} \mathbf{f}_1(t, \mathbf{y}_1) \\ \mathbf{f}_2(t, \mathbf{y}_2) \\ \vdots \\ \mathbf{f}_J(t, \mathbf{y}_J) \end{pmatrix}, \qquad \boldsymbol{\gamma} \equiv \begin{pmatrix} \boldsymbol{\alpha} \\ \mathbf{0} \\ \vdots \\ \mathbf{0} \end{pmatrix}; \tag{2.4.6}$$

and the square matrices of order nJ

$$P \equiv \begin{pmatrix} A & 0 & 0 & \cdots & 0 \\ 0 & I & 0 & \cdots & 0 \\ 0 & 0 & I & \cdots & 0 \\ \vdots & & & & \vdots \\ 0 & 0 & 0 & \cdots & I \end{pmatrix},$$

$$Q \equiv \begin{pmatrix} 0 & 0 & 0 & \cdots & B \\ -I & 0 & 0 & \cdots & 0 \\ 0 & -I & 0 & \cdots & 0 \\ \vdots & & & & \vdots \\ 0 & 0 & 0 & -I & 0 \end{pmatrix}. \tag{2.4.7}$$

In (2.4.7) the identity matrix I is of order n and the blocks of zeros are also of order n.

Under modest smoothness conditions on $\mathbf{f}(x, \mathbf{y})$, the boundary-value problem (2.4.1) for n first-order equations on $a \leq x \leq b$ can be shown to be equivalent to the boundary-value problem (2.4.5) for nJ first-order equations on $0 \leq t \leq 1$. Clearly one parallel shooting procedure for solving (2.4.1) consists in applying ordinary shooting, as in Section 2.3, to (2.4.5). For this purpose we must solve the initial-value problem

$$\frac{d\mathbf{U}}{dt} = \mathbf{F}(t, \mathbf{U}), \qquad \mathbf{U}(0) = \mathbf{s}, \tag{2.4.8a}$$

for a first-order system of nJ equations. We try to pick the nJ-dimensional initial vector, $\mathbf{s}$, such that

$$\mathbf{\Phi}(\mathbf{s}) \equiv P\mathbf{s} + Q\mathbf{U}(\mathbf{s}; 1) - \boldsymbol{\gamma} = \mathbf{0}. \tag{2.4.9}$$

Of course Newton's method is advocated for solving this system. To employ it we compute, along with the solutions of the initial-value problem (2.4.8a), the nJ-order matrix solution, $W(\mathbf{s}, t) \equiv \partial \mathbf{U}/\partial \mathbf{s}$, of the variational system

$$\frac{dW}{dt} = \frac{\partial \mathbf{F}(t, \mathbf{U}(\mathbf{s}; t))}{\partial \mathbf{Y}} W, \qquad W(0) = I. \tag{2.4.10a}$$

The iterates are then given by $\mathbf{s}^{(\nu+1)} = \mathbf{s}^{(\nu)} + \Delta\mathbf{s}^{(\nu)}$, where

$$[P + QW(\mathbf{s}^{(\nu)}; 1)]\,\Delta\mathbf{s}^{(\nu)} = -\mathbf{\Phi}(\mathbf{s}^{(\nu)}). \tag{2.4.11}$$

The computations involved in carrying out the above procedure are not nearly as complicated as they might seem. This is due to the special form of $\mathbf{F}(t, \mathbf{Y})$ defined in (2.4.6). In fact, if we introduce the n-vectors $\mathbf{s}_j$ such that $\mathbf{s} = (\mathbf{s}_1^T, \mathbf{s}_2^T, \ldots, \mathbf{s}_J^T)^T$, then the system (2.4.8a) is in fact

$$\frac{d\mathbf{u}_j(t)}{dt} = \mathbf{f}_j(t, \mathbf{u}_j), \qquad \mathbf{u}_j(0) = \mathbf{s}_j, \qquad j = 1, 2, \ldots, J. \tag{2.4.8b}$$

This is J first-order systems of n equations and each system is independent of the others. Thus these J initial-value problems can be solved independently of each other. In fact the solution of the set of initial-value problems (2.4.8) is ideally suited for computation on *parallel computers* (which are at present being designed). The same is of course true of the variational system (2.4.10) for the matrix W of order nJ. If we define the J matrices, W_j, of order n by

$$\frac{dW_j}{dt} = \frac{\partial \mathbf{f}_j(t, \mathbf{u}_j(\mathbf{s}_j; t))}{\partial \mathbf{u}_j} W_j, \qquad W_j(0) = I, \qquad j = 1, 2, \ldots, J, \tag{2.4.10b}$$

then $W(\mathbf{s}, t) = \operatorname{diag}\{W_j(\mathbf{s}_j; t)\}$. This follows since $W_j = \partial\mathbf{u}_j/\partial\mathbf{s}_j$ and $\partial\mathbf{u}_i/\partial\mathbf{s}_j \equiv 0$ if $i \neq j$. The only coupling of the systems (2.4.8b) and (2.4.10b) for different values of j occurs in the algebraic problem of solving the linear system (2.4.11). We examine below some questions relating to the nonsingularity of the coefficient matrix in Equation (2.4.11). In particular the explicit form of the inverse of this matrix can be deduced under special circumstances (see Problem 2.4.3).

We first observe that the nJ-order matrix $(P + Q)$ is nonsingular if the nth-order matrix $(A + B)$ is nonsingular. In fact, with the definitions

$$R \equiv (A + B)^{-1}, \qquad S \equiv -RB, \qquad T \equiv RA = I + S, \tag{2.4.12a}$$

it is easily verified that

$$(P + Q)^{-1} = \begin{pmatrix} R & S & S & \cdots & S \\ R & T & S & \cdots & S \\ R & T & T & \cdots & \vdots \\ \vdots & & & & S \\ R & T & T & \cdots & T \end{pmatrix}. \qquad (2.4.12b)$$

A derivation of this result is indicated in Problem 2.4.2. Now the coefficient matrix in Equation (2.4.11) can be written as

$$(P + Q)[I + (P + Q)^{-1}Q(W(\mathbf{s}^{(\nu)}; 1) - I)],$$

and hence it is nonsingular if

$$\|(P + Q)^{-1}Q\|_\infty \, \|W(\mathbf{s}; 1) - I\|_\infty < 1. \qquad (2.4.13)$$

Using (2.4.12) and (2.4.7) it follows that

$$\|(P + Q)^{-1}Q\|_\infty \le M \equiv (J + 1)m, \qquad (2.4.14a)$$

where

$$m \equiv \max\{\|(A + B)^{-1}B\|_\infty, \|(A + B)^{-1}A\|_\infty\}.$$

Furthermore, just as in the proof of Theorem 1.2.6, we find from (2.4.10b) and the form of W that

$$\|W(\mathbf{s}; 1) - I\|_\infty \le \max_{1 \le j \le J} \left[\exp\left(\Delta_j \int_0^1 k(x_{j-1} + t\Delta_j)\, dt\right) - 1\right], \qquad (2.4.14b)$$

where $k(x)$ is, as usual, the bound

$$k(x) \ge \left\|\frac{\partial \mathbf{f}(x, \mathbf{y})}{\partial \mathbf{y}}\right\|_\infty, \qquad a \le x \le b.$$

We see that taking all the Δ_j "small" reduces the bound in (2.4.14b). But since $\sum_1^J \Delta_j = b - a$, this implies "large" values for J which increases the bound in (2.4.14a). If we assume that $k(x)$ is bounded on $[a, b]$ and take subintervals of equal length, $\Delta_j = (b - a)/J$, $j = 1, 2, \ldots, J$, then the inequality (2.4.13) is satisfied if

$$b - a < \frac{J \ln [1 + (1/M)]}{\max_{a \le x \le b} k(x)}.$$

On the other hand, Theorem 1.2.6 is valid if we replace the hypothesis (2.2.18e) by the stronger condition

$$b - a < \frac{\ln [1 + (1/m)]}{\max_{a \le x \le b} k(x)}.$$

For large J and m the above inequalities are almost equivalent, since then

$$\ln\left(1+\frac{1}{m}\right)\approx\frac{1}{m},\qquad J\ln\left(1+\frac{1}{(J+1)m}\right)\approx\frac{J}{(J+1)m}.$$

We should also observe that when (2.4.13) is satisfied, the proof of Theorem 1.2.6 applies to the boundary-value problem (2.4.5) to show that it has a unique solution.

What we have shown above is, essentially, that the parallel shooting procedure does not make matters *worse* than they were for the original initial-value problem. We have not been able to show, for instance, that the length of the interval $[a, b]$ over which our proof of existence and uniqueness holds, can be increased. But the purpose of the parallel shooting method is to overcome certain practical difficulties that occur in ordinary shooting. While actual computations verify its usefulness in special cases, we may also give some theoretical justification as follows. In solving the initial-value problems (2.3.2) and (2.4.8) numerically, errors are of course introduced. If the same stable scheme of order p, say, is used in each case with the same net spacing h, and the functions $\mathbf{f}(x, \mathbf{u})$ and $\mathbf{F}(t, \mathbf{U})$ are sufficiently smooth, then the numerical errors at points of the intervals $[a, b]$ and $[0, 1]$ can be bounded by

$$|\mathbf{u}(x_i)-\mathbf{u}_i|\le h^pM_1\exp[K_1|x_0-x_i|],$$
$$|\mathbf{U}(t_i)-\mathbf{U}_i|\le h^pM_2\exp[K_2|t_0-t_i|].$$

Some estimates of this form are derived in Section 1.3. The constants M_1 and M_2 depend in a simple algebraic manner on bounds for the functions $\mathbf{f}$ and $\mathbf{F}$ and possibly some of their derivatives. However, the constants K_1 and K_2 are essentially the Lipschitz constants for $\mathbf{f}$ and $\mathbf{F}$, respectively, or polynomials in these constants. Then if we take $\Delta_j = |b-a|/J$, $j = 1, 2, \ldots, J$, in the subdivision (2.4.2) it is clear from (2.4.3) and (2.4.6) that

$$K_2 \doteq K_1\frac{|b-a|}{J}.$$

Then since solutions of (2.3.2) at $x = b$ correspond to those of (2.4.8) at $t = 1$, we see that the *bound on the error in the numerical solution is reduced exponentially by parallel shooting* [that is, the bound is proportional to $(\exp[K_1|b-a|])^{1/J}$ rather than to $(\exp[K_1|b-a|])$]. The constant M_2 is at worst larger than M_1 by a factor which is a small power of J. To show the detailed dependence of the quantities M_1, M_2, K_1, and K_2 on bounds for $\mathbf{f}$, $\mathbf{F}$, and their derivatives is rather complicated. Problems 1.3.3–6 contain some results which should clarify matters. More details can be found in Isaacson and Keller, Chapter 8, Sections 2 and 3. Very explicit error estimates are contained in Henrici (1962) and (1963).

A schematic diagram of the parallel shooting scheme presented above is shown in Figure 2.4.1. By analogy it is easy to indicate other parallel shooting schemes which may in many cases be more efficient. For instance, if we agree to take $J = 2N$, so that there is always an even number of subintervals, we can shoot from each odd-labeled subdivision point toward each of its two adjacent even-labeled points. A glance at Figure 2.4.2 for the special case $J = 4$ should suffice. Here there are only two n-vectors $\mathbf{s}_1$ and $\mathbf{s}_2$ to be determined [by applying continuity at x_2, that is $\mathbf{u}_2(1) = \mathbf{u}_3(1)$, and the appropriate boundary conditions on $\mathbf{u}_1(1)$ and $\mathbf{u}_4(1)$]. The continuity conditions at x_1 and x_3 are automatically satisfied. We do not bother with a detailed formulation of this case as the diagram should suffice. In this manner the systems replacing (2.4.9) and (2.4.11) are only half the order they would be if all shooting were in the same direction for the same number of subintervals.

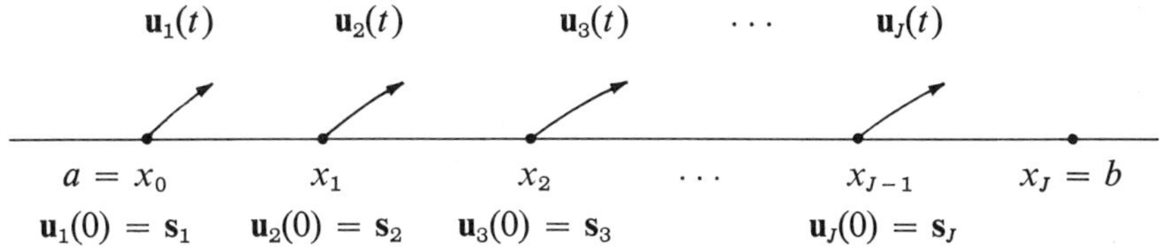

Figure 2.4.1

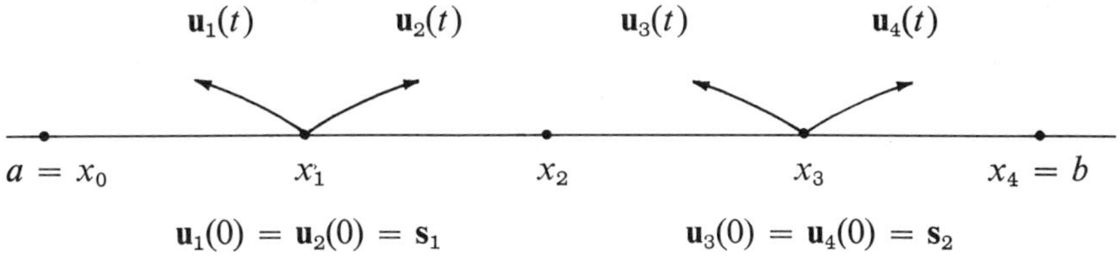

Figure 2.4.2

A rather common special case of the above modification occurs for $J = 2$ and is generally described in terms of shooting from each endpoint and matching at some interior point. In fact all of our schemes are just as well considered to be multiple matching generalizations of this well-known case.

If it is known that all solutions of a given system of differential equations decay in one direction then all integrations should be done in that direction. However if solutions grow more or less equally in both directions then there is no preferred direction and the more efficient process of shooting in both directions should be used.

A rough practical guide to the choice of subintervals to be used in parallel shooting can be based on the old-fashioned technique (when calculating with fixed point arithmetic) of rescaling the solution as it grows. That is, integrate the initial-value problem

$$\mathbf{y}' = \mathbf{f}(x, \mathbf{y}), \qquad \mathbf{y}(a) = \boldsymbol{\xi}$$

using some "typical" initial value $\boldsymbol{\xi}$ on some sufficiently fine net $\{x_\nu\}$ with $x_0 = a$. After each step of the integration test to see if the growth condition

$$\|\mathbf{y}(x_\nu)\| > R\|\mathbf{y}(x_0)\|,$$

where R is some selected reasonable growth factor, say $R = 10^3$ (the choice of R depends upon the machine word length, as well as other factors). When this test is passed, take x_ν to be one of the points in (2.4.2a), replace $\|\mathbf{y}(x_0)\|$ in the test by the new value, $\|\mathbf{y}(x_\nu)\|$, and continue the integration and testing. Some experimenting with choices of $\boldsymbol{\xi}$ and R may be required in very difficult cases.

2.4.1 Power Series

Power series are occasionally applied or suggested as a means for solving boundary-value problems. Their application is in fact a variant of the initial-value method. For example, if $\mathbf{f}(x, \mathbf{y})$ in Equation (2.4.1a) is an analytic function of the $n + 1$ variables $(x, \mathbf{y})$, then we may seek power-series solutions in the form

$$\mathbf{y}(x) = \sum_{k=0}^{\infty} \mathbf{a}_k (x - a)^k. \tag{2.4.15}$$

Using this in the expanded form of Equation (2.4.1a) and equating coefficients of like powers of $(x - a)$, we obtain (recursive) formulae for the coefficients $\mathbf{a}_k$, $k = 1, 2, \ldots$, in terms of the initial point a, and the leading coefficients $\mathbf{a}_0$ [i.e., $\mathbf{a}_k = \mathbf{a}_k(\mathbf{a}_0)$].

Now $\mathbf{a}_0$ is to be determined so that the boundary conditions (2.4.1b) are satisfied. This yields the system

$$A\mathbf{a}_0 + B \sum_{k=0}^{\infty} \mathbf{a}_k (b - a)^k - \boldsymbol{\alpha} = 0. \tag{2.4.16}$$

Since the $\mathbf{a}_k$ for $k \geq 1$ are functions of $\mathbf{a}_0$ the system (2.4.16) can be considered a transcendental system of equations in $\mathbf{a}_0$. [Of course if there are p independent conditions on $\mathbf{y}(a)$ in (2.4.1b), or equivalently on $\mathbf{a}_0$ in (2.4.1b), then the system is easily reduced to one containing only $q = n - p$ equations and unknowns.]

However, if power series are employed to solve the initial-value problem (2.3.2) then the resulting transcendental system $\boldsymbol{\phi}(\mathbf{s}) = 0$, with $\boldsymbol{\phi}(\mathbf{s})$ defined in (2.3.3), is identical to the system (2.4.16) if we set $\mathbf{s} \equiv \mathbf{a}_0$. In this sense the power-series procedure is but a special case of the initial-value method.

To justify the power-series method in any case requires a study of the convergence of the appropriate series (2.4.15) over the interval $a \leq x \leq b$. Thus, at best, the method has rather limited applicability. In actual calculations we do not use (2.4.15) but some truncated version, say,

$$\mathbf{u}_N(x) = \sum_{k=0}^{N} \mathbf{a}_k(x - a)^k. \tag{2.4.17}$$

The error committed in this way is formally analogous to the truncation error introduced when solving the initial-value problem (2.4.1) by some numerical scheme. While the calculations using (2.4.17) are always well-defined, the formal result as $N \to \infty$ may be nonsense if the radius of convergence is too small, that is, less than $b - a$. (As indicated in Section 2.3 the schemes based on direct numerical integration of the initial-value problem have no such limitation imposed by radius-of-convergence difficulties.)

However, there are several ways in which the power-series method may be salvaged. One way is by direct analytic continuation from a to b by expansions about a sequence of intermediate points, x_j, $j = 1, 2, \ldots, J$. This procedure is essentially the same as using the one-step integration scheme known as the Taylor expansion method to solve the initial-value problem (2.3.2). When the motivation is power series one would employ many terms in the expansions of form (2.4.17) and few "expansion points" x_j, that is, small J. Conversely, many closely-spaced "net points," x_j, and few terms in the Taylor series would be used in schemes motivated by numerical integration. The difference in point of view depends, of course, on which limiting process is intended, $\max_j |x_j - x_{j+1}| \to 0$, or $N \to \infty$; only in the latter case is analyticity required.

Some other ways in which power series may be used are suggested by the parallel shooting variants discussed above. For instance, the solution can be expanded about each endpoint and the two series matched at some common interior point. Then two unknown leading-coefficient vectors, say $\mathbf{a}_0$ and $\mathbf{b}_0$, must be determined by the matching conditions and the boundary conditions. Obviously the solution could be expanded about N interior points, matched at $N - 1$ interior points separating these expansion points, and the boundary conditions imposed to determine N unknown leading-coefficient vectors. For instance, the odd-labeled points in Figure 2.4.2 may be taken as the origins for expansions, and at the even-labeled interior points the appropriate series would be matched. The convergence problems and questions of accuracy in such power-series methods are untreated in the literature.

Problems

2.4.1 The problem $y'' = m^2 \sinh q^2 y$, $y(0) = y(1) = 0$ has the unique solution $y(x) \equiv 0$. Show that the initial-value problem

$$u'' = m^2 \sinh q^2 u, \qquad u(0) = 0, \qquad u'(0) = s,$$

has a singularity located at approximately

$$x_\infty = \frac{1}{qm} \log \frac{8m}{qs} + \cdots.$$

Thus in order that $x_\infty > 1$, that is, lie outside [0, 1], the initial parameter s must satisfy

$$s \le \frac{8m}{q} e^{-mq}.$$

For $m = q = 4$ the initial parameter s must be accurate to within e^{-16}. [This problem is from B. A. Troesch (1960)]. [HINT: By integrating $y'y'' = [\frac{1}{2}(y')^2]'$, the solution can be obtained in the implicit form: $x = \int_0^u [\cdots]\, du$. Setting $u = \infty$, we obtain an expression for x_∞ which can be estimated by expanding the integrand appropriately.]

2.4.2 For the matrix $(P + Q)$ determined by Equation (2.4.7) find the elementary block transformations, T_j, such that

$$(P + Q)T_{J-1}T_{J-2}\cdots T_1 = \begin{pmatrix} (A+B) & B & B & \cdots & B \\ & I & 0 & \cdots & 0 \\ & 0 & I & \cdots & 0 \\ \vdots & & & & \vdots \\ & & & & 0 \\ 0 & & \cdots & & I \end{pmatrix}.$$

Use the above and the forms of T_j to deduce the result in (2.4.12).

2.4.3 Using the fact that $W = \operatorname{diag}\{W_j\}$ and the assumption that the nth-order matrix $(A + BW_J \cdots W_1)$ is nonsingular, derive an explicit representation for the inverse of the nJ-order matrix $(P + QW)$. [HINT: Reduce $(P + QW)$ to upper-triangular form with first row $(A + BW_J \cdots W_1)$, $BW_J \cdots W_2, \ldots, BW_J$ in a manner similar to that of Problem 2.4.2. Find the inverse as the product of triangular matrices in analogy with (2.4.12).]

2.4.4 Formulate the parallel shooting scheme implied by Figure 2.4.2 (generalized to $J = 2N$) for the boundary-value problem (2.4.1). Examine the linear system obtained by applying Newton's method to solve for the nN-dimensional vector $\mathbf{s}$.

2.4.5 Consider the boundary-value problem of order $n = 2m$

$$\mathbf{y}' = \mathbf{f}(x, \mathbf{y}, \mathbf{z}), \qquad A\mathbf{y}(a) = \boldsymbol{\alpha}, \qquad \mathbf{z}' = \mathbf{g}(x, \mathbf{y}, \mathbf{z}), \qquad B\mathbf{z}(b) = \boldsymbol{\beta},$$

where $\mathbf{y}$, $\mathbf{z}$, $\mathbf{f}$, $\mathbf{g}$, $\boldsymbol{\alpha}$, and $\boldsymbol{\beta}$ are m-dimensional and the mth-order matrices A and B are nonsingular. Formulate the parallel shooting schemes of both types, Figures 2.4.1 and 2.4.2, for the same $J = 2N$ intervals for this problem. Compare the application of Newton's method in each case and formally determine the relevant inverse matrices. Discuss the solution when $\mathbf{f}$ and $\mathbf{g}$ are linear in $\mathbf{y}$ and $\mathbf{z}$.

SUPPLEMENTARY REFERENCES AND NOTES

Section 2.1 A technique for reducing the effect of cancellation errors in some linear boundary-value problems is given in Godunov (1961). This procedure has been made more practical by S. Conti (1966), whose scheme can be formulated as a special form of parallel shooting.

Section 2.2 Shooting methods for nonlinear second-order problems are described by Collatz (1960) and Fox (1957).

Section 2.3 The Newton method applied to shooting with somewhat specialized boundary conditions is described in Goodman and Lance (1956). Rather than solve a small-order linear system to obtain the corrections to the initial data they integrate (numerically) the adjoint system backwards.

Since the variational systems are linear, predictor-corrector schemes are better replaced by the corrector alone, properly solved [see Riley, Bennett, and McCormick (1967)].

Section 2.4 A limiting form of parallel shooting yields a finite-difference scheme (that is, when the modified Euler one-step method is used over each interval). Multiple shooting in various forms has been considered by, among others: Fox (1960), Morrison, Riley, and Zancanaro (1962), and Kalnins (1964). For linear problems, Conti's (1966) procedure is closely related. However, one of the most important features of parallel shooting—the exponential reduction in error growth—does not seem to have been recognized previously.

For an example of the use of power series in solving nonlinear boundary-value problems see Reiss, Greenberg, and Keller (1957) or Weinitishke (1960), who employs analytic continuation.

CHAPTER 3

FINITE-DIFFERENCE METHODS

3.1 Linear Second-Order Equations

We again consider the single linear second-order equation

$$Ly(x) \equiv -y'' + p(x)y' + q(x)y = r(x), \qquad a < x < b, \quad (3.1.1a)$$

which is now subject to the special two-point boundary conditions

$$y(a) = \alpha, \qquad y(b) = \beta. \quad (3.1.1b)$$

More general boundary conditions will be discussed later. A unique solution, $y(x)$, of (3.1.1) exists by the Corollary to Theorem 1.2.2 if $p(x)$, $q(x)$, $r(x)$ are continuous on $[a, b]$ and $q(x)$ is positive there. But since these functions are continuous on a closed bounded interval, there must exist positive constants P^*, Q^*, and Q_* such that

$$|p(x)| \leq P^*, \qquad 0 < Q_* \leq q(x) \leq Q^*, \qquad a \leq x \leq b. \quad (3.1.2)$$

(It should be observed that the conditions here imposed on $p(x)$, $q(x)$, and $r(x)$ are much more restrictive than those required in Section 2.1 for the application of initial-value methods.) We shall now study finite-difference methods for computing approximations to the solution of the boundary-value problem (3.1.1).

On the interval $[a, b]$ we place a uniform net, say

$$x_j = a + jh, \qquad j = 0, 1, \ldots, J + 1, \qquad h = \frac{b - a}{J + 1}. \quad (3.1.3)$$

To approximate $y(x)$ on this net we define a net function $\{u_j\}$ as the solution of a system of finite-difference equations which are in some sense an approximation to the problem (3.1.1). An obvious such difference formulation is

$$L_h u_j \equiv -\left(\frac{u_{j+1} - 2u_j + u_{j-1}}{h^2}\right) + p(x_j)\left(\frac{u_{j+1} - u_{j-1}}{2h}\right) + q(x_j)u_j \tag{3.1.4a}$$

$$= r(x_j), \qquad 1 \leq j \leq J;$$

$$u_0 = \alpha, \qquad u_{J+1} = \beta. \tag{3.1.4b}$$

At each interior net point, x_j, the derivatives in Equation (3.1.1a) have been replaced by corresponding centered difference quotients to give Equations (3.1.4a). We proceed to show that the linear system (3.1.4) can be solved by a simple algorithm, if h is sufficiently small, and then we estimate the accuracy of this numerical solution.

The result of multiplying the Equations (3.1.4a) by $h^2/2$ can be written as

$$\frac{h^2}{2} L_h u_j \equiv a_j u_{j-1} + b_j u_j + c_j u_{j+1} = \frac{h^2}{2} r(x_j), \qquad 1 \leq j \leq J, \tag{3.1.5a}$$

where

$$\begin{aligned} a_j &\equiv -\frac{1}{2}\left[1 + \frac{h}{2} p(x_j)\right], \\ b_j &\equiv \left[1 + \frac{h^2}{2} q(x_j)\right], \qquad 1 \leq j \leq J, \\ c_j &\equiv -\frac{1}{2}\left[1 - \frac{h}{2} p(x_j)\right], \end{aligned} \tag{3.1.5b}$$

Now the system (3.1.4) is, in vector notation,

$$A\mathbf{u} = \mathbf{r}, \tag{3.1.6a}$$

where we have introduced the J-dimensional vectors

$$\mathbf{u} \equiv \begin{pmatrix} u_1 \\ u_2 \\ \vdots \\ u_J \end{pmatrix}, \qquad \mathbf{r} \equiv \begin{pmatrix} r_1 \\ r_2 \\ \vdots \\ r_J \end{pmatrix} \equiv \frac{h^2}{2} \begin{pmatrix} r(x_1) \\ r(x_2) \\ \vdots \\ r(x_J) \end{pmatrix} - \begin{pmatrix} a_1\alpha \\ 0 \\ \vdots \\ 0 \\ c_J\beta \end{pmatrix}, \tag{3.1.6b}$$

and the J-order matrix

$$A = \begin{pmatrix} b_1 & c_1 & 0 & \cdot & \cdot & \cdot & 0 \\ a_2 & b_2 & c_2 & & & & \\ & \cdot & \cdot & \cdot & & & \cdot \\ \cdot & & \cdot & \cdot & \cdot & & \cdot \\ \cdot & & & \cdot & \cdot & \cdot & \cdot \\ \cdot & & & & a_{J-1} & b_{J-1} & c_{J-1} \\ 0 & \cdot & \cdot & \cdot & 0 & a_J & b_J \end{pmatrix}. \tag{3.1.6c}$$

A matrix of the form (3.1.6c), with nonzero elements only on the diagonal and the two adjacent codiagonals, is called a *tridiagonal* matrix. This special form frequently permits a very efficient application of the Gaussian elimination procedure, accounting for the occurrence of the known zero elements.

Let us derive this procedure quite formally, for solving any system of the form (3.1.6), and then justify its application when the coefficients (3.1.5b) are used. We assume that A is nonsingular and can be factored into the product

$$A = LU,$$

where

$$L \equiv \begin{pmatrix} \beta_1 & 0 & \cdot & \cdot & 0 \\ a_2 & \beta_2 & & & \cdot \\ 0 & \cdot & \cdot & & \cdot \\ \cdot & & \cdot & \cdot & 0 \\ 0 & \cdot & 0 & a_J & \beta_J \end{pmatrix}, \qquad U \equiv \begin{pmatrix} 1 & \gamma_1 & 0 & \cdot & 0 \\ 0 & 1 & \gamma_2 & & \cdot \\ \cdot & & \cdot & \cdot & 0 \\ \cdot & & & \cdot & \gamma_{J-1} \\ 0 & \cdot & \cdot & 0 & 1 \end{pmatrix}.$$

It follows that the β_j and γ_j must satisfy

$$\begin{aligned} &\beta_1 = b_1, \qquad \gamma_1 = c_1/\beta_1; \\ &\beta_j = b_j - a_j\gamma_{j-1}, \qquad j = 2, 3, \ldots, J; \\ &\gamma_j = c_j/\beta_j, \qquad j = 2, 3, \ldots, J-1. \end{aligned} \tag{3.1.7a}$$

The system (3.1.6a) can now be replaced by an equivalent pair of systems, say

$$L\mathbf{z} = \mathbf{r}, \qquad U\mathbf{u} = \mathbf{z}.$$

But since L and U are triangular, the solutions of these systems are easily obtained as

$$z_1 = r_1/\beta_1, \qquad z_j = (r_j - a_j z_{j-1})/\beta_j, \qquad j = 2, 3, \ldots, J; \tag{3.1.7b}$$

and

$$u_J = z_J, \qquad u_j = z_j - \gamma_j u_{j+1}, \qquad j = J-1, J-2, \ldots, 1. \tag{3.1.7c}$$

Thus, in summary, our formal procedure for solving Equation (3.1.6a) with coefficient matrix of the form (3.1.6c) is to compute the quantities β_j and γ_j in (3.1.7a), then evaluate the "intermediate solution," z_j, in (3.1.7b); and finally, u_j is given in (3.1.7c).

The only way in which the direct factorization procedure (3.1.7) can fail is for some β_j to vanish. This difficulty can frequently be avoided by means of the following.

THEOREM 3.1.1. *Let the elements of A in* (3.1.6c) *satisfy*

$$|b_j| > |a_j| + |c_j|, \qquad j = 1, 2, \ldots, J; \qquad (a_1 \equiv c_J \equiv 0).$$

Then A is nonsingular and the quantities β_j and γ_j in (3.1.7a) *are bounded by*

$$\text{(a)} \quad |\gamma_j| < 1, \qquad \text{(b)} \quad |b_j| - |a_j| \le |\beta_j| \le |b_j| + |a_j|.$$

Proof. If $\beta_j \neq 0$ for $1 \le j \le J$ the factorization $A = LU$ is valid. Then $\det A = (\det L)(\det U) = \beta_1\beta_2 \cdots \beta_J \neq 0$, so that A is nonsingular.

From the hypothesis, $|\gamma_1| = |c_1/b_1| < 1$. For an inductive proof of (a) assume $|\gamma_i| < 1$ for $i \le j - 1$. But we know that

$$\gamma_j = c_j/(b_j - a_j\gamma_{j-1})$$

and thus

$$|\gamma_j| \le \frac{|c_j|}{|b_j| - |a_j|\,|\gamma_{j-1}|} \le \frac{|c_j|}{|b_j| - |a_j|} < 1,$$

so part (a) follows. Now we use $|\gamma_j| < 1$ in $\beta_j = b_j - a_j\gamma_{j-1}$ and take absolute values to conclude part (b). ∎

Returning to our finite-difference problem, we have the following obvious corollary.

COROLLARY. *Let $p(x)$ and $q(x)$ satisfy* (3.1.2) *and the net spacing h satisfy*

$$h \le \frac{2}{P^*}.$$

Then the finite-difference system (3.1.4) *or* (3.1.6) *with coefficients given in* (3.1.5) *has a unique solution, $\{u_j\}$, given by* (3.1.7).

Proof. From (3.1.2) and (3.1.5b) we have

$$|b_j| \ge 1 + \frac{h^2}{2} Q_*.$$

But if $h \le 2/P^*$, then

$$|a_j| = \frac{1}{2}\left[1 + \frac{h}{2}p(x_j)\right], \qquad |c_j| = \frac{1}{2}\left[1 - \frac{h}{2}p(x_j)\right],$$

and so

$$|a_j| + |c_j| = 1.$$

Now the hypothesis of Theorem 3.1.1 is satisfied and the corollary follows. ∎

To estimate the error in the numerical solution of boundary-value problems by finite-difference methods, we can employ a stability theory exactly analogous to that used in Section 1.3 for numerical solutions of initial-value problems. We first define the *local truncation errors*, $\tau_j[v]$, in L_h, as an approximation to L, for any smooth function $v(x)$, by

$$\tau_j[v] \equiv L_h v(x_j) - Lv(x_j), \qquad 1 \leq j \leq J. \tag{3.1.8}$$

If $v(x)$ has continuous fourth derivatives on $[a, b]$, then for L as defined in (3.1.1a) and L_h as defined in (3.1.4a),

$$\begin{aligned}\tau_j[v] &= -\left[\frac{v(x_j + h) - 2v(x_j) + v(x_j - h)}{h^2} - v''(x_j)\right] \\ &\qquad + p(x_j)\left[\frac{v(x_j + h) - v(x_j - h)}{2h} - v'(x_j)\right] \\ &= -\frac{h^2}{12}\,[v''''(\xi_j) - 2p(x_j)v'''(\eta_j)], \qquad 1 \leq j \leq J.\end{aligned} \tag{3.1.9}$$

Here ξ_j and η_j are values in $[x_{j-1}, x_{j+1}]$ which come from the application of Taylor's theorem. Thus from the first lines of (3.1.9) we find that L_h *is consistent with* L; that is, $\tau_j[v] \to 0$ as $h \to 0$, for all functions $v(x)$ having a continuous second derivative on $[a, b]$. Further, L_h *has second-order accuracy* (in approximating L) for functions, $v(x)$, with continuous fourth derivatives on $[a, b]$. If $p(x) \equiv 0$ it is not difficult to devise fourth-order-accurate difference approximations to L (see Problem 3.3.1).

The linear difference operator L_h is said to be *stable* if for sufficiently small h there is a positive constant M, independent of h, such that

$$|v_j| \leq M\left\{\max(|v_0|, |v_{J+1}|) + \max_{1 \leq i \leq J} |L_h v_i|\right\}, \qquad 0 \leq j \leq J + 1, \tag{3.1.10}$$

for all net functions $\{v_j\}$. We note that stability is solely a property of the finite-difference approximation L_h. Before exploiting the consequences of stability we shall establish this property for the operator in (3.1.4a). We have the following.

THEOREM 3.1.2. *Let* L_h *be defined by* (3.1.4a) *or* (3.1.5) *where* $p(x)$ *and* $q(x)$ *satisfy* (3.1.2). *Then for all net spacing* h *such that*

$$h \leq \frac{2}{P^*},$$

and all net functions $\{v_j\}$, *the inequality* (3.1.10) *holds with the constant*

$$M = \max(1, 1/Q_*);$$

that is, L_h *is stable.*

Proof. From the definition in (3.1.5a) we have the identity

$$b_j v_j \equiv -a_j v_{j-1} - c_j v_{j+1} + \frac{h^2}{2} L_h v_j, \qquad 1 \le j \le J.$$

Since $h \le 2/P^*$, it follows from (3.1.5b) and (3.1.2) that

$$b_j \ge 1 + \frac{h^2}{2} Q_* > 1, \qquad |a_j| + |c_j| = 1.$$

Taking absolute values in the above identity, we now get

$$\left(1 + \frac{h^2}{2} Q_*\right)|v_j| \le \max_{0 \le i \le J+1} |v_i| + \frac{h^2}{2} \max_{1 \le i \le J} |L_h v_i|, \qquad 1 \le j \le J.$$

If $\max_{0 \le i \le J+1} |v_i|$ occurs for i in $1 \le i \le J$, then the inequality above implies, if we choose the appropriate index j, that

$$\max_{0 \le i \le J+1} |v_i| \le \frac{1}{Q_*} \max_{1 \le i \le J} |L_h v_i|.$$

In this case clearly for any j in $1 \le j \le J$, with $M \equiv \max(1, 1/Q_*)$,

$$\begin{aligned} |v_j| \le \frac{1}{Q_*} \max_{1 \le i \le J} |L_h v_i| &\le M \max_{1 \le i \le J} |L_h v_i| \\ &\le M\left\{\max(|v_0|, |v_{J+1}|) + \max_{1 \le i \le J} |L_h v_i|\right\}. \end{aligned}$$

But if $\max_{0 \le i \le J+1} |v_i|$ occurs for $i = 0$ or $i = J + 1$ the result (3.1.10) follows trivially since $M \ge 1$. ▌

One consequence of stability is the fact that the difference equations (3.1.4) have a unique solution. This follows since the homogeneous system can have only the trivial solution, $u_j \equiv 0$. We have previously given a constructive proof of this result in the Corollary to Theorem 3.1.1, under the same hypothesis. A more important application of stability is in obtaining the following error estimate.

THEOREM 3.1.3. *Let $p(x)$ and $q(x)$ satisfy* (3.1.2) *and h satisfy $h \le 2/P^*$. Then the numerical solution $\{u_j\}$ of* (3.1.4) *and solution $y(x)$ of* (3.1.1) *satisfy, with* $M \equiv \max(1, 1/Q_*)$,

$$|u_j - y(x_j)| \le M \max_{1 \le i \le J} |\tau_i[y]|, \qquad 0 \le j \le J + 1.$$

If $y(x)$ has four continuous derivatives on $[a, b]$, *then*

$$|u_j - y(x_j)| \le M \frac{h^2}{12}(M_4 + 2P^* M_3), \qquad 0 \le j \le J + 1,$$

where $M_\nu \equiv \max_{a \le x \le b} |d^\nu y(x)/dx^\nu|$; $\nu = 3, 4$.

Proof. From (3.1.4a) and (3.1.1), evaluated at $x = x_j$, we have by the linearity of L_h and the definition (3.1.8)

$$L_h[u_j - y(x_j)] = r(x_j) - L_h y(x_j) = Ly(x_j) - L_h y(x_j) = -\tau_j[y].$$

But from Equations (3.1.1b) and (3.1.4b),

$$u_0 - y(x_0) = u_{J+1} - y(x_{J+1}) = 0.$$

Now we apply (3.1.10) with $v_j \equiv u_j - y(x_j)$ and recall (3.1.9) to obtain the theorem. ∎

In Problems 3.1.2 and 3.1.3 we show how the above results can be extended to apply to Equation (3.1.1a), subject to more general boundary conditions.

3.1.1 *Difference Corrections and $h \to 0$ Extrapolation*

The difference scheme (3.1.4) has been shown to yield an approximation to the solution of the boundary-value problem (3.1.1) to within an error that is $\mathcal{O}(h^2)$. For somewhat more special equations a slightly improved difference scheme yields $\mathcal{O}(h^4)$ errors (see Problem 3.3.1). We shall briefly examine two ways in which, with additional calculations, the scheme (3.1.4) can be made to yield $\mathcal{O}(h^4)$ accuracy. These error-reduction procedures are Richardson's *deferred approach to the limit* or, as we prefer to call it, *extrapolation to zero mesh-width*, and Fox's (1957) method of *difference corrections.*

The theoretical basis for both methods is the same, namely that there exists some function $e(x)$, independent of the net spacing h, such that the error has the form

$$[y(x_j) - u_j] = h^2 e(x_j) + \mathcal{O}(h^4), \qquad 0 \le j \le J + 1. \qquad (3.1.11)$$

Suppose we can compute $\{E_j\}$, an $\mathcal{O}(h^2)$ approximation to $\{e(x_j)\}$; then clearly

$$\bar{u}_j \equiv u_j + h^2 E_j$$

is an $\mathcal{O}(h^4)$ approximation to $y(x_j)$ on the net. This is essentially the difference-correction method and there may be various ways in which the E_j can be determined.

For the $h \to 0$ extrapolation we solve (3.1.4) twice, with the net spacings h and $h/2$. Let the respective solutions of these difference problems be denoted by $\{u_i(h)\}$ and $\{u_j(h/2)\}$. For any point x common to both nets, say $x = jh = 2j(h/2)$, we have from (3.1.11)

$$\tfrac{1}{3}\{4[y(x) - u_{2j}(h/2)] - [y(x) - u_j(h)]\} = \mathcal{O}(h^4).$$

Thus an $\mathcal{O}(h^4)$ approximation to $y(x)$ on the net with spacing h is given by

$$\bar{u}_j \equiv \tfrac{4}{3}u_{2j}(h/2) - \tfrac{1}{3}u_j(h), \qquad 0 \leq j \leq J + 1.$$

A derivation of (3.1.11) is contained in the proof of the following.

THEOREM 3.1.4. *Let $p(x)$ and $q(x)$ satisfy* (3.1.2) *and h satisfy $h < 2/P^*$. In addition let $p(x)$, $q(x)$, and $r(x)$ be so smooth*† *that $y(x)$, the solution of the boundary-value problem* (3.1.1), *has a continuous sixth derivative on $[a, b]$. Then* (3.1.11) *holds with $\{u_j\}$, the solution of* (3.1.4), *and $e(x)$, the solution of the boundary-value problem*

$$Le(x) = \theta(x), \qquad a < x < b, \tag{3.1.12a}$$

$$e(a) = e(b) = 0; \tag{3.1.12b}$$

where

$$\theta(x) \equiv -\tfrac{1}{12}[y^{(\text{iv})}(x) - 2p(x)y^{(\text{iii})}(x)]. \tag{3.1.13}$$

Proof. We first note, by the Corollary to Theorem 1.2.2, that the boundary-value problem (3.1.12) has a unique solution. Further, since $\theta(x)$ has a continuous second derivative this solution, $e(x)$, must have a continuous fourth derivative on $[a, b]$.

Now define the net function $\{e_j\}$ by

$$e_j \equiv h^{-2}[y(x_j) - u_j], \qquad 0 \leq j \leq J + 1.$$

Using (3.1.1a), (3.1.4a), and (3.1.8) we obtain

$$\begin{aligned} L_h e_j &= h^{-2}[L_h y(x_j) - L_h u_j] \\ &= h^{-2}[L_h y(x_j) - Ly(x_j)] + h^{-2}[Ly(x_j) - L_h u_j] \\ &= h^{-2}\tau_j[y], \qquad 1 \leq j \leq J. \end{aligned}$$

But by using the continuity of $y^{(\text{vi})}(x)$ the evaluation (3.1.9) of the local truncation error can be done more precisely to yield

$$\tau_j[y] = h^2\theta(x_j) + \mathcal{O}(h^4).$$

Thus we have

$$L_h e_j = \theta(x_j) + \mathcal{O}(h^2), \qquad 1 \leq j \leq J. \tag{3.1.14a}$$

In addition, Equations (3.1.1b) and (3.1.4b) yield

$$e_0 = e_{J+1} = 0. \tag{3.1.14b}$$

† It is sufficient that $p(x)$, $q(x)$, and $r(x)$ have continuous fourth derivatives on $[a, b]$.

From Equation (3.1.12a) evaluated at $x = x_j$ and Equations (3.1.14a) we get now

$$\begin{aligned} L_h[e(x_j) - e_j] &= L_h e(x_j) - Le(x_j) - \mathcal{O}(h^2) \\ &= \tau_j[e] + \mathcal{O}(h^2) \\ &= \mathcal{O}(h^2), \qquad 1 \le j \le J, \end{aligned}$$

where we have used the smoothness of $e(x)$ in estimating $\tau[e]$. But Theorem 3.1.2 is applicable and so from the stability of L_h, that is, from (3.1.10) with v_j replaced by $e(x_j) - e_j$, we deduce that

$$|e(x_j) - e_j| \le \mathcal{O}(h^2).$$

Then multiplying by h^2 yields (3.1.11). ∎

An important by-product of this proof is the determination of various difference problems of the form (3.1.14), whose solutions can be used in the difference-correction procedure. Clearly as in the above proof any net function $\{E_j\}$ defined by

$$L_h E_j = \Theta_j, \qquad 1 \le j \le J, \tag{3.1.15a}$$

$$E_0 = E_{J+1} = 0, \tag{3.1.15b}$$

satisfies, as shown in Problem 3.1.7,

$$|e(x_j) - E_j| \le M|\theta(x_j) - \Theta_j| + \mathcal{O}(h^2).$$

Thus we need only determine Θ_j such that

$$\theta(x_j) - \Theta_j = \mathcal{O}(h^2) \tag{3.1.16}$$

and then the difference-corrected solution

$$\bar{u}_j \equiv u_j + h^2 E_j$$

is an $\mathcal{O}(h^4)$ approximation to $y(x_j)$.

One way in which Θ_j to satisfy (3.1.16) can be obtained is to evaluate $\theta(x)$ in terms of $y'(x)$ and $y(x)$. That is, using the fact that

$$y''(x) = p(x)y' + q(x)y - r(x),$$

and differentiating twice, we obtain a relation of the form

$$\theta(x) = A(x)y'(x) + B(x)y(x) + C(x), \tag{3.1.17a}$$

where $A(x)$, $B(x)$, and $C(x)$ are expressions given in terms of $p(x)$, $q(x)$, $r(x)$ and their first two derivatives [see Problem 3.1.4]. Now we claim that

$$\Theta_j \equiv A(x_j)\frac{(u_{j+1} - u_{j-1})}{2h} + B(x_j)u_j + C(x_j), \qquad j = 1, 2, \ldots, J \tag{3.1.17b}$$

satisfies (3.1.16). Clearly from (3.1.11), since $e(x)$ is sufficiently smooth,

$$\frac{u_{j+1} - u_{j-1}}{2h} = y'(x_j) + h^2 e'(x_j) + \mathcal{O}(h^2),$$

and the result easily follows.

A more direct way to define Θ_j so as to satisfy (3.1.16) is to form some obvious finite-difference analog of $\theta(x)$ defined in (3.1.13), using the numerical solution u_j in place of the actual solution $y(x_j)$. This is in fact the procedure employed by Fox (1957) in originating the difference-correction method. From Equations (3.1.15a) we note that the Θ_j are only required at interior net points. But since third- and fourth-order derivatives of $y(x)$ occur in $\theta(x)$ it is clear that unsymmetric differences, or some other device, must be used near the endpoints of the interval. One trick devised by Fox for this purpose is simply to compute the numerical solution u_j at points exterior to $[a, b]$ and then to use centered differences.

The above procedures can frequently be employed to obtain approximate solutions of higher-order accuracy than the $\mathcal{O}(h^4)$ indicated here. Of course even more differentiability is required of the solution and the error expansion (3.1.11) is replaced by, say,

$$[y(x_j) - u_j] = h^2 e(h, x_j) + \mathcal{O}(h^{2m}),$$

where $m \geq 2$. If $e(h, x_j)$ can be expressed as a polynomial in h^2 of degree at most $m - 1$, then the problem is reduced to obtaining sufficiently accurate approximations to the "coefficient" functions. We pose the details as an exercise. This extension of the difference correction or $h \to 0$ extrapolation seems to be the only theoretically justified procedure for obtaining arbitrary (high) order accuracy by finite differences (at present).

Problems

3.1.1 Find coefficients A_j, B_j, C_j so that

$$L_h u_j \equiv A_j u_{j-1} + B_j u_j + C_j u_{j+1}$$

approximates

$$Ly(x) \equiv -y''(x) + q(x)y(x),$$

to fourth order for all solutions $v(x)$ of $Lv = 0$ which have six continuous derivatives.

[HINT: expand $L_h v(x_j)$ about x_j by Taylor's theorem to sixth order in h. But since $Lv = 0$ we have

$$\tau[v] = L_h v - Lv \equiv L_h v - Lv - (Lv)' - (Lv)''.]$$

3.1.2 In place of (3.1.1b) let us impose the boundary conditions

$$\begin{aligned} a_0 y(a) - a_1 y'(a) &= \alpha, \quad & a_0 \geq 0, \quad & a_1 \geq 0, \\ b_0 y(b) + b_1 y'(b) &= \beta, \quad & b_0 \geq 0, \quad & b_1 \geq 0, \end{aligned} \qquad a_0 + b_0 \neq 0.$$

Now let the difference equations be

$$L_h u_j = r(x_j), \qquad 0 \leq j \leq J + 1,$$

$$a_0 u_0 - a_1 \frac{u_1 - u_{-1}}{2h} = \alpha, \qquad b_0 u_{J+1} + b_1 \frac{u_{J+2} - u_J}{2h} = \beta,$$

where L_h is as defined in (3.1.4a). Show that for $h < 2/P^*$ these equations have a unique solution and derive explicit formulas for computing this solution based on Theorem 3.1.1 (that is, extend the Corollary to Theorem 3.1.1).

3.1.3 Use the results of the above problem to estimate the error in the numerical scheme described there.

3.1.4 Determine the functions $A(x)$, $B(x)$, and $C(x)$ to be used in (3.1.17a) by differentiating the equation $y'' = p(x)y' + q(x)y - r(x)$ twice and eliminating y'' and y'''. Note that $\theta(x)$ is defined in (3.1.13).

3.1.5 To solve the boundary-value problem

$$Ly \equiv y'' - q(x)y = r(x), \qquad y(a) = y(b) = 0,$$

use a difference scheme of the form: $u_0 = u_{J+1} = 0$;

$$\begin{aligned} L_h u &\equiv \frac{[u_{j+1} - 2u_j + u_{j-1}]}{h^2} - [\alpha_1 q_{j+1} u_{j+1} + \alpha_0 q_j u_j + \alpha_{-1} q_{j-1} u_{j-1}] \\ &= [\alpha_1 r_{j+1} + \alpha_0 r_j + \alpha_{-1} r_{j-1}], \qquad j = 1, 2, \ldots, J; \end{aligned}$$

where $h = (b - a)/(J + 1)$ and $q_{j+1} = q(x_{j+1})$ etc.

(a) Determine α_1, α_0, α_{-1} such that the local truncation error is $\mathcal{O}(h^4)$, for the solution $y(x)$, assuming y^{iv}, q^{iv}, and r^{iv} continuous. Note that $y^{\text{iv}} - [qy]'' = r''$.

(b) If $q(x) \geq Q_* > 0$, show that, for sufficiently small h,

$$|u_j - y(x_j)| \leq \frac{h^4}{720} \frac{2M_6 + 5N_4 + 5R_4}{Q_*}, \qquad 0 \leq j \leq J + 1,$$

where $M_6 \geq |y^{\text{vi}}|$, $N_4 \geq |(qy)^{\text{iv}}|$, $R_4 \geq |r^{\text{iv}}|$ on $[a, b]$.

3.1.6 Consider the boundary-value problem

$$(a(x)y')' - p(x)y' - q(x)y = r(x); \qquad y(a) = y(b) = 0$$

and the corresponding difference problem

$$\left\{a\left(x_j + \frac{h}{2}\right)\left[\frac{u_{j+1} - u_j}{h^2}\right] - a\left(x_j - \frac{h}{2}\right)\left[\frac{u_j - u_{j-1}}{h^2}\right]\right\}$$
$$- p(x_j)\left[\frac{u_{j+1} - u_{j-1}}{2h}\right] - q(x_j)u_j = r(x_j),$$
$$j = 1, 2, \ldots, J, \qquad u_0 = u_{J+1} = 0.$$

(a) If y^{iv} and a''' are continuous, show that the truncation error in this scheme is $\mathcal{O}(h^2)$.

(b) If $q(x) \geq Q_*$ and $A^* \geq a(x) \geq A_* > 0$, show that

$$|u_j - y(x_j)| \leq \frac{A^*}{A_* Q_*} \|\tau\|,$$

provided that $A_* - (h/2)p(x_j) \geq 0$ for $j = 1, 2, \ldots, J$. [HINT: Proceed as in the proof of Theorem 3.1.1 to demonstrate stability of the difference scheme but now divide by $|a_j| + |c_j| = a_j + c_j \geq 2A_*$ before bounding the coefficients.]

3.1.7 From (3.1.12), (3.1.13), and (3.1.15) deduce that

$$L_h(e(x_j) - E_j) = [\theta(x_j) - \Theta_j] + \mathcal{O}(h^2), \qquad 1 \leq j \leq J;$$
$$e(a) - E_0 = 0, \qquad e(b) - E_{J+1} = 0.$$

Then apply Theorem 3.1.2 to get

$$|e(x_j) - E_j| \leq M|\theta(x_j) - \Theta_j| + \mathcal{O}(h^2).$$

3.2 Nonlinear Second-Order Equations

We now apply finite-difference methods to boundary-value problems of the form

$$\mathscr{L}y(x) \equiv -y'' + f(x, y, y') = 0, \qquad a < x < b, \tag{3.2.1a}$$

$$y(a) = \alpha, \qquad y(b) = \beta. \tag{3.2.1b}$$

In order that Theorem 1.2.2 be valid we assume that $f(x, y, z)$ has continuous derivatives which satisfy

$$\left|\frac{\partial f}{\partial z}\right| \leq P^*, \qquad 0 < Q_* \leq \frac{\partial f}{\partial y} \leq Q^*, \tag{3.2.2}$$

for some positive constants P^*, Q^*, and Q_*.

The uniform net (3.1.3) will be used and on this net an obvious difference approximation to the boundary-value problem (3.2.1) is given by

$$\mathscr{L}_h u_j \equiv -\left(\frac{u_{j+1} - 2u_j + u_{j-1}}{h^2}\right) + f\left(x_j, u_j, \frac{u_{j+1} - u_{j-1}}{2h}\right) = 0, \qquad 1 \leq j \leq J, \quad (3.2.3a)$$

$$u_0 = \alpha, \qquad u_{J+1} = \beta. \quad (3.2.3b)$$

Again centered-difference quotients have replaced derivatives at interior net points. The resulting difference equations (3.2.3) are in general nonlinear and we shall employ iterative methods to solve them. In fact one of these techniques also yields a proof of the existence and uniqueness of a solution of the difference problem. But first we consider the question of convergence and error estimates for the numerical solution.

The local truncation error, $\tau_j[v]$, is defined and evaluated essentially as in (3.1.9) to yield

$$\tau_j[v] \equiv \mathscr{L}_h(x_j) - \mathscr{L}v(x_j)$$
$$= -\frac{h^2}{12}\left[v''''(\xi_j) - 2\frac{\partial f(x_j, v(x_j), v'(\eta_j))}{\partial z} v'''(\zeta_j)\right], \qquad 1 \leq j \leq J. \quad (3.2.4)$$

Here $v(x)$ is any function with a continuous fourth derivative on $[a, b]$ and ξ_j, η_j, and ζ_j are points in $[x_{j-1}, x_{j+1}]$. The definition and proof of stability for $\mathscr{L}_h$ are contained in the following.

THEOREM 3.2.1. *Let $\mathscr{L}_h$ be defined by* (3.2.3a) *where $f(x, y, z)$ has continuous derivatives satisfying* (3.2.2). *Then for all net spacing h such that*

$$h \leq \frac{2}{P^*},$$

$\mathscr{L}_h$ is stable in the sense that for all net functions $\{v_j\}$ and $\{w_j\}$

$$|v_j - w_j| \leq M\left\{\max\left(|v_0 - w_0|, |v_{J+1} - w_{J+1}|\right) + \max_{1 \leq i \leq J} |\mathscr{L}_h v_i - \mathscr{L}_h w_i|\right\}, \qquad 0 \leq j \leq J + 1,$$

where $M = \max(1, 1/Q_*)$.

Proof. By the mean-value theorem we easily obtain

$$\frac{h^2}{2}[\mathscr{L}_h v_i - \mathscr{L}_h w_i] = a_i[v_{i-1} - w_{i-1}] + b_i[v_i - w_i] + c_i[v_{i+1} - w_{i+1}], \quad (3.2.5a)$$

where

$$a_i \equiv -\frac{1}{2}\left\{1 + \frac{h^2}{2}\,\partial f\left(x_i, w_i + \theta_i[v_i - w_i], \frac{w_{i+1} - w_{i-1}}{2h}\right.\right.$$

$$\left.\left. + \theta_i \frac{[v_{i+1} - w_{i+1}] - [v_{i-1} - w_{i-1}]}{2h}\right)\Big/ \partial z\right\},$$

$$b_i \equiv \left\{1 + \frac{h^2}{2}\,\partial f\left(x_i, w_i + \theta_i[v_i - w_i], \frac{w_{i+1} - w_{i-1}}{2h}\right.\right.$$

$$\left.\left. + \theta_i \frac{[v_{i+1} - w_{i+1}] - [v_{i-1} - w_{i-1}]}{2h}\right)\Big/ \partial y\right\}, \qquad (3.2.5b)$$

$$c_i \equiv -1 - a_i, \qquad 0 < \theta_i < 1, \qquad 1 \le j \le J.$$

But from (3.2.2) and $h \le 2/P^*$ we get

$$|a_i| + |c_i| = 1, \qquad b_i \ge 1 + h^2 Q_*/2$$

and the proof now follows exactly as that of Theorem 3.1.2. ∎

The error estimate can now be stated as the following.

COROLLARY. *Let $f(x, y, z)$ have continuous derivatives which satisfy* (3.2.2). *Then the numerical solution $\{u_j\}$ of the difference equations* (3.2.3) *and the solution $y(x)$ of the boundary-value problem* (3.2.1) *satisfy, with $M \equiv \max(1, 1/Q_*)$,*

$$|u_j - u(x_j)| \le M \max_{1 \le i \le J} |\tau_i[y]|, \qquad 0 \le j \le J + 1.$$

If $y(x)$ has a continuous fourth derivative on $[a, b]$, then

$$|u_j - y(x_j)| \le M \frac{h^2}{12}(M_4 + 2P^*M_3), \qquad 0 \le j \le J + 1.$$

Proof. The proof is essentially the same as that of Theorem 3.1.3 with the evaluation (3.2.4) for $\tau_j[y]$. ∎

Whenever $f(x, y, z)$ is not linear in y and z the difference Equations (3.2.3) form a nonlinear system. To solve such a system or indeed to demonstrate existence of a solution we could apply the general procedures indicated in Section 1.4. We shall in fact employ a functional iteration scheme for which the Contracting Mapping theorem is valid.

To devise our iteration scheme we multiply (3.2.3a) by $h^2/2$, add ωu_j to each side and, assuming $\omega \ne -1$, the result can be written as

$$u_j = (1 + \omega)^{-1}\left[\tfrac{1}{2}(u_{j+1} + u_{j-1}) + \omega u_j - \frac{h^2}{2} f\left(x_j, u_j, \frac{u_{j+1} - u_{j-1}}{2h}\right)\right],$$

$$1 \le j \le J, \qquad (3.2.6a)$$

$$u_0 = \alpha, \qquad u_{J+1} = \beta. \qquad (3.2.6b)$$

Clearly this system is equivalent to that in (3.2.3) for any finite $\omega \neq -1$. It is in the canonical form

$$\mathbf{u} = \mathbf{g}(\mathbf{u}), \qquad \mathbf{u} \equiv (u_0, u_1, \ldots, u_{J+1})^T, \tag{3.2.6c}$$

where the components $g_j(\mathbf{u})$ are defined by the right-hand sides of Equations (3.2.6a, b). The functional iteration implied by (3.2.6) is

$$u_j^{(0)} = \text{arbitrary}, \qquad 1 \leq j \leq J; \tag{3.2.7a}$$

$$u_j^{(\nu+1)} = (1+\omega)^{-1}\left[\frac{1}{2}(u_{j+1}^{(\nu)} + u_{j-1}^{(\nu)}) + \omega u_j^{(\nu)} - \frac{h^2}{2} f\left(x_j, u_j^{(\nu)}, \frac{u_{j+1}^{(\nu)} - u_{j-1}^{(\nu)}}{2h}\right)\right],$$

$$1 \leq j \leq J, \qquad \nu = 0, 1, \ldots; \tag{3.2.7b}$$

$$u_0^{(\nu)} = \alpha, \qquad u_{J+1}^{(\nu)} = \beta, \qquad \nu = 0, 1, \ldots. \tag{3.2.7c}$$

This is an explicit iteration scheme [in contrast to implicit schemes where linear systems must be solved; see Newton's method (3.2.10) below]. The fact that the iterates $\{u_j^{(\nu)}\}$ converge to a solution of (3.2.3) for an appropriate choice of ω is but part of the content of the following.

THEOREM 3.2.2. *Let $f(x, y, z)$ have continuous derivatives which satisfy* (3.2.2). *Then the system of difference equations* (3.2.3) *have a unique solution for each h such that*

$$h \leq \frac{2}{P^*}.$$

This solution is the limit of the iterates $\{u_j^{(\nu)}\}$ as $\nu \to \infty$ defined by (3.2.7) *with any finite ω satisfying*

$$\omega \geq \frac{h^2}{2} Q^*.$$

The convergence factor for this scheme is at most

$$\lambda(\omega) \equiv 1 - \frac{(h^2/2)Q_*}{1+\omega}.$$

Proof. Let $\mathbf{g}(\mathbf{u})$ be as defined in (3.2.6); then by the definition of $\mathscr{L}_h$ we can write

$$g_j(\mathbf{u}) \equiv \begin{cases} \alpha, & j = 0, \\ u_j - (1+\omega)^{-1}\dfrac{h^2}{2}\mathscr{L}_h u_j, & 1 \leq j \leq J, \\ \beta, & j = J+1. \end{cases}$$

Now Taylor's theorem as used in (3.2.5) implies, for any pair of net functions $\{v_j\}$ and $\{w_j\}$, that

$$g_j(\mathbf{v}) - g_j(\mathbf{w}) = \begin{cases} 0, & j = 0; \\ (1+\omega)^{-1}[-a_j(v_{j-1} - w_{j-1}) + (1 + \omega - b_j) \\ \qquad \times (v_j - w_j) - c_j(v_{j+1} - w_{j+1})], & 1 \le j \le J; \\ 0, & j = J + 1. \end{cases}$$

The coefficients here are defined in (3.2.5b). Thus with $h \le 2/P^*$ and $\omega \ge h^2Q^*/2$ we have $-a_j \ge 0$, $(1 + \omega - b_j) \ge 0$ and $-c_j \ge 0$ so that upon taking absolute values,

$$|g_j(\mathbf{v}) - g_j(\mathbf{w})| \le \frac{1 + \omega - a_j - b_j - c_j}{1 + \omega} \max_i |v_i - w_i| \le \lambda(\omega) \max_i |v_i - w_i|, \quad 0 \le j \le J + 1.$$

That is, in the maximum norm, $\mathbf{g}(\mathbf{u})$ is Lipschitz-continuous,

$$|\mathbf{g}(\mathbf{v}) - \mathbf{g}(\mathbf{w})| \le \lambda(\omega)|\mathbf{v} - \mathbf{w}|,$$

with constant $\lambda(\omega) < 1$ for $\omega \ge h^2Q^*/2$. The theorem now follows from Theorem 1.4.1 (with $\rho = \infty$) and the fact that (3.2.6) and (3.2.3) have identical solutions for finite positive ω. ∎

It is important to observe that the scheme (3.2.7) converges for *any initial estimate* $u_j^{(0)}$, $1 \le j \le J$, provided $\omega \ge h^2Q^*/2$. As far as our analysis shows the best value for ω is the limiting value

$$\omega = \omega^* \equiv \frac{h^2}{2} Q^*.$$

We easily see that $\lambda(\omega) > \lambda(\omega^*)$ if $\omega > \omega^*$. Of course, even with this choice the convergence may be quite slow since

$$\lambda(\omega) = 1 - \mathcal{O}(h^2)$$

can be very close to unity. Thus we may wish to consider alternative iteration schemes for solving (3.2.3) and of these Newton's method can be shown to be applicable.

To define the Newton iterations we first write Equations (3.2.3a) in the form

$$\boldsymbol{\phi}(\mathbf{u}) = 0, \tag{3.2.8a}$$

where

$$\mathbf{u} \equiv \begin{pmatrix} u_1 \\ u_2 \\ \vdots \\ u_J \end{pmatrix}, \qquad \boldsymbol{\phi}(\mathbf{u}) \equiv \begin{pmatrix} \phi_1(\mathbf{u}) \\ \phi_2(\mathbf{u}) \\ \vdots \\ \phi_J(\mathbf{u}) \end{pmatrix}, \qquad \phi_j(\mathbf{u}) \equiv \frac{h^2}{2}\mathscr{L}_h u_j,$$

$$1 \le j \le J. \quad (3.2.8b)$$

Now the Jacobian of $\boldsymbol{\phi}(\mathbf{u})$ is easily found to be the Jth-order tridiagonal matrix

$$A(\mathbf{u}) \equiv \frac{\partial \boldsymbol{\phi}(\mathbf{u})}{\partial \mathbf{u}} = \begin{pmatrix} B_1(\mathbf{u}) & C_1(\mathbf{u}) & 0 & \cdots & 0 \\ A_2(\mathbf{u}) & B_2(\mathbf{u}) & C_2(\mathbf{u}) & \cdots & \\ \vdots & & & & \vdots \\ & & A_{J-1}(\mathbf{u}) & B_{J-1}(\mathbf{u}) & C_{J-1}(\mathbf{u}) \\ 0 & \cdots & 0 & A_J(\mathbf{u}) & B_J(\mathbf{u}) \end{pmatrix}, \quad (3.2.9a)$$

where

$$A_j(\mathbf{u}) \equiv -\frac{1}{2}\left[1 + \frac{h}{2}\frac{\partial f}{\partial z}\left(x_j, u_j, \frac{u_{j+1} - u_{j-1}}{2h}\right)\right], \qquad 2 \le j \le J;$$

$$B_j(\mathbf{u}) \equiv \left[1 + \frac{h^2}{2}\frac{\partial f}{\partial y}\left(x_j, u_j, \frac{u_{j+1} - u_{j-1}}{2h}\right)\right], \qquad 1 \le j \le J; \qquad (3.2.9b)$$

$$C_j(\mathbf{u}) \equiv -\frac{1}{2}\left[1 - \frac{h}{2}\frac{\partial f}{\partial z}\left(x_j, u_j, \frac{u_{j+1} - u_{j-1}}{2h}\right)\right], \qquad 1 \le j \le J - 1.$$

In computing $\phi_1(\mathbf{u})$, $\phi_J(\mathbf{u})$, $A_J(\mathbf{u})$, $B_1(\mathbf{u})$, $B_J(\mathbf{u})$, and $C_1(\mathbf{u})$ we use $u_0 \equiv \alpha$ and $u_{J+1} \equiv \beta$ so that (3.2.3b) is always satisfied. Now, with any initial estimate $\mathbf{u}^{(0)}$ of the quantities u_j, $1 \le j \le J$, we define

$$\mathbf{u}^{(\nu+1)} = \mathbf{u}^{(\nu)} + \Delta\mathbf{u}^{(\nu)}, \qquad \nu = 0, 1, 2, \ldots, \qquad (3.2.10a)$$

where $\Delta\mathbf{u}^{(\nu)}$ is the solution of

$$A(\mathbf{u}^{(\nu)})\,\Delta\mathbf{u}^{(\nu)} = -\boldsymbol{\phi}(\mathbf{u}^{(\nu)}), \qquad \nu = 0, 1, 2, \ldots. \qquad (3.2.10b)$$

If the function $f(x, y, z)$ satisfies (3.2.2) and $h \le 2/P^*$, it follows as in the proof of the Corollary to Theorem 3.1.1 that the linear system (3.2.10b) has a unique solution, $\Delta\mathbf{u}^{(\nu)}$, for any $\mathbf{u}^{(\nu)}$. Further, this solution is easily computed by means of the algorithm described in (3.1.7) for solving (3.1.6). Thus Newton's method can be applied in attempting to solve (3.2.3) or its equivalent (3.2.8). In order for this method to converge it is sufficient (see Theorem 1.4.3) that the initial iterate $\mathbf{u}^{(0)}$ be "close" to the solution. But by Theorem

3.2.2 we can obtain close estimates to the solution by applying the iteration scheme (3.2.7). A reasonable procedure is thus to determine the initial Newton iterate by first computing several iterates of the explicit scheme.

The treatment of more general linear boundary conditions than those in (3.2.1b) is easily included in appropriate modifications of the difference scheme (3.2.3); see Problems 3.2.1, 3.2.2. The difference-correction and extrapolation-to-zero-mesh-width procedures can frequently be applied to the nonlinear problems treated here. The basic result required is an extension of Theorem 3.1.4 contained in Problem 3.2.3.

Difference schemes and corresponding iterations are frequently suggested by analytical attempts to solve or approximate the solution of nonlinear boundary-value problems. When there is some evidence that the analytical procedures are effective there may be advantages in such approaches. However, the replacement of derivatives by difference quotients finally yields a difference scheme which must be examined independently.

To illustrate, we consider a common analytical procedure, which is to linearize about some approximate solution and then solve the linearized problem to obtain a correction. Of course this procedure can be continued to yield an iteration scheme and we formulate it that way. Thus let $y^{(\nu)}(x)$ be some approximation to the solution of (3.2.1) with say $y^{(\nu)}(a) = \alpha$ and $y^{(\nu)}(b) = \beta$. Then if $e^{(\nu)}(x) = y(x) - y^{(\nu)}(x)$ is the error, we have

$$-[y^{(\nu)} + e^{(\nu)}]'' + f(x, [y^{(\nu)} + e^{(\nu)}], [y^{(\nu)} + e^{(\nu)}]') = 0.$$

Assuming $e^{(\nu)}(x)$ to be small and $f(x, y, z)$ sufficiently smooth, we have

$$-[y^{(\nu)} + e^{(\nu)}]'' + \frac{\partial f}{\partial z}(x, y^{(\nu)}, y^{(\nu)\prime})e^{(\nu)\prime} + \frac{\partial f}{\partial y}(x, y^{(\nu)}, y^{(\nu)\prime})e^{(\nu)} + f(x, y^{(\nu)}, y^{(\nu)\prime}) = \mathcal{O}((e^{(\nu)})^2 + (e^{(\nu)\prime})^2).$$

Neglecting the second-order terms on the right-hand side above, we get the linearized problem for $e^{(\nu)}(x)$

$$-e^{(\nu)''} + \frac{\partial f}{\partial z}(x, y^{(\nu)}, y^{(\nu)\prime})e^{(\nu)\prime} + \frac{\partial f}{\partial y}(x, y^{(\nu)}, y^{(\nu)\prime})e^{(\nu)} = y^{(\nu)''} - f(x, y^{(\nu)}, y^{(\nu)\prime}), \quad (3.2.11a)$$

$$e^{(\nu)}(a) = e^{(\nu)}(b) = 0. \quad (3.2.11b)$$

Of course this procedure is just a form of Newton's method (applied to a nonlinear operator equation in a function space rather than in a finite dimensional space). A study of the convergence of $y^{(\nu)}(x) + e^{(\nu)}(x)$ as $\nu \to \infty$ is beyond our present subject [see, for example, Kantorovich and Akilov (1964), pp. 735–739]. However, let us assume that it converges in the anticipated second-order fashion [that is, $e^{(\nu+1)} = \mathcal{O}(e^{(\nu)2})$].

To carry out the above scheme numerically, we need only solve the sequence of linear problems (3.2.11). If we employ the difference technique of Section 3.1, with $y^{(\nu)\prime}(x_j)$ replaced by centered difference quotients in the coefficients f, $\partial f/\partial y$, and $\partial f/\partial z$, then *we obtain exactly the system* (3.2.10) with $\Delta u_j^{(\nu)}$ approximating $e^{(\nu)}(x_j)$ and $u_j^{(\nu)}$ approximating $y^{(\nu)}(x_j)$. Thus our accuracy can be no better than that of the numerical solution $\{u_j\}$ determined by the difference scheme (3.2.3). Of course we could use initial-value methods as in section 2.1 for solving (3.2.11). In this case greater accuracy in approximating $e^{(\nu)}(x_j)$ is easily obtained.

Another analytical scheme to approximate the solution of (3.2.1), based on solving linear boundary-value problems, follows from writing (3.2.1a) as

$$y'' - \omega y = f(x, y, y') - \omega y.$$

Then with arbitrary $y^{(0)}(x)$ satisfying $y^{(0)}(a) = \alpha$, $y^{(0)}(b) = \beta$ we define $\{y^{(\nu)}(x)\}$ by

$$y^{(\nu+1)''} - \omega y^{(\nu+1)} = f(x, y^{(\nu)}, y^{(\nu)\prime}) - \omega y^{(\nu)}, \tag{3.2.12a}$$

$$y^{(\nu+1)}(a) = \alpha, \qquad y^{(\nu+1)}(b) = \beta. \tag{3.2.12b}$$

For a range of values of ω it can be shown (see Section 4.1) that $y^{(\nu)}(x) \to y(x)$ if $f(x, y, z)$ satisfies appropriate conditions. If the difference method of Section 3.1 is used to approximate the solution of (3.2.12), we obtain an implicit iteration scheme for solving the difference equations (3.2.3). The resulting procedure is related to but not quite the same as that in (3.2.7).

Problems

3.2.1 Replace (3.2.1b) by

$$a_0 y(a) - a_1 y'(a) = \alpha, \qquad b_0 y(b) + b_1 y'(b) = \beta,$$
$$a_0 > 0, \qquad a_1 \geq 0, \qquad b_0 \geq 0, \qquad b_1 \geq 0.$$

Apply (3.2.3a) for $j = 0$ and $j = J + 1$ and approximate the above by

$$a_0 u_0 - a_1 \frac{u_1 - u_{-1}}{2h} = \alpha, \qquad b_0 u_{J+1} + b_1 \frac{u_{J+2} - u_J}{2h} = \beta.$$

Prove convergence of $\{u_j\} \to \{y(x_j)\}$ if $y(x)$ has four continuous derivatives and (3.2.1a) holds on $a \leq x \leq b$.

3.2.2 Modify (3.2.7) to apply to the difference scheme of Problem 3.2.1 and prove the analog of Theorem 3.2.2.

3.2.3 State and prove an extension of Theorem 3.1.4 which applies to the solution $y(x)$ of (3.2.1) and numerical solution $\{u_j\}$ of (3.2.3).

3.2.4 Consider, in place of (3.2.3), the difference equations

$$u_0 = \alpha, \qquad u_{J+1} = \beta,$$

$$\frac{u_{j+1} - 2u_j + u_{j-1}}{h^2} = f\left(x_j, \frac{u_{j+1} + u_{j-1}}{2}, \frac{u_{j+1} - u_{j-1}}{2h}\right),$$

$$j = 1, 2, \ldots, J.$$

(a) Show that $|u_j - y(x_j)| = \mathcal{O}(h^2)$, where $y(x)$ is the four times continuously differentiable solution of (3.2.1), (3.2.2) holds, $h \leq 2/P^*$, and $y''''(x)$, $\partial f/\partial y$, and $\partial f/\partial y'$ are continuous.

(b) Under the above assumptions, prove convergence of the iterations: $u_0^{(\nu+1)} = u_{J+1}^{(\nu+1)} = 0$,

$$u_j^{(\nu+1)} = \frac{1}{2}[u_{j+1}^{(\nu)} + u_{j-1}^{(\nu)}] - \frac{h^2}{2}f\left(x_j, \frac{u_{j+1}^{(\nu)} + u_{j-1}^{(\nu)}}{2}, \frac{u_{j+1}^{(\nu)} - u_{j-1}^{(\nu)}}{2h}\right),$$

$$j = 1, 2, \ldots, J.$$

Does this converge for all net spacing?

3.2.5 Show in detail that the centered difference approximations to the system of linear differential equations (3.2.11) yield a linear algebraic system identical to that in (3.2.10).

3.3 Linear and Nonlinear Systems

The difference methods discussed in Sections 3.1 and 3.2 are quite special as they were devised for second-order (scalar) equations. It would not be difficult to write down obvious generalizations that might be applicable to systems of coupled second-order equations. But as even this is rather limited, we shall consider here, as in Section 2.3, the general systems of n first-order equations subject to linear two-point boundary conditions

$$\text{(a)} \quad L\mathbf{y} \equiv \mathbf{y}' - \mathbf{f}(x, \mathbf{y}) = 0; \qquad \text{(b)} \quad A\mathbf{y}(a) + B\mathbf{y}(b) = \boldsymbol{\alpha}. \qquad (3.3.1)$$

As previously indicated, a very general class of problems can be reduced to this form, including, of course, various systems of linear differential equations and periodic boundary conditions.

In the present discussion we take the net points on $[a, b]$ as

$$x_j = a + jh, \qquad j = 0, 1, \ldots, J; \qquad h = \frac{b - a}{J}. \qquad (3.3.2)$$

The use of nonuniform spacing causes no difficulties and we employ the uniform net (3.3.2) merely for notational convenience. We denote by the

n-dimensional vectors $\mathbf{u}_j$ approximations to the corresponding values of the solution $\mathbf{y}(x_j)$ of (3.3.1) at the points of our net. One obvious system of difference equations for the determination of these approximations is

$$L_h\mathbf{u}_j \equiv \frac{\mathbf{u}_j - \mathbf{u}_{j-1}}{h} - \mathbf{f}\left(x_{j-1/2}, \frac{\mathbf{u}_j + \mathbf{u}_{j-1}}{2}\right) = 0, \qquad j = 1, 2, \ldots, J; \tag{3.3.3a}$$

and the boundary conditions become

$$A\mathbf{u}_0 + B\mathbf{u}_J - \boldsymbol{\alpha} = 0. \tag{3.3.3b}$$

The scheme in (3.3.3a) is known as the centered-difference method when used for the equation (3.3.1a) subject to initial conditions. The nonlinear term in (3.3.3a) might have been chosen as

$$\tfrac{1}{2}[\mathbf{f}(x_j, \mathbf{u}_j) + \mathbf{f}(x_{j-1}, \mathbf{u}_{j-1})],$$

and the resulting scheme is called the modified Euler method. We find our choice more convenient, if not necessarily more accurate. Some discussion of the above choice is to be found in Problem 3.3.3.

The Equations (3.3.3), of $J + 1$ sets of n equations each, are the difference equations whose solution is to approximate that of (3.3.1) on the net. We shall examine the problem of solving these difference equations and shall also estimate their accuracy in approximating $\mathbf{y}(x_j)$. First, we rewrite them in a more uniform notation. Let the $n(J + 1)$-dimensional vector $\mathbf{U}$ be defined by

$$\mathbf{U} \equiv \begin{pmatrix} \mathbf{u}_0 \\ \mathbf{u}_1 \\ \vdots \\ \mathbf{u}_J \end{pmatrix}.$$

Then Equations (3.3.3) can be written as the system of $n(J + 1)$ equations

$$\boldsymbol{\Phi}(\mathbf{U}) \equiv \begin{pmatrix} A\mathbf{u}_0 + B\mathbf{u}_J - \boldsymbol{\alpha} \\ hL_h\mathbf{u}_1 \\ \vdots \\ hL_h\mathbf{u}_J \end{pmatrix} = \mathbf{0}. \tag{3.3.4}$$

We now see one basic difference, at least in point of view, between the initial-value methods and the finite-difference methods. In initial-value methods some unknowns, the initial values, are somehow determined first; then, in a definite order the other unknowns are determined recursively so as to be accurate approximations to solutions of the differential equations, and only when the last variables are computed are the boundary conditions employed. In finite-difference schemes no particular variables are preferred and the differential equations and boundary conditions are presumably treated simultaneously. [In some iterative attempts at solving the system (3.3.4) one might proceed recursively guessing at $\mathbf{u}_0$, say, then solving the equations in (3.3.3a), exactly or approximately, in the order $j = 1, 2, \ldots, J$ and finally checking (3.3.3b) to change the value of $\mathbf{u}_0$. But this procedure is then in fact an initial-value method; it is in general a rather poor one, since there are much better schemes than the centered-difference method for integrating the system (3.3.1a) over the net (3.3.2).] From this point of view the parallel shooting schemes of Section 2.4 are combinations of initial-value and finite-difference methods. The integration of the initial-value problem over each interval of length Δ_j corresponds to the use of (3.3.3a) over the corresponding interval. Indeed we shall see great similarities in some of our present analysis to that in Section 2.4.

It is instructive to consider systems of linear differential equations first, and so we take

$$\mathbf{f}(x, \mathbf{y}) \equiv K(x)\mathbf{y} + \mathbf{f}_0(x), \tag{3.3.5}$$

where $K(x)$ is an nth-order matrix with continuous elements on $[a, b]$. Using this form we find that the system of difference equations (3.3.4) reduces to the linear form

$$\mathbf{\Phi}(\mathbf{U}) \equiv \mathscr{L}_h\mathbf{U} - \boldsymbol{\gamma} = 0. \tag{3.3.6a}$$

Here the $n(J + 1)$th-order matrix $\mathscr{L}_h$ and vector $\boldsymbol{\gamma}$ are

$$\mathscr{L}_h \equiv \begin{pmatrix} A & 0 & 0 & \cdots & 0 & B \\ -L_1 & R_1 & 0 & & \cdots & 0 \\ 0 & -L_2 & R_2 & 0 & \cdots & 0 \\ \vdots & & & & & \vdots \\ 0 & 0 & 0 & \cdots & -L_J & R_J \end{pmatrix}, \tag{3.3.6b}$$

$$\boldsymbol{\gamma} \equiv \begin{pmatrix} \boldsymbol{\alpha} \\ h\mathbf{f}_0(x_{1/2}) \\ h\mathbf{f}_0(x_{3/2}) \\ \vdots \\ h\mathbf{f}_0(x_{J-1/2}) \end{pmatrix},$$

where we have used the notation for nth-order matrices

$$R_j \equiv I - \frac{h}{2} K(x_{j-1/2}), \qquad L_j \equiv I + \frac{h}{2} K(x_{j-1/2}), \qquad j = 1, 2, \ldots, J. \tag{3.3.6c}$$

Under somewhat general conditions we can show that the matrix $\mathscr{L}_h$ is nonsingular. We have in fact the following.

THEOREM 3.3.1. *Let* $\mathbf{f}(x, \mathbf{y})$ *be given by Equation* (3.3.5), *where* $K(x)$ *is continuous on* $[a, b]$ *and satisfies*

$$\max_{a \le x \le b} \|K(x)\|_\infty \le K. \tag{3.3.7a}$$

Let the matrices A and B satisfy

$$(A + B) \text{ nonsingular}. \tag{3.3.7b}$$

Finally let the interval $[a, b]$ *be so small that*

$$|b - a| < \frac{\ln [1 + (1/m)]}{K}; \qquad m \equiv \|(A + B)^{-1}B\|_\infty. \tag{3.3.7c}$$

Then the boundary-value problem (3.3.1) *and, for all net spacing* $h < 2/K$, *the finite-difference equations* (3.3.3) *have unique solutions for all* $\boldsymbol{\alpha}$ *and bounded integrable* $\mathbf{f}_0(x)$.

Proof. The fact that the linear boundary-value problem (3.3.1), with (3.3.5), has a unique solution follows from Theorem 1.2.5. It only remains to show that the matrix $\mathscr{L}_h$ in (3.3.6) is nonsingular for small h.

Since $\|K(x)\|_\infty \le K$ by (3.3.7a), we are assured that for $h < 2/K$ the matrices L_j and R_j in (3.3.6c) are nonsingular (see Isaacson and Keller (1966), p. 16 or pp. 135–136). We define nth-order matrices P_j and the $n(J + 1)$th-order diagonal matrix D as

$$P_j \equiv R_j^{-1} L_j, \qquad j = 1, 2, \ldots, J; \qquad D \equiv \begin{pmatrix} I & 0 & \cdots & 0 \\ 0 & R_1 & & \vdots \\ \vdots & & & 0 \\ 0 & \cdots & 0 & R_J \end{pmatrix} \tag{3.3.8a}$$

and then form

$$D^{-1}\mathscr{L}_h = \begin{pmatrix} A & 0 & 0 & \cdots & 0 & B \\ -P_1 & I & 0 & & \cdots & 0 \\ \vdots & & & & & \vdots \\ & & & & & 0 \\ 0 & & \cdots & & -P_J & I \end{pmatrix}.$$

Elementary block transformations can be employed to triangularize the above matrix. Specifically, with the definitions

$$T_1 \equiv \begin{pmatrix} I & 0 & \cdots & 0 \\ P_1 & I & & \\ \vdots & & & \vdots \\ 0 & \cdots & & I \end{pmatrix}, \qquad T_2 \equiv \begin{pmatrix} I & 0 & 0 & \cdots & 0 \\ 0 & I & 0 & \cdots & \\ 0 & P_2 & I & \cdots & \vdots \\ \vdots & & & & \\ 0 & \cdots & & & I \end{pmatrix}, \ldots,$$

$$T_J \equiv \begin{pmatrix} I & \cdots & & 0 \\ & & & \vdots \\ \vdots & & & \\ & & I & 0 \\ 0 & \cdots & P_J & I \end{pmatrix}, \tag{3.3.8b}$$

we obtain the triangular matrix

$$D^{-1}\mathscr{L}_h T_J \cdots T_1 = \begin{pmatrix} (A + B\pi_1) & B\pi_2 & \cdots & B\pi_J & B \\ 0 & I & & \cdots & 0 \\ \vdots & & & & \vdots \\ 0 & & \cdots & 0 & I \end{pmatrix}. \tag{3.3.8c}$$

Here we have used the abbreviations

$$\pi_J \equiv P_J; \qquad \pi_j = \pi_{j+1}P_j, \qquad j = 1, 2, \ldots, J - 1. \tag{3.3.8d}$$

Since D and the T_j, $j = 1, 2, \ldots, J$ are nonsingular, it follows from (3.3.8c) that $\mathscr{L}_h$ is nonsingular if and only if the nth-order matrix $(A + B\pi_1)$ is nonsingular.

Since $(A + B)$ is nonsingular by (3.3.7b), we write

$$(A + B\pi_1) = (A + B)[I + (A + B)^{-1}B(\pi_1 - I)].$$

With $h < 2/K$ it can be shown, as in Problem 3.3.1, that

$$\|\pi_1 - I\|_\infty \leq e^{K|b-a|} - 1.$$

Then, using (3.3.7c), we see that

$$\|(A + B)^{-1}B(\pi_1 - I)\|_\infty \leq m(e^{K|b-a|} - 1) < 1,$$

and so $(A + B\pi_1)$ is nonsingular. ∎

The above derivation of (3.3.8) is essentially the same as that used to deduce (2.4.12). The estimate of $\|\pi_1 - I\|_\infty$ is related to that in (1.2.17), but is slightly more involved. By writing down the inverse of $\mathscr{L}_h$ we obtain an explicit representation for the solution of the finite-difference problem (3.3.3) for the linear case where $\mathbf{f}$ is given by (3.3.5). From (3.3.8b) we easily find this inverse in the form:

$$\mathscr{L}_h^{-1} = T_J \cdots T_1 \begin{pmatrix} (A + B\pi_1)^{-1} & \cdots & 0 \\ 0 & I & \cdots & 0 \\ \vdots & & & \vdots \\ 0 & \cdots & & I \end{pmatrix} \begin{pmatrix} I & -B\pi_2 & \cdots & -B\pi_J & -B \\ 0 & I & & \cdots & 0 \\ \vdots & & & & \vdots \\ 0 & & \cdots & 0 & I \end{pmatrix} D^{-1}. \tag{3.3.9}$$

Again we point out that the condition $(A + B)$ nonsingular can be eliminated. For h sufficiently small, it can be shown that $(A + B\pi_1)$ is nonsingular if $(A + B\Omega_a^b\{K\})$ is nonsingular (see Problem 3.3.7). But this latter condition is, recalling the proof of Theorem 1.2.5 and remarks following, just the necessary and sufficient condition for the existence of a unique solution to (3.3.1) and (3.3.5).

Next we turn to the nonlinear case and show, under conditions quite similar to those of Theorem 1.2.6, that a unique solution of the difference equations (3.3.3) exists. This is done by means of an iteration scheme which could also be employed in practice to compute the difference approximation. These results are the content of the following.

THEOREM 3.3.2. *Let* $\mathbf{f}(x, \mathbf{u})$ *satisfy on* R: $a \le x \le b$, $|\mathbf{u}| < \infty$ *the conditions*

(a) $\mathbf{f}(x, \mathbf{u})$ *continuous*;

(b) $\dfrac{\partial f_i(x, \mathbf{u})}{\partial u_j}$ *continuous*, $i, j = 1, 2, \ldots, n$; (3.3.10)

(c) $\left\|\dfrac{\partial \mathbf{f}(x, \mathbf{u})}{\partial \mathbf{u}}\right\|_\infty \le K$.

Furthermore, let the matrices A and B, the scalar K and the length of the interval, $|b - a|$, *satisfy*

(d) $(A + B)$ *nonsingular*;

(e) $K|b - a| \le \ln\left(1 + \dfrac{\lambda}{m}\right)$; (3.3.10)

for some λ *in* $0 < \lambda < 1$ *where*

$$m \equiv \max\{\|(A + B)^{-1}B\|_\infty, \|(A + B)^{-1}A\|_\infty\}.$$

Then the boundary-value problem (3.3.1) *and, for all* $h = |b - a|/J$, *the finite-difference problems* (3.3.3) *have solutions which are unique.*

In particular the solution of the difference equations (3.3.3) *is the limit of the sequence* $\{\mathbf{U}^{(\nu)}\}$, *with* $\mathbf{U}^{(0)}$ *arbitrary, defined by*

$$\text{(a)}\quad \mathbf{u}_j^{(\nu+1)} - \mathbf{u}_{j-1}^{(\nu+1)} = h\mathbf{f}\left(x_{j-1/2}, \frac{\mathbf{u}_j^{(\nu)} + \mathbf{u}_{j-1}^{(\nu)}}{2}\right), \qquad j = 1, 2, \ldots, J, \tag{3.3.11}$$

$$\text{(b)}\quad A\mathbf{u}_0^{(\nu+1)} + B\mathbf{u}_J^{(\nu+1)} = \boldsymbol{\alpha}.$$

Proof. Obviously the hypothesis of Theorem 1.2.6 in Chapter 1 is implied by (3.3.10), and so the existence and uniqueness of the solution to the problem (3.3.1) are established.

We shall write the difference equations (3.3.3) in a form from which it can be shown that the iteration scheme in (3.3.11) comes from a contracting map. First we observe that by setting $h = 0$ in (3.3.6) the matrices R_j and L_j reduce to the nth-order identity, and $\mathscr{L}_h$ becomes simply

$$\mathscr{L}_0 \equiv (P + Q), \tag{3.3.12}$$

where P and Q are the $n(J + 1)$th-order matrices defined by (2.4.7). It follows from (3.3.10d) that $\mathscr{L}_0$ is nonsingular, and in fact $\mathscr{L}_0^{-1}$ is given by (2.4.12). Thus the difference equations (3.3.3) or their equivalent form (3.3.4) have the same solutions as the system

$$\mathbf{U} = \mathbf{U} - \mathscr{L}_0^{-1}\boldsymbol{\Phi}(\mathbf{U}) \equiv \mathbf{G}(\mathbf{U}). \tag{3.3.13}$$

We now leave to Problem 3.3.2 the simple demonstration that, with the same $\mathbf{U}^{(0)}$, the iterates $\mathbf{U}^{(\nu+1)} = \mathbf{G}(\mathbf{U}^{(\nu)})$ are identical with those in (3.3.11).

It only remains to show that $\mathbf{G}(\mathbf{U})$ is contracting. A direct computation gives

$$\frac{\partial \mathbf{G}}{\partial \mathbf{U}} = \frac{h}{2}\mathscr{L}_0^{-1}\begin{pmatrix} 0 & 0 & \cdots & & 0 \\ K_1 & K_1 & & \cdots & \\ 0 & K_2 & K_2 & \cdots & \\ \vdots & & & & \vdots \\ 0 & \cdots & & K_J & K_J \end{pmatrix}, \tag{3.3.14}$$

where the nth-order matrices K_j are defined by

$$K_j \equiv \frac{\partial \mathbf{f}[x_{j-1/2}, (\mathbf{u}_j + \mathbf{u}_{j-1})/2]}{\partial \mathbf{u}}, \qquad j = 1, 2, \ldots, J.$$

Using (2.4.12) we obtain, on multiplying out in the above and taking the norm,

$$\left\|\frac{\partial \mathbf{G}}{\partial \mathbf{U}}\right\|_\infty \le \frac{h}{2}\cdot 2KJm.$$

Here we have used (3.3.10c) to bound $\|K_j\|_\infty \leq K$. Since $Jh = |b - a|$, it now follows from (3.3.10e) that

$$\left\|\frac{\partial \mathbf{G}}{\partial \mathbf{U}}\right\|_\infty \leq m \ln\left(1 + \frac{\lambda}{m}\right) < \lambda < 1. \quad \blacksquare \tag{3.3.15}$$

In many cases the iteration scheme (3.3.11) will converge too slowly to be of practical value, and so we consider the application of Newton's method for solving (3.3.3) or equivalently (3.3.4). With some initial guess, $\mathbf{U}^{(0)}$, of the solution we now compute the sequence $\{\mathbf{U}^{(\nu)}\}$ by

$$\mathbf{U}^{(\nu+1)} = \mathbf{U}^{(\nu)} + \Delta\mathbf{U}^{(\nu)}, \qquad \nu = 0, 1, 2, \ldots,$$

where $\Delta\mathbf{U}^{(\nu)}$ is the solution of the linear algebraic system

$$\frac{\partial \mathbf{\Phi}(\mathbf{U}^{(\nu)})}{\partial \mathbf{U}} \Delta\mathbf{U}^{(\nu)} = -\mathbf{\Phi}(U^{(\nu)}).$$

As usual in our study, we need only verify the nonsingularity of the coefficient matrix in this system to insure the convergence of Newton's method (since Theorem 1.4.3 is applicable). However, using the definition of $\mathbf{G}(\mathbf{U})$ in (3.3.13), it follows that

$$\frac{\partial \mathbf{\Phi}(\mathbf{U})}{\partial \mathbf{U}} = \mathscr{L}_0^{-1}\left[I - \frac{\partial \mathbf{G}(\mathbf{U})}{\partial \mathbf{U}}\right].$$

From (3.3.15) we deduce that the matrix $[I - \partial\mathbf{G}/\partial\mathbf{U}]$ is nonsingular and hence, under the hypothesis of Theorem 3.3.2, Newton's method is applicable.

We finally turn to the question of the accuracy of the finite-difference solution. Conditions which insure us that the error is $\mathcal{O}(h^2)$ are contained in

THEOREM 3.3.3. *Let the hypothesis of Theorem* 3.3.2 *hold and in addition let* $\mathbf{f}(x, \mathbf{u})$ *have two continuous derivatives with respect to x and* $\mathbf{u}$ *on* $a \leq x \leq b$, $|\mathbf{u}| < \infty$. *Then the solution* $\mathbf{y}(x)$ *of the boundary-value problem* (3.3.1) *and the approximate solution* $\mathbf{u}_j$ *defined by the difference problem* (3.3.3) *satisfy*

$$|\mathbf{y}(x_j) - \mathbf{u}_j| = \mathcal{O}(h^2), \qquad j = 0, 1, \ldots, J.$$

Proof. Under the conditions on $\mathbf{f}$ we are assured that $\mathbf{y}(x)$ has three continuous derivatives and thus

$$\frac{\mathbf{y}(x_j) - \mathbf{y}(x_{j-1})}{h} - \mathbf{y}'(x_{j-1/2}) = \mathcal{O}(h^2),$$

$$\frac{\mathbf{y}(x_j) + \mathbf{y}(x_{j-1})}{2} - \mathbf{y}(x_{j-1/2}) = \mathcal{O}(h^2).$$

From (3.3.1a) at $x = x_{j-1/2}$ and (3.3.3a) we obtain, with $\mathbf{e}_j \equiv \mathbf{y}(x_j) - \mathbf{u}_j$,

$$\frac{\mathbf{e}_j - \mathbf{e}_{j-1}}{h} - K_j \frac{\mathbf{e}_j + \mathbf{e}_{j-1}}{2} = \mathcal{O}(h^2), \qquad j = 1, 2, \ldots, J.$$

Here each row of the matrix K_j is a corresponding row of $\partial\mathbf{f}/\partial\mathbf{u}$ evaluated at some point $(x, \mathbf{u})$ with $x = x_{j-1/2}$,

$$\mathbf{u} = \frac{\theta}{2}(\mathbf{u}_j + \mathbf{u}_{j-1}) + \frac{(1-\theta)}{2}(\mathbf{y}(x_j) + \mathbf{y}(x_{j-1})), \qquad 0 < \theta < 1.$$

From (3.3.1b) and (3.3.3b) we obtain

$$A\mathbf{e}_0 + B\mathbf{e}_J = 0.$$

Combining the above results into matrix form using $\mathscr{L}_0$ of (3.3.12) and $\mathbf{E} \equiv (\mathbf{e}_0^T, \mathbf{e}_1^T, \ldots, \mathbf{e}_J^T)^T$, we get

$$\mathscr{L}_0\mathbf{E} = \frac{h}{2}\begin{pmatrix} 0 & 0 & & \cdots & 0 \\ K_1 & K_1 & & \cdots & \\ 0 & K_2 & K_2 & \cdots & \vdots \\ \vdots & & & & \\ 0 & & \cdots & K_J & K_J \end{pmatrix}\mathbf{E} + \mathcal{O}(h^3).$$

This can be written, in an obvious notation, as

$$\mathbf{E} = \frac{h}{2}\mathscr{L}_0^{-1}K\mathbf{E} + \mathscr{L}_0^{-1}\mathcal{O}(h^3).$$

The coefficient matrix $h/2\mathscr{L}_0^{-1}K$, which enters here, is quite similar to $\partial\mathbf{G}/\partial\mathbf{U}$ in (3.3.14). The elements of the K_j are not evaluated at the same points in the two cases but by (3.3.10) we find, just as in (3.3.15), that

$$\left\|\frac{h}{2}\mathscr{L}_0^{-1}K\right\|_\infty < \lambda.$$

Taking norms in the error equation, we find that

$$\|\mathbf{E}\|_\infty \le \lambda\|\mathbf{E}\|_\infty + \mathcal{O}(h^2)$$

and, since $\lambda < 1$,

$$\|\mathbf{E}\|_\infty \le \mathcal{O}(h^2).$$

We have set $\|\mathscr{L}_0^{-1}\mathcal{O}(h^3)\|_\infty = \mathcal{O}(h^2)$ since $\|\mathscr{L}_0^{-1}\|_\infty \le (J + 2)m$ and $\mathcal{O}(h^3)$ represents a vector. ▌

3.3.1 *Difference Corrections and $h \to 0$ Extrapolation for Systems*

We can frequently improve the $\mathcal{O}(h^2)$ accuracy of the finite difference solution, $\mathbf{u}_j$, defined in (3.3.3) by the application of difference corrections or $h \to 0$ extrapolation. These procedures are justified in the present case if we can show that there is some vector-valued function, $\mathbf{e}(x)$, such that the exact solution, $\mathbf{y}(x)$, of (3.3.1) and the numerical solution, $\mathbf{u}_j$, are related by

$$\mathbf{y}(x_j) = \mathbf{u}_j + h^2\mathbf{e}(x_j) + \mathcal{O}(h^4), \qquad j = 0, 1, \ldots, J. \tag{3.3.16}$$

A derivation of this result is quite similar to that of (3.1.11) (see Theorem 3.1.4) and is based on the following.

THEOREM 3.3.4. *Let* $\mathbf{f}(x, \mathbf{y})$, *A and B satisfy the hypothesis of Theorem* 3.3.3 *and in addition* $\mathbf{f}$ *be so smooth that the solution* $\mathbf{y}(x)$ *of* (3.3.1) *has a continuous fifth derivative*† *on* $[a, b]$. *Then* (3.3.16) *holds with* $\{\mathbf{u}_j\}$ *the solution of* (3.3.3) *and* $\mathbf{e}(x)$ *the solution of the linear boundary-value problem:*

$$\begin{aligned} &\text{(a)} \quad \mathbf{e}' = K(x)\mathbf{e} + \boldsymbol{\theta}(x), \qquad a < x < b, \\ &\text{(b)} \quad A\mathbf{e}(a) + B\mathbf{e}(b) = 0; \end{aligned} \tag{3.3.17}$$

where

$$K(x) \equiv \frac{\partial \mathbf{f}(x, \mathbf{y}(x))}{\partial \mathbf{y}}, \qquad \boldsymbol{\theta}(x) \equiv \frac{1}{24}\mathbf{y}^{(''')}(x) - \frac{1}{4}K(x)\mathbf{y}^{('')}(x). \tag{3.3.18}$$

Proof. Let $\mathbf{v}(x)$ be the unique solution of the initial-value problem

$$\mathbf{v}' = K(x)\mathbf{v} + \boldsymbol{\theta}(x), \qquad \mathbf{v}(a) = \mathbf{0}.$$

Then define the n-vector $\boldsymbol{\alpha}$ by

$$\boldsymbol{\alpha} = B\mathbf{v}(b).$$

Now the problem (3.3.17) is reduced to solving the boundary-value problem

$$\mathbf{w}' = K(x)\mathbf{w}, \qquad A\mathbf{w}(a) + B\mathbf{w}(b) = \boldsymbol{\alpha}$$

since then

$$\mathbf{e}(x) = \mathbf{w}(x) + \mathbf{v}(x).$$

But Theorem 1.2.5 implies that the boundary-value problem for $\mathbf{w}$ has a unique solution. Thus we conclude that the problem (3.3.17) also has a unique solution.

Since $\mathbf{y}(x)$ has a continuous fifth derivative we see that $K(x)$ must have at least a continuous third derivative and so $\boldsymbol{\theta}(x)$ has a continuous second

† We need only require a Lipschitz-continuous fourth derivative and the theorem is valid. However, we are not seeking the weakest conditions.

derivative. But then $\mathbf{e}(x)$, a solution of (3.3.17a), must have a continuous third derivative.

With the definitions

$$\mathbf{e}_j \equiv h^{-2}[\mathbf{y}(x_j) - \mathbf{u}_j], \qquad j = 0, 1, \ldots, J \tag{3.3.19}$$

we obtain from (3.3.3a) and (3.1.1a) evaluated at $x = x_{j-1/2}$

$$\mathbf{e}_j = \mathbf{e}_{j-1} + h^{-1}\left[\mathbf{f}\left(x_{j-1/2}, \mathbf{y}(x_{j-1/2})\right) - \mathbf{f}\left(x_{j-1/2}, \frac{\mathbf{u}_j + \mathbf{u}_{j-1}}{2}\right)\right] + \frac{h}{24}\mathbf{y}^{(''')}(x_{j-1/2}) + \mathcal{O}(h^3).$$

By Theorem 3.3.3 we have $[\mathbf{y}(x_j) - \mathbf{u}_j] = \mathcal{O}(h^2)$, and a Taylor expansion yields

$$\frac{\mathbf{y}(x_j) + \mathbf{y}(x_{j-1})}{2} - \mathbf{y}(x_{j-1/2}) = \frac{h^2}{4}\mathbf{y}^{('')}(x_{j-1/2}) + \mathcal{O}(h^4).$$

Then several Taylor expansions yield

$$\left[\mathbf{f}\left(x_{j-1/2}, \mathbf{y}(x_{j-1/2})\right) - \mathbf{f}\left(x_{j-1/2}, \frac{\mathbf{u}_j + \mathbf{u}_{j-1}}{2}\right)\right]$$
$$= \frac{\partial \mathbf{f}(x_{j-1/2}, y(x_{j-1/2}))}{\partial \mathbf{y}}\left[h^2\left(\frac{\mathbf{e}_j + \mathbf{e}_{j-1}}{2}\right) - \frac{h^2}{4}\mathbf{y}^{('')}(x_{j-1/2})\right] + \mathcal{O}(h^4),$$

and, using this above, we find that

$$\mathbf{e}_j = \mathbf{e}_{j-1} + \frac{h}{2}K(x_{j-1/2})(\mathbf{e}_j + \mathbf{e}_{j-1}) + h\boldsymbol{\theta}(x_{j-1/2}) + \mathcal{O}(h^3),$$
$$j = 1, 2, \ldots, J. \tag{3.3.20a}$$

From (3.3.1b) and (3.3.3b) we get

$$A\mathbf{e}_0 + B\mathbf{e}_J = 0. \tag{3.3.20b}$$

We have already shown that $\mathbf{e}(x)$ has three continuous derivatives. So it now follows, by applying the analysis in the proof of Theorem 3.3.3 to the boundary-value problem (3.3.17) and the difference problem (3.3.20), that

$$\mathbf{e}(x_j) - \mathbf{e}_j = \mathcal{O}(h^2), \qquad j = 0, 1, \ldots, J.$$

Recalling the definition (3.3.19), we finally deduce (3.3.16). ∎

The applications of the results contained in (3.3.16) and (3.3.17) are quite similar to the corresponding results in Section 3.1.1. For the $h \to 0$

extrapolation we find, in an obvious notation, that

$$\bar{\mathbf{u}}_j = \frac{4}{3}\mathbf{u}_{2j}\left(\frac{h}{2}\right) - \frac{1}{3}\mathbf{u}_j(h)$$

satisfies

$$|\mathbf{y}(x_j) - \bar{\mathbf{u}}_j| = \mathcal{O}(h^4), \qquad j = 0, 1, \ldots, J.$$

Thus with two computations of the form (3.3.3), using $h = [b - a]/J$ and $h = [b - a]/2J$, respectively, we obtain an $\mathcal{O}(h^4)$ approximation.

The difference correction is again based on computing an $\mathcal{O}(h^2)$ accurate approximation to $\mathbf{e}(x)$ as defined in (3.3.17). However, in addition to the fact that $\boldsymbol{\theta}(x)$ is not known exactly, we also see that the coefficient $K(x)$ cannot be precisely evaluated (since $y(x)$ is in general unknown). Of course, if we employ the difference solution $\mathbf{u}_j$, we get

$$\frac{\partial \mathbf{f}(x_j, \mathbf{u}_j)}{\partial \mathbf{y}} = K(x_j) + \mathcal{O}(h^2).$$

It can be shown that with this approximation and some $\mathcal{O}(h^2)$ approximation, $\boldsymbol{\Theta}_j$, to $\boldsymbol{\theta}(x_j)$, a difference problem whose solutions are $\mathcal{O}(h^2)$ approximations to $\mathbf{e}(x_j)$ can be formulated (see Problem 3.3.4). Of course as is implied by the name of this procedure we may approximate $\boldsymbol{\theta}(x_j)$ by using appropriate difference quotients of the numerical solution to replace the derivatives in (3.3.18). When $\mathbf{f}(x, \mathbf{y})$ is linear in $\mathbf{y}$ the difficulty with $K(x)$ does not occur, and $\boldsymbol{\theta}(x)$ can be written in terms of $\mathbf{y}(x)$ and higher derivatives of given functions. [This is analogous to the treatment of the second-order scalar case, where $\theta(x)$ in (3.1.13) was reduced to (3.1.17a).]

Problems

3.3.1* Let $\pi_1 = (R_J^{-1}L_J)\cdots(R_1^{-1}L_1)$, where R_j and L_j are as defined in (3.3.6c) and $h < 2/K$. Show that $\|\pi_1 - I\| \le e^{K|b-a|} - 1$. [HINT: It can be shown (see Isaacson and Keller [1966], p. 15) that

$$R_j^{-1} = I + \sum_{\nu=1}^{\infty} ((h/2)K(x_{j-1/2}))^{\nu}.$$

Using this J times, we get $\pi_1 = I + E$, where E contains first and higher powers of h but no terms independent of h. Then estimate

$$\|\pi_1 - I\|_\infty = \|E\|_\infty = (1 + \|E\|_\infty) - 1,$$

using the facts that $\|K(x)\|_\infty < K$ and

$$\|R_j^{-1}\| \le \frac{1}{1 - (h/2)K}, \qquad \|R_j^{-1} - I\|_\infty \le \frac{1}{1 - (h/2)K} - 1,$$

$$\left(\frac{1 + (h/2)K}{1 - (h/2)K}\right)^J \le e^{K|b-a|}$$

since $h = |b - a|/J$. See also Problems 3.3.7 and 1.2.8.]

3.3.2 Using the matrix $\mathscr{L}_0$ of (3.3.12) and the vector function $\mathbf{\Phi}$ defined in (3.3.4), define $\mathbf{F}(\mathbf{U}) \equiv \mathscr{L}_0\mathbf{U} - \mathbf{\Phi}(\mathbf{U})$. Then from (3.3.13) we have that $\mathbf{G}(\mathbf{U}) = \mathscr{L}_0^{-1}\mathbf{F}(\mathbf{U})$. Verify that the iterates in (3.3.11) are simply

$$\mathscr{L}_0\mathbf{U}^{(\nu+1)} = \mathbf{F}(\mathbf{U}^{(\nu)}).$$

3.3.3 Examine the validity of Theorems 3.3.2 and 3.3.3 if, in (3.3.3a), the term $\mathbf{f}(x_{j-1/2}, (\mathbf{u}_j + \mathbf{u}_{j-1})/2)$ is replaced by $\frac{1}{2}[\mathbf{f}(x_j, \mathbf{u}_j) + \mathbf{f}(x_{j-1}, \mathbf{u}_{j-1})]$.

3.3.4 Let a difference problem for approximating the solution $\mathbf{e}(x)$ of the boundary-value problem (3.3.17) be of the form

$$\frac{\mathbf{E}_j - \mathbf{E}_{j-1}}{h} = [K(x_{j-1/2}) + \mathcal{O}(h^2)]\frac{\mathbf{E}_j + \mathbf{E}_{j-1}}{2} + [\mathbf{\theta}(x_j) + \mathcal{O}(h^2)], \qquad j = 1, 2, \ldots, J;$$

$$A\mathbf{E}_0 + B\mathbf{E}_J = 0.$$

Show that under the hypothesis of Theorem 3.3.1, for h sufficiently small,

$$|\mathbf{e}(x_j) - \mathbf{E}_j| = \mathcal{O}(h^2), \qquad j = 0, 1, \ldots, J.$$

3.3.5 Newton's method (in function space) for solving the boundary-value problem (3.3.1) consists in determining a sequence of functions $\{\mathbf{y}^{(\nu)}(x)\}$, where $\mathbf{y}^{(\nu+1)}(x) = \mathbf{y}^{(\nu)}(x) + \mathbf{e}^{(\nu)}(x)$ and $\mathbf{e}^{(\nu)}(x)$ is the solution of the linear boundary-value problem

$$\mathbf{e}^{(\nu)\prime}(x) - \mathbf{f}_y(x, \mathbf{y}^{(\nu)}(x))\mathbf{e}^{(\nu)}(x) = \mathbf{f}(x, \mathbf{y}^{(\nu)}(x)) - \mathbf{y}^{(\nu)\prime}(x),$$
$$A\mathbf{e}^{(\nu)}(a) + B\mathbf{e}^{(\nu)}(b) = \boldsymbol{\alpha} - A\mathbf{y}^{(\nu)}(a) - B\mathbf{y}^{(\nu)}(b).$$

Show that the centered-difference approximation to this system on the net (3.3.2) yields the same algebraic problem as that obtained by employing the usual Newton procedure to solve the algebraic system (3.3.3) [see formulation after Equation (3.3.15)].

3.3.6 In the parallel shooting formulation (2.4.5) use the apparently very crude approximation to (2.4.5a)

$$\mathbf{Y}(1) - \mathbf{Y}(0) = \mathbf{F}\left(\frac{1}{2}, \frac{\mathbf{Y}(1) + \mathbf{Y}(0)}{2}\right).$$

Show that with (2.4.5b) the resulting difference approximation to the problem (2.3.1) [or equivalently (2.4.1)] is identical to the centered-difference scheme (3.3.3) provided $\Delta_j = h$ for $j = 1, 2, \ldots, J$. Thus, in a sense, difference methods can be obtained as special cases of parallel shooting techniques.

3.3.7 Show that π_1, defined in (3.3.8d), satisfies

$$\pi_1 = \mathop{\Omega}_a^b \{K\} + \mathcal{O}(h^2)$$

if $K(x)$ is twice continuously differentiable on $[a, b]$. [HINT: Define $S_0 = I$,

$$S_j - S_{j-1} = \frac{h}{2} K(x_{j-1/2})(S_j + S_{j-1}), \qquad j = 1, 2, \ldots, J,$$

and note that $S_J = \pi_1$. Show that $\{S_j\}$ converges to the solution of

$$Y' = K(x)Y, \; Y(a) = I.]$$

SUPPLEMENTARY REFERENCES AND NOTES

Section 3.1 The derivation of difference approximations to linear differential operators is discussed by Fox (1957), Kantorovich and Krylov (1958), and Babuška, Práger, and Vitásek (1966). Detailed studies of the properties of the coefficient matrices for various difference schemes are given by Varga (1962). These result in more precise error estimates. Variational methods leading to difference equations, or other Ritz approximations, are discussed by Farrington, Gregory, and Taub (1957), Kantorovich and Krylov (1958), and Varga (1965).

Our convergence proof uses neither the maximum principle nor any fancy properties of matrices. With them we could get stronger results, such as allowing $q(x) = 0$.

It is not clear (or perhaps even true) that an arbitrarily high-order difference approximation to the linear differential operator results in correspondingly high-order-accurate approximations to the solution. Thus *repeated* difference corrections and $h \to 0$ extrapolations are at present the only theoretically justified means for obtaining arbitrarily high-order accuracy using difference methods, see for example Pereyra (1966).

Section 3.2 A very thorough study of difference methods applied to $y'' = f(x, y)$ with $f_y \geq 0$ is contained in Henrici (1962), and Lees (1966) allows $f_y < 0$. Difference corrections are also studied in these works, and interesting generalizations are discussed by Pereyra (1966). See also Brown (1962), who employs nonuniform nets. For $f_y \geq 0$ and $f_{yy} < 0$ (that is, concave nonlinearities), Kalaba (1959) shows the applicability of Newton's method (in the continuous form), and Wendroff (1966) justifies it for the difference equations as well. Such applications of Newton's method are sometimes called "quasilinearization" as in Bellman and Kalaba (1965), but the new term seems superfluous. A general study of the equivalence of differencing and then applying Newton's method with the application of Newton's method and then differencing is given by Ortega and Rheinboldt (1965).

Section 3.3 Difference methods for first-order systems are rarely treated in the literature. However, for many of the special boundary conditions occurring in practical problems (for example, separated end conditions) the difference equations are in block-tridiagonal form and hence are easily solved. We do not (in general) advocate using three-point difference equations for first-order systems (that is, $\mathbf{u}_{j+1} - \mathbf{u}_{j-1} = 2h\mathbf{f}(x_j, \mathbf{u}_j)$), since stability problems may arise. Also, special treatment is required at the endpoints to obtain as many equations as unknowns. The application of Galerkin's method to first-order systems has been studied by Urabe (1966), and is in a sense a generalization of difference methods using piecewise linear approximating functions (see Appendix 1). Sylvester and Meyer (1965) employ Newton's method, presumably without being aware of the fact, to the difference scheme (3.3.3); see Problem 3.3.5 to clarify their approach.

CHAPTER 4

INTEGRAL-EQUATION METHODS

4.1 Green's Functions; Equivalent Integral Equations

Many of the numerical methods in Section 1.3 were suggested by first replacing the initial-value problem by an integral equation and then applying quadrature formulae to the integral equation. The same can be done for boundary-value problems, but the derivation of equivalent integral equations is somewhat more complicated. It is based on the determination of the Green's function for a *linear* boundary-value problem.

The Green's function for a linear boundary-value problem is roughly analogous to the inverse of the coefficient matrix in a linear system of equations. In brief, let the boundary-value problem be, for example,

$$Ly(x) \equiv (p(x)y'(x))' - q(x)y(x) = r(x), \qquad a \le x \le b, \tag{4.1.1a}$$

$$y(a) = 0, \qquad y(b) = 0; \tag{4.1.1b}$$

where $p(x) > 0$ and $q(x) \ge 0$. Then the Green's function, $g(x, \xi)$, is a function such that the solution of (4.1.1) is given by

$$y(x) = -\int_a^b g(x, \xi)r(\xi)\,d\xi. \tag{4.1.2}$$

This representation is to be valid for all inhomogeneous terms $r(x)$ satisfying appropriate smoothness conditions. Thus the Green's function, g, is determined by the differential operator L in (4.1.1a) and the boundary conditions (4.1.1b).

It is not difficult to show that $g(x, \xi)$ is uniquely defined by the following conditions:

(a) $g(x, \xi)$ is continuous in x for fixed ξ and $g(a, \xi) = g(b, \xi) = 0$. (4.1.3)

(b) The first and second x-derivatives of $g(x, \xi)$ are continuous for $x \ne \xi$ and at $x = \xi$ the jump condition,

$$\left.\frac{dg(x, \xi)}{dx}\right|_{x=\xi_-}^{x=\xi_+} = -\left.\frac{1}{p(\xi)}\right|, \quad \text{is satisfied}.$$

(c) $Lg(x, \xi) = 0$ for all $x \neq \xi$.

We now have the basic theorem.

THEOREM 4.1.1. *The function* $y(x)$ *is a solution of* (4.1.1) *if and only if it is given by Equation* (4.1.2), *where* $g(x, \xi)$ *is the Green's function as defined in* (4.1.3).

Proof. The proof of this theorem follows by forming Ly from Equation (4.1.2) and using (4.1.3b) when differentiating to get (4.1.1). Then assuming $y(x)$ to satisfy (4.1.1), we multiply this equation by $g(\xi, x)$ and integrate with respect to x, using partial integration to get (4.1.2) with x and ξ interchanged. The details can be found in Courant-Hilbert, Vol. I (1953), pp. 535 et seq., and are left to the reader as an exercise. ∎

If the boundary conditions (4.1.1b) are replaced by inhomogeneous conditions, a simple modification of Equation (4.1.2) yields the solution (see Problem 4.1.1). More general boundary conditions are easily treated as in Problem 4.1.2.

To construct the Green's function we first determine two nontrivial solutions $y_1(x)$ and $y_2(x)$ of the homogeneous equation $Ly = 0$ such that $y_1(a) = 0$ and $y_2(b) = 0$. Then we have

$$g(x, \xi) = A\begin{cases} y_1(x)y_2(\xi), & x < \xi; \\ y_2(x)y_1(\xi), & x > \xi. \end{cases} \tag{4.1.4a}$$

The quantity A is determined from condition (4.1.3b) as

$$A = -\{p(\xi)[y_2'(\xi)y_1(\xi) - y_1'(\xi)y_2(\xi)]\}^{-1}. \tag{4.1.4b}$$

However, since

$$\frac{d}{d\xi}A^{-1} = p[y_2''y_1 - y_1''y_2] + p'[y_2'y_1 - y_1'y_2] = y_1Ly_2 - y_2Ly_1 = 0,$$

we see that A is indeed a constant.

We now consider several ways in which Green's functions can be used to reduce *nonlinear* boundary-value problems to integral equations. Let us first treat the problem

$$Ly = f(x, y, y'), \tag{4.1.5a}$$

$$y(a) = y(b) = 0, \tag{4.1.5b}$$

where L is as defined in (4.1.1a). Under the assumption that this problem has a solution $y(x)$, it follows from Theorem 4.1.1, by letting $r(x) \equiv f(x, y(x), y'(x))$, that the solution satisfies

$$y(x) = -\int_a^b g(x, \xi)f(\xi, y(\xi), y'(\xi))\, d\xi. \tag{4.1.6}$$

Conversely any solution $y(x)$ of Equation (4.1.6) satisfies (4.1.5) and hence the equivalence of the boundary-value problem (4.1.5) with the integro-differential equation (4.1.6) is demonstrated. If the boundary conditions (4.1.5b) are replaced by inhomogeneous conditions, then the corresponding integral equation (4.1.6) is modified by the addition of an inhomogeneous term (see Problem 4.1.1).

We have assumed above that the operator L was given as defined in (4.1.1a). However, by simply changing the definition of $f(x, y, y')$ we could obtain a different operator, a corresponding Green's function and hence an integral equation different from (4.1.6) but still equivalent to (4.1.5). As an illustration of this procedure we consider the problem:

$$L_0 y \equiv y''(x) = f(x, y), \qquad y(0) = y(1) = 0. \tag{4.1.7}$$

The Green's function for L_0, subject to the indicated boundary conditions, is easily found to be

$$g_0(x, \xi) = \begin{cases} x(1 - \xi), & x < \xi; \\ (1 - x)\xi, & x > \xi. \end{cases}$$

Thus the problem (4.1.7) is equivalent to the integral equation

$$y(x) = -\int_0^1 g_0(x, \xi) f(\xi, y(\xi))\, d\xi. \tag{4.1.8}$$

However, by subtracting $k^2 y$ from each side of the differential equation in (4.1.7) we have the equivalent boundary-value problem

$$L_k y \equiv y''(x) - k^2 y(x) = f(x, y(x)) - k^2 y(x), \qquad y(0) = y(1) = 0. \tag{4.1.9}$$

The Green's function for L_k and the indicated boundary conditions is now

$$g_k(x, \xi) = \frac{1}{k \sinh k} \begin{cases} \sinh kx \sinh k(1 - \xi), & x < \xi; \\ \sinh k(1 - x) \sinh k\xi, & x > \xi. \end{cases} \tag{4.1.10}$$

Thus from (4.1.9) we obtain the integral equation

$$y(x) = \int_0^1 g_k(x, \xi)[k^2 y(\xi) - f(\xi, y(\xi))]\, d\xi, \tag{4.1.11}$$

which must be equivalent to the boundary-value problem (4.1.7). The usefulness of this procedure in the present case can be demonstrated by actually using (4.1.11) to solve (4.1.7). We have the following.

THEOREM 4.1.2. *Let f_y be continuous and satisfy* $0 \le \partial f(x, y)/\partial y \le N$ *for* $x \in [0, 1]$ *and all* y. *Then a unique solution of* (4.1.7) *exists and for any* k

such that $k^2 \geq N$ it is given by the limit of the convergent sequence of functions

$$y^{(0)}(x) \equiv 0, \tag{4.1.12a}$$

$$y^{(\nu+1)}(x) = \int_0^1 g_k(x, \xi)[k^2 y^{(\nu)}(\xi) - f(\xi, y^{(\nu)}(\xi))]\, d\xi, \qquad \nu = 0, 1, \ldots . \tag{4.1.12b}$$

Proof. The functions $y^{(\nu)}(x)$ are uniformly continuous on [0, 1] by the continuity of the Green's function. Thus we need only show that they form a Cauchy sequence to conclude that they have a uniformly-continuous limit function $y(x)$. To do this we form

$$\begin{aligned} e^{(\nu+1)}(x) &\equiv y^{(\nu+1)}(x) - y^{(\nu)}(x) \\ &= \int_0^1 g_k(x, \xi)\left[k^2 - \frac{\partial f}{\partial y}(\xi, y^{(\nu)}(\xi) - \theta(\xi)e^{(\nu)}(\xi))\right] e^{(\nu)}(\xi)\, d\xi, \end{aligned}$$

where Taylor's theorem has been used and $0 \leq \theta(\xi) \leq 1$. We note that $g_k(x, \xi) \geq 0$, and since $k^2 \geq N$ the bracket in the integrand satisfies $0 \leq [k^2 - (\partial f/\partial y)] \leq k^2$. Then, calling

$$\|e^{(\nu)}\| \equiv \max_{0 \leq x \leq 1} |e^{(\nu)}(x)|,$$

we obtain

$$\begin{aligned} |e^{(\nu+1)}(x)| &\leq \int_0^1 g_k(x, \xi) k^2\, d\xi \cdot \|e^{(\nu)}\| \\ &= \left(1 - \frac{\cosh k(\frac{1}{2} - x)}{\cosh (k/2)}\right) \cdot \|e^{(\nu)}\| \\ &\leq \left(1 - \frac{1}{\cosh (k/2)}\right) \cdot \|e^{(\nu)}\| \equiv \mu_k \|e^{(\nu)}\|. \end{aligned}$$

Since this holds for all $x \in [0, 1]$, it follows that

$$\|e^{(\nu+1)}\| \leq \mu_k \|e^{(\nu)}\|; \qquad \nu = 1, 2, \ldots,$$

where $\mu_k \equiv (1 - 1/\cosh (k/2)) < 1$. We deduce from this that $\|e^{(\nu+1)}\| \leq \mu_k^\nu \|e^{(1)}\|$ and hence that $\{y^{(\nu)}(x)\}$ is a Cauchy sequence.

We may then take the limit in (4.1.12b) as $\nu \to \infty$ and find that the limit function $y(x)$ satisfies the integral equation (4.1.11). Since this equation is equivalent to (4.1.7), we have demonstrated the existence of a solution to the boundary-value problem. If two solutions $u(x)$ and $y(x)$ exist they both satisfy (4.1.11), and by the above argument

$$\|u - y\| \leq \mu_k \|u - y\|.$$

Thus $\|u - y\| = 0$ and uniqueness follows. ∎

The sequence of functions defined in (4.1.12) are called the *Neumann iterates* for the integral equation (4.1.11) with initial iterate zero. The corresponding iterates for any continuous nonzero initial estimate $y^{(0)}(x)$ would also converge to a solution. It should be observed that the iterates $y^{(\nu)}(x)$ can also be defined as the solutions of the sequence of linear boundary-value problems:

$$y^{(\nu+1)''}(x) - k^2 y^{(\nu+1)}(x) = f(x, y^{(\nu)}(x)) - k^2 y^{(\nu)}(x), \qquad y^{(\nu+1)}(0) = 0,$$
$$y^{(\nu+1)}(1) = 0.$$

Of course this is but a special case of the scheme suggested in (3.2.12). Thus, Theorem 4.1.2 yields a proof of convergence for this scheme in the case indicated.

We must recall that the existence of a unique solution of (4.1.7), provided $\partial f/\partial y > 0$, is implied by Theorem 1.2.2. However, the above proof of this fact is *constructive* and suggests rather obvious numerical methods for approximating the solution. Theorem 4.1.2 is in fact a contracting mapping theorem for an integral operator on a function space, quite analogous to Theorem 1.4.1. For a more general discussion from the viewpoint of functional analysis see Collatz (1960), pp. 34–42.

It is important to consider systems of integral equations by means of which quite general boundary-value problems can be treated. For example (4.1.6) is a special case of the integro-differential equation

$$y(x) = \int_a^b F[x, \xi; y(\xi), y'(\xi)]\, d\xi. \tag{4.1.13a}$$

Under appropriate smoothness conditions on the functions $y(x)$ and $F_x(x, \xi; y, y')$, the derivative $y'(x)$ must satisfy

$$y'(x) = \int_a^b F_x[x, \xi; y(\xi), y'(\xi)]\, d\xi. \tag{4.1.13b}$$

Thus we see that boundary-value problems of the form (4.1.5) can be replaced by a system of integral equations.

As another example, we consider a system of boundary-value problems of the general form

$$\left.\begin{aligned} &\text{(a)}\quad L_\nu y_\nu(x) \equiv (p_\nu(x) y_\nu'(x))' - q_\nu(x) y_\nu(x) = f_\nu(x; y_1, \ldots, y_n), \\ &\qquad\qquad\qquad\qquad\qquad\qquad\qquad\qquad a \le x \le b, \\ &\text{(b)}\quad y_\nu(a) = 0, \qquad y_\nu(b) = 0, \end{aligned}\right\} \quad 1 \le \nu \le n. \tag{4.1.14}$$

where $p_\nu(x) > 0$ and $q_\nu(x) \ge 0$ for all ν.

If $g_\nu(x, \xi)$ is the Green's function for the differential operator L_ν, subject to the homogeneous boundary conditions (4.1.14b), then the solution of (4.1.14) must satisfy

$$y_\nu(x) = -\int_a^b g_\nu(x, \xi) f_\nu(\xi; y_1(\xi), \ldots, y_n(\xi))\, d\xi, \qquad 1 \le \nu \le n. \quad (4.1.15)$$

Conversely we see that any twice continuously differentiable solution of (4.1.15) is a solution of (4.1.14). (It is assumed here that all functions $p_\nu'(x)$, $q_\nu(x)$, and $f_\nu(x; y_1, \ldots, y_n)$ are continuous.) If the boundary conditions are not homogeneous then, as before, inhomogeneous terms must be included. If more general boundary conditions than those in (4.1.14b) are to be treated (but with the y_ν still uncoupled), we need only use the appropriate Green's functions. [If the boundary conditions are coupled the situation is considerably more complicated. However, if we associate the νth pair of conditions containing $y_\nu(a)$ and $y_\nu(b)$ with the νth equation in (4.1.14a) and consider $y_\mu(a)$ and $y_\mu(b)$ for $\mu \neq \nu$ as inhomogeneous terms, an equivalent system of integral equations is easily derived. This system then involves values of the dependent variables at the endpoints, and a theoretical analysis is rather complicated. But there are frequently no practical difficulties in the numerical solution of such systems by the methods in Section 4.2.]

The systems (4.1.13) and (4.1.15) are special cases of a rather general system of n coupled integral equations which can be written as

$$\mathbf{y}(x) = \int_a^b \mathbf{F}(x, \xi; \mathbf{y}(\xi))\, d\xi. \quad (4.1.16)$$

A constructive existence and uniqueness proof for this system is easily obtained if the integrand satisfies appropriate conditions. We have in fact the following.

THEOREM 4.1.3. *Let the continuous functions* $F_i(x, \xi; \mathbf{y})$ *have continuous derivatives,* $\partial F_i(x, \xi; \mathbf{y})/\partial y_j$ *on* $a \le x,\ \xi \le b$, $|\mathbf{y}| < \infty$, *for* $i, j = 1, 2, \ldots, n$. *Further for any vector-valued function* $\mathbf{z}(\xi)$ *continuous on* $a \le \xi \le b$ *let*

$$\int_a^b \sum_{j=1}^n \left| \frac{\partial F_i}{\partial y_j}(x, \xi; \mathbf{z}(\xi)) \right| d\xi \le \mu < 1, \qquad i = 1, 2, \ldots, n, \qquad a \le x \le b. \quad (4.1.17)$$

Then the integral equation (4.1.16) *has a unique continuous solution* $\mathbf{y}(x)$, *which is the limit of the convergent sequence of functions*

$$\text{(a)}\quad \mathbf{y}^{(0)}(x) = 0$$
$$\text{(b)}\quad \mathbf{y}^{(\nu+1)}(x) = \int_a^b \mathbf{F}(x, \xi; \mathbf{y}^{(\nu)}(\xi))\, d\xi, \qquad \nu = 0, 1, \ldots. \quad (4.1.18)$$

Proof. The proof is quite similar to that of Theorem 4.1.2, using the Contracting Mapping principle. The details are left to Problem 4.1.4. ▌

Problems

4.1.1 Let $y_0(x)$ be the solution of the boundary-value problem

$$Ly_0 = 0; \qquad y_0(a) = \alpha, \qquad y_0(b) = \beta.$$

Then show that the solution of the problem

$$Ly = r(x), \qquad y(a) = \alpha, \qquad y(b) = \beta$$

is

$$y(x) = y_0(x) - \int_a^b g(x, \xi)r(\xi)\, d\xi.$$

Here L is as defined in (4.1.1a) and $g(x, \xi)$ is the Green's function in (4.1.2). The function $y_0(x)$ can be determined as a linear combination of $y_1(x)$ and $y_2(x)$ as used in (4.1.4).

4.1.2 Define the Green's function for the differential operator L of (4.1.1a), subject to the boundary conditions

$$a_0 y(a) + a_1 y'(a) = 0, \qquad b_0 y(b) - b_1 y'(b) = 0.$$

4.1.3 Prove that the Green's function $g(x, \xi)$, as defined in (4.1.3) for the operator L in (4.1.1a), is symmetric; that is,

$$g(x, \xi) = g(\xi, x).$$

[This is always true of *self-adjoint* differential operators; that is, if for all u and v vanishing at $x = a$ and $x = b$, $\int_a^b uLv\, dx = \int_a^b vLu\, dx$.]

4.1.4 Carry out the details in the proof of Theorem 4.1.3. [HINT: If $\mathbf{e}^{(\nu)}(\xi) \equiv \mathbf{u}^{(\nu+1)}(\xi) - \mathbf{u}^{(\nu)}(\xi)$ is continuous, then

$$F_i(x, \xi; \mathbf{u}^{(\nu)}(\xi) + \mathbf{e}^{(\nu)}(\xi)) = F_i(x, \xi; \mathbf{u}^{(\nu)}(\xi)) + \sum_j \frac{\partial F_i}{\partial y_j}(x, \xi; \mathbf{u}^{(\nu)}(\xi) + \theta_i(\xi)\mathbf{e}^{(\nu)}(\xi))e_j^{(\nu)}(\xi),$$

where $\theta_i(\xi)$ in $0 \le \theta_i \le 1$ is a continuous function of ξ on $[a, b]$.]

4.1.5 Show that the Green's function for $Lu \equiv -u'' - 4u$, subject to $u(0) = u'(1) = 0$, is

$$g(x, t) = \frac{1}{2\cos 2}\begin{cases} \sin 2x \cos 2(1 - \xi), & x < \xi, \\ \cos 2(1 - x)\sin 2\xi, & x > \xi. \end{cases}$$

4.2 *Numerical Solution of Integral Equations*

We now consider numerical methods for approximating the solution of integral equations. If these methods are effective, then they also furnish approximations to the solution of corresponding boundary-value problems. We shall first consider the special integral equation (4.1.11), obtained from the boundary-value problem (4.1.7) or equivalently from (4.1.9), and then discuss the obvious extensions to more general systems of integral equations of the forms (4.1.15) and (4.1.16).

The net points x_j, $j = 1, 2, \ldots, J$, are *not* required to be equally spaced, but we take them such that

$$0 \leq x_1 < x_2 \cdots < x_J \leq 1.$$

The net function $\{u_j\}$ which is to approximate $y(x_j)$ is defined as the solution of the system of equations

$$u_i = \sum_{j=1}^{J} \alpha_j g_k(x_i, x_j)[k^2 u_j - f(x_j, u_j)], \qquad i = 1, 2, \ldots, J. \tag{4.2.1}$$

The quantities α_j are the coefficients for a quadrature formula over [0, 1] with nodes at the points x_j. Thus for each value $x = x_i$ we use the same approximation to the corresponding integral in (4.1.11). This is just a convenience and is more efficient for storage purposes. More "accurate" schemes based, for example, on weighted Gaussian-type quadrature formulae, do not have this feature and will be discussed later.

We require that the quadrature scheme used in (4.2.1) satisfy

$$\begin{aligned} &\text{(a)} \quad \alpha_j \geq 0, \qquad j = 1, 2, \ldots, J. \\ &\text{(b)} \quad \lim_{J \to \infty} E_J\{F(x)\} = 0, \end{aligned} \tag{4.2.2}$$

for all $F(x)$ which are continuous on [0, 1]. Here we have defined the quadrature error in the formula using the coefficients α_j and nodes x_j as

$$E_J\{F(\xi)\} \equiv \int_0^1 F(\xi)\, d\xi - \sum_{j=1}^{J} \alpha_j F(x_j). \tag{4.2.3}$$

Thus we want nonnegative coefficients and convergence for all *continuous* integrands. (This last condition (4.2.2b) is imposed because $g_k(x, \xi)$, and hence the integrand in Equation (4.1.11), is continuous on $0 \leq \xi \leq 1$ but has a discontinuous first derivative at $\xi = x$.) We say that the quadrature scheme has *degree of precision* N if $E_J\{\xi^n\} = 0$ for $n = 0, 1, \ldots, N$ and $E_J\{\xi^{N+1}\} \neq 0$. Then all polynomials of degree N or less are integrated exactly by the scheme.

Let us consider first the question of convergence of the approximate solution, u_j, to the exact solution of the integral equation (4.1.11). Later we treat the problem of solving this nonlinear system by iteration. The local truncation errors, τ_i, of the approximation (4.2.1) are defined by

$$\tau_i = E_J\{g_k(x_i, \xi)[k^2 y(\xi) - f(\xi, y(\xi))]\}, \qquad i = 1, 2, \ldots, J. \tag{4.2.4}$$

Now we can state the basic error estimate as a theorem.

THEOREM 4.2.1. *Let the quadrature formula with nodes* $\{x_j\}$ *and coefficients* $\{\alpha_j\}$ *satisfy* (4.2.2) *and let* f *and* $\partial f/\partial y$ *be continuous and satisfy* $0 \le \partial f/\partial y \le M$ *for all* $x \in [0, 1]$ *and all* y. *Then for any* k *such that* $k^2 \ge M$ *there exists an integer* J_k *and positive quantities* ε_{Jk} *such that for all* $J \ge J_k$

$$|u_i - y(x_i)| \le \left(\varepsilon_{Jk} + \cosh\frac{k}{2}\right)\|\tau\|, \qquad i = 1, 2, \ldots, J. \tag{4.2.5a}$$

Here $\{u_i\}$ *is the solution of* (4.2.2), $y(x)$ *is the solution of* (4.1.11) *and*

$$\lim_{J\to\infty} \varepsilon_{Jk} = 0, \qquad \lim_{J\to\infty} \|\tau\| = 0. \tag{4.2.5b}$$

Proof. We use the definitions

$$e_j \equiv u_j - y(x_j), \qquad \|e\| \equiv \max_{1\le j\le J} |e_j|, \qquad \|\tau\| \equiv \max_{1\le j\le J} |\tau_j|.$$

Then, using Taylor's theorem and the continuity of $\partial f/\partial y$, we deduce from (4.2.1) and (4.2.4) that

$$e_i = \sum_{j=1}^{J} \alpha_j g_k(x_i, x_j)[k^2 - \tilde{f}_{y,j}]e_j - \tau_i, \qquad i = 1, 2, \ldots, J.$$

Here $\tilde{f}_{y,j}$ is an appropriate intermediate value of $\partial f/\partial y$. Taking absolute values above and recalling that $\alpha_j \ge 0$, $0 \le k^2 - f_y \le k^2$, and $g(x, \xi) \ge 0$, we get

$$|e_i| \le \left[\sum_{j=1}^{J} \alpha_j k^2 g_k(x_i, x_j)\right] \cdot \|e\| + \|\tau\|, \qquad i = 1, 2, \ldots, J. \tag{4.2.6}$$

From the definition (4.2.3) it follows that

$$\left[\sum_{j=1}^{J} \alpha_j k^2 g_k(x_i, x_j)\right] = \int_0^1 g_k(x_i, \xi)k^2\, d\xi - E_J\{k^2 g_k(x_i, \xi)\},$$

$$\le \left[1 - \frac{1}{\cosh(k/2)}\right] + k^2|E_J\{g_k(x_i, \xi)\}|, \qquad i = 1, 2, \ldots, J.$$

However, the functions $g_k(x_i, \xi)$ are continuous functions of ξ on [0, 1] for all $i = 1, 2, \ldots, J$. Thus by the convergence property (4.2.2b) we can make $|E_J\{g_k(x_i, \xi)\}|$ arbitrarily small by taking J sufficiently large. Let J_k be an integer such that for all $J \ge J_k$:

$$|E_J\{g_k(x_i, \xi)\}| < \frac{1}{k^2 \cosh(k/2)}, \qquad i = 1, 2, \ldots, J.$$

Now define the quantities ε_{Jk} by

$$\varepsilon_{Jk} \equiv \left(\frac{1}{\cosh(k/2)} - k^2\|E_J\{g_k(x, \xi)\}\|\right)^{-1} - \cosh\frac{k}{2},$$

where

$$\|E_J\{g_k(x, \xi)\}\| = \max_{1\le i\le J} |E_J\{g_k(x_i, \xi)\}|.$$

Clearly $\varepsilon_{Jk} \geq 0$ for $J \geq J_k$ and $\lim_{J\to\infty} \varepsilon_{Jk} = 0$. Combining the above, we have, for $J \geq J_k$,

$$\left[\sum_{j=1}^{J} \alpha_j k^2 g_k(x_i, x_j)\right] \leq 1 - \frac{1}{\varepsilon_{Jk} + \cosh(k/2)}; \qquad i = 1, 2, \ldots, J.$$

This result in (4.2.6) implies that

$$\|e\| \leq \left(\varepsilon_{Jk} + \cosh\frac{k}{2}\right)\|\tau\|,$$

and the theorem clearly follows. ∎

It should be noted that the error bound in (4.2.5) estimates the order of convergence of the approximate solution to the exact solution by the order of convergence of the quadrature formula applied to the integrand in Equation (4.1.11). To get more detailed estimates of the error we must specify a particular quadrature scheme and then examine the corresponding quadrature error for integrands of the indicated form.

A particularly simple example is furnished by employing the *trapezoidal rule* with equally-spaced nodes. Thus we take $x_j = jh$, $h = 1/J$, $\alpha_1 = \alpha_J = \frac{1}{2}$, and $\alpha_j = 1$, $j = 2, 3, \ldots, J - 1$. For brevity let us introduce the notation

$$G(x, \xi) \equiv g_k(x, \xi)[k^2 y(\xi) - f(\xi, y(\xi))],$$

where $y(x)$ is the solution of (4.1.11). Since Theorem 4.2.1 is valid for the trapezoidal rule we need only estimate the errors in applying this rule to approximate

$$\int_0^1 G(x_i, \xi)\, d\xi.$$

These errors are

$$E_J\{G(x_i, \xi)\} = \int_0^1 G(x_i, \xi)\, d\xi - \sum_{j=1}^{J} \alpha_j G(x_i, x_j), \qquad i = 1, 2, \ldots, J.$$

But by introducing $\alpha_{ij} = (1 - \frac{1}{2}\delta_{ij})\alpha_j$ we can write them as

$$E_J\{G(x_i, \xi)\} = \left\{\int_0^{x_i} G(x_i, \xi)\, d\xi - \sum_{j=1}^{i} \alpha_{ij} G(x_i, x_j)\right\}$$
$$+ \left\{\int_{x_i}^1 G(x_i, \xi)\, d\xi - \sum_{j=i}^{J} \alpha_{ij} G(x_i, x_j)\right\}, \qquad 1 \leq i \leq J.$$

Thus for $0 < x_i < 1$ the error is the sum of two quadrature errors employing the trapezoidal rule over $[0, x_i]$ and $[x_i, 1]$, respectively. More important, however, is the fact that the discontinuity of the first derivative of the integrand only occurs at the endpoints of these intervals. The same is true for

$x_i = 0$ and $x_i = 1$. Assuming sufficient differentiability of $f(x, y(x))$, we can apply the usual error estimates for the trapezoidal rule [see Isaacson and Keller (1966), p. 318] to each of the bracketed terms above to get

$$|E_J\{G(x_i, \xi)\}| \le h^2 M,$$

where

$$M = \frac{1}{12} \max_{0 \le x \le 1} \left[\max_{\substack{\xi \in [0, x], \\ \xi \in [x, 1]}} \left| \frac{d^2 G(x, \xi)}{d\xi^2} \right| \right].$$

Using this result in Theorem 4.2.1 we find that *the trapezoidal rule yields accuracy which is at least* $\mathcal{O}(1/J^2)$.

It can be shown that the conditions in (4.2.2) are satisfied by any quadrature formula with positive coefficients whose degree of precision becomes unbounded as the number of nodes becomes infinite. Thus Theorem 4.2.1 is valid for ordinary Gaussian quadrature formulae. It is also valid for various composite quadrature formulae such as Simpson's rule. However, since the integrand in (4.1.11) does not, in general, have continuous derivatives, the usual estimates of the error in such higher-order accurate schemes can not be employed. Indeed, in some exceptional cases, the use of the trapezoidal rule in (4.2.1) may yield more accurate approximations to the exact solution of (4.1.11) than would be obtained by using Simpson's rule or Gaussian quadrature (with the same number of nodes). But these higher-order schemes are frequently quite accurate even when the standard error estimates are not valid [see Davis and Rabinowitz (1967), p. 122].

To circumvent this difficulty, caused by the presence of the Green's function in the integrand, we can employ special weighted quadrature formulae. That is, for each x_i we approximate an integral of the form

$$\int_0^1 g_k(x_i, \xi)\phi(\xi)\, d\xi, \qquad i = 1, 2, \ldots, J \tag{4.2.7a}$$

by a sum of the form

$$\sum_{j=1}^{J} \beta_{ij}\phi(x_j), \qquad i = 1, 2, \ldots, J. \tag{4.2.7b}$$

Again we require the equivalent of (4.2.2); nonnegative coefficients $\beta_{ij} \ge 0$ and convergence for all continuous functions $\phi(x)$,

$$\lim_{J \to \infty} E_{i,J}\{\phi(\xi)\} \equiv \lim_{J \to \infty} \left[\int_0^1 g_k(x_i, \xi)\phi(\xi)\, d\xi - \sum_{j=1}^{J} \beta_{ij}\phi(x_j) \right] = 0,$$

$$i = 1, 2, \ldots, J. \tag{4.2.8}$$

In (4.2.7b) we have actually introduced J different weighted quadrature formulae and so must now retain J^2 coefficients, β_{ij}, $i, j = 1, 2, \ldots, J$. The

ith scheme in (4.2.7b) is said to have degree of precision N if $E_{i,J}\{\xi^n\} = 0$ for $n = 1, 2, \ldots, N$ and $E_{i,J}\{\xi^{N+1}\} \neq 0$. If the degree of precision is at least zero, then

$$\sum_{j=1}^{J} \beta_{ij} = \int_0^1 g_k(x_i, \xi)\, d\xi = k^{-2}\left(1 - \frac{\cosh k(\frac{1}{2} - x_i)}{\cosh k/2}\right). \tag{4.2.9}$$

We do not study here the derivation of such schemes. Let it suffice to say that with J nodes, weighted quadrature formulae (4.2.7b) with degrees of precision $N_i \leq J$ can be determined [see Isaacson and Keller (1966), pp. 331–334].

In place of (4.2.1), we now consider the approximating system

$$u_i = \sum_{j=1}^{J} \beta_{ij}[k^2 u_j - f(x_j, u_j)], \qquad i = 1, 2, \ldots, J. \tag{4.2.10}$$

It is straightforward to prove a result similar to Theorem 4.2.1. In fact, if we require that (4.2.9) hold, then we can drop the small quantities corresponding to ε_{Jk} in (4.2.5). We leave the statement and proof of this result to Problem 4.2.1.

The application of either of the above procedures to systems of integral equations of the form (4.1.15) is quite clear. When using the weighted quadrature formulae, however, we must determine nJ^2 coefficients, that is, J^2 of them, for each Green's function $g_\nu(x, \xi)$, $\nu = 1, 2, \ldots, n$. For the more general systems of the form (4.1.16), the weighted formulae may not be appropriate. Thus we approximate their solutions by the set of n-vectors $\{\mathbf{u}_j\}$ which satisfy

$$\mathbf{u}_i = \sum_{j=1}^{J} \alpha_j \mathbf{F}(x_i, x_j; \mathbf{u}_j), \qquad i = 1, 2, \ldots, J. \tag{4.2.11}$$

A convergence proof for this case is again analogous to that of Theorem 4.2.1. We have the following.

THEOREM 4.2.2. *Let the quadrature formula with nodes* $\{x_j\}$ *and coefficients* $\{\alpha_j\}$ *satisfy* (4.2.2). *Let* $\mathbf{F}(x, \xi; \mathbf{y})$ *satisfy the hypothesis of Theorem* 4.1.3. *Then there exists an integer* J_0 *and positive quantities* $\varepsilon_J < 1 - \mu$ *such that for each* $J \geq J_0$:

$$|\mathbf{u}_i - \mathbf{y}(x_i)| \leq \frac{1}{1 - \mu - \varepsilon_J} \|\tau\|, \qquad i = 1, 2, \ldots, J.$$

Here $\{\mathbf{u}_i\}$ *is the solution of* (4.2.11), $\mathbf{y}(x)$ *is the solution of* (4.1.16), $\lim_{J\to\infty} \varepsilon_J = 0$ *and*

$$\|\tau\| = \max_{\substack{1\leq i\leq J,\\ 1\leq \nu\leq n}} E_J\{F_\nu(x_i, \xi; \mathbf{y}(\xi))\}.$$

Proof. The proof follows closely that of Theorem 4.2.1, using the expansion in Problem 4.1.4; we leave the details to Problem 4.2.2. ∎

We now turn to the problems of solving the nonlinear systems (4.2.1), (4.2.10), or (4.2.11). Of course part of our task is to show that these systems have solutions which are unique. Under appropriate conditions the obvious functional iteration schemes can be used to demonstrate these results. The details should be clear by now, so we are content to sketch the procedure as applied to the system (4.2.1).

The hypothesis of Theorem 4.2.1 is assumed to hold, and we take $k^2 \geq M$ and $J \geq J_k$. A sequence of net functions $\{u_j^{(\nu)}\}$, $\nu = 0, 1, 2, \ldots$ is defined as follows:

$$\text{(a)} \quad u_i^{(0)} = \text{arbitrary}, \qquad i = 1, 2, \ldots, J;$$

$$\text{(b)} \quad u_i^{(\nu+1)} = \sum_{j=1}^{J} \alpha_j g_k(x_i, x_j)[k^2 u_j^{(\nu)} - f(x_j, u_j^{(\nu)})], \qquad i = 1, 2, \ldots, J. \tag{4.2.12}$$

We first prove that $\{u_j^{(\nu)}\}$ is a Cauchy sequence (in ν, for each j) by the procedures used in Theorems 4.1.2 and 4.2.1. That is, with the definitions $e_i^{(\nu+1)} \equiv u_i^{(\nu+1)} - u_i^{(\nu)}$, we get from (4.2.12b) for $\nu + 1$ and ν

$$|e_i^{(\nu+1)}| = \left|\sum_{j=1}^{J} \alpha_j g_k(x_i, x_j)[k^2 - f_{y,j}]e_j^{(\nu)}\right| \leq \left[\sum_{j=1}^{J} \alpha_j g_k(x_i, x_j)k^2\right] \|e^{(\nu)}\|$$
$$\leq \left(1 - \frac{1}{\varepsilon_{Jk} + \cosh(k/2)}\right)\|e^{(\nu)}\| \leq \mu_k \|e^{(\nu)}\|, \qquad i = 1, 2, \ldots, J.$$

Thus we get

$$\|e^{(\nu+1)}\| \leq \mu_k \|e^{(\nu)}\|,$$

and since $\mu_k < 1$ the $\{u_j^{(\nu)}\}$ forms a Cauchy sequence whose limit, say $\{u_j\}$, satisfies (4.2.1). Existence of a solution is thus demonstrated and uniqueness easily follows since for any other solution $\{v_j\}$ we obtain

$$\|u - v\| \leq \mu_k \|u - v\|,$$

and hence $\{u_j\} \equiv \{v_j\}$. With essentially no more difficulty the systems (4.2.10) and (4.2.11) can be treated analogously.

It should be stressed that the indicated functional iterations converge for *any* initial guess at the solution. But the rate of convergence may be quite slow; in the above case μ_k can be very near unity. In seeking more-rapidly-convergent schemes Newton's method is again a likely choice. To derive it for the system (4.2.1) we replace u_j by $u_j^{(\nu)} + \Delta u_j^{(\nu)}$, expand in powers of Δu

and drop all second- and higher-order terms to get the linear system

$$\Delta u_i^{(\nu)} = \sum_{j=1}^{J} \alpha_j g_k(x_i, x_j)[k^2 - f_y(x_j, u_j^{(\nu)})] \Delta u_j^{(\nu)} + r_i^{(\nu)}, \qquad i = 1, 2, \ldots \tag{4.2.13a}$$

with

$$r_i^{(\nu)} \equiv \sum_{j=1}^{J} \alpha_j g_k(x_i, x_j)[k^2 u_j^{(\nu)} - f(x_j, u_j^{(\nu)})] - u_i^{(\nu)}. \tag{4.2.13b}$$

The scheme is then

$$u_i^{(0)} = \text{arbitrary}, \qquad u_i^{(\nu+1)} = u_j^{(\nu)} + \Delta u_i^{(\nu)}, \qquad \nu = 0, 1, \ldots,$$

where the $\Delta u_i^{(\nu)}$ are as defined in (4.2.13). To show that this linear system is nonsingular, so that Newton's method is well defined, we need only observe that the coefficient matrix is diagonally dominant (provided $k^2 \geq M$ and $J \geq J_k$, as in Theorem 4.2.1). A "sufficiently close" initial estimate to insure convergence (by Theorem 1.4.3) can be obtained by using the scheme (4.2.12) for several iterations.

Finally we point out that Newton's method as defined above is also suggested by first linearizing the integral equation (4.1.11) about some approximate solution, say $y^{(\nu)}(x)$, to obtain a correction $\Delta y^{(\nu)}(x)$ as the solution of

$$\Delta y^{(\nu)}(x) = \int_0^1 g_k(x, \xi)[k^2 - f_y(\xi, y^{(\nu)}(\xi))] \Delta y^{(\nu)}(\xi)\, d\xi + r^{(\nu)}(x), \tag{4.2.14a}$$

where

$$r^{(\nu)}(x) = \int_0^1 g_k(x, \xi)[k^2 y^{(\nu)}(\xi) - f(\xi, y^{(\nu)}(\xi))]\, d\xi - y^{(\nu)}(x). \tag{4.2.14b}$$

Then if the linear integral equation (4.2.14) is numerically approximated, in the obvious way, we obtain (4.2.13). Thus even if the continuous iterates $y^{(\nu+1)}(x) = y^{(\nu)}(x) + \Delta y^{(\nu)}(x)$, $\nu = 0, 1, \ldots$ converge quite rapidly to the solution $y(x)$ of (4.1.11), the accuracy of the corresponding numerical approximation is determined as in Theorem 4.2.1. These considerations are exactly analogous to those in (3.2.11) et seq. The reader is urged to consider Newton's method for both the discrete problem (4.2.11) and the corresponding system of integral equations (4.1.16) [see Problems 4.2.3 and 4.2.4].

Problems

4.2.1 Prove the following THEOREM 4.2.1′: *Let the quadrature formula* (4.2.7b) *have nonnegative coefficients and degree of precision at least zero. Let $f(x, y)$ satisfy the hypothesis of Theorem* 4.2.1. *Then for any $k^2 > M$ the solutions $\{u_j\}$ of* (4.2.10) *and $y(x)$ of* (4.1.11) *satisfy:*

$$|u_i - y(x_i)| \leq \cosh\frac{k}{2} \max_{1 \leq j \leq J} |E_{j,J}\{[k^2 y(\xi) - f(\xi, y(\xi))]\}|, \qquad i = 1, 2, \ldots, J.$$

4.2.2 Carry out the details in the proof of Theorem 4.2.2.

4.2.3 Formulate the application of Newton's method for the solution of the nonlinear system (4.2.11). Under the conditions of Theorems 4.1.3 and 4.2.2, show that for sufficiently large J the relevant coefficient matrix is always nonsingular.

4.2.4 Derive the linear integral equations resulting from the application of Newton's method to the nonlinear system of integral equations (4.1.16). Let the continuous iterates defined in this way be approximated by employing a quadrature formula to evaluate the integrals on some net. Can the algebraic problem of Problem 4.2.3 be obtained in this way?

4.2.5 (a) Replace the sequence of linear differential equations in (3.2.12) by a corresponding sequence of centered difference equations. Write these equations in the vector form

$$A\mathbf{v}^{(\nu+1)} = \mathbf{F}(\mathbf{v}^{(\nu)})$$

and determine the matrix A and vector function $\mathbf{F}(\mathbf{v})$.

(b) Write the iteration scheme (4.2.12) for solving the numerical approximation (4.2.1) to the integral equation (4.1.11) in the vector form

$$\mathbf{u}^{(\nu+1)} = B\mathbf{G}(\mathbf{u}^{(\nu)}),$$

and determine the matrix B and vector function $\mathbf{G}(\mathbf{u})$.

(c) Discuss the relation between the two algebraic systems above if the original boundary-value problems to be solved were identical and $\omega = k^2$. Is $B = A^{-1}$ when the trapezoidal rule is used in (4.1.11)? Compare operational counts in evaluating $\mathbf{v}^{(\nu+1)}$ and $\mathbf{u}^{(\nu+1)}$ when A is tridiagonal and B has essentially J^2 nonzero elements (that is, $h = 1/J$).

4.2.6 With a little more care in bounding the integral in the proof of Theorem 4.1.2, we may allow f_y to be "slightly" negative.

THEOREM 4.2.3. *Let f_y be continuous and satisfy, for some $k > 0$ and θ in $0 < \theta \leqslant 1$,*

$$k^2 \frac{1-\theta}{1-\cosh k/2} \leqslant \frac{\partial f(x, y)}{\partial y} \leqslant k^2 \tag{4.2.15}$$

for all $x \in [0, 1]$ and all y. Then a unique solution of (4.1.7) *exists and is given as the limit of the sequence of iterates $\{y^{(\nu)}(x)\}$ defined in* (4.1.12). [HINT: Use the bound $(k^2 - f_y) \leqslant (k^2 - \min f_y)$. The convergence factor is now $\mu = 1 - \theta/\cosh(h/2)$.] Much better results allowing $f_y < 0$ are given by M. Lees (1966).

4.2.7 The requirement that f satisfy appropriate conditions for all y is very severe. It is not difficult to eliminate such conditions. For example, one such weakening of the hypothesis can be stated as follows.

THEOREM 4.2.4. *Let $M > 0$ and $k > 0$ be such that*

$$|f(x, y)| \leqslant \frac{k^2}{\cosh k/2 - 1} M \qquad (4.2.16)$$

for all $x \in [0, 1]$ and y in $|y| \leqslant M$. In addition let f_y satisfy (4.2.15) *with some $\theta \in (0, 1]$ for all $x \in [0, 1]$ and y in $|y| \leqslant M$. Then* (4.1.7) *has a unique solution satisfying*

$$|y(x)| \leqslant M,$$

and it is the limit of the iterates $\{y^{(\nu)}(x)\}$ in (4.1.12). [HINT: By induction show that $|y^{(\nu)}(x)| \leqslant M$, and then the proof of Theorem 4.2.3 is applicable.]

SUPPLEMENTARY REFERENCES AND NOTES

Section 4.1 Conversion of a boundary-value problem to an integral equation is one of the standard devices used in proving existence theorems [see Hartman (1964) and Courant-Hilbert (1953)]. There are procedures other than using Green's functions for replacing differential equation problems by equivalent integral equations. In particular, for first-order systems, an integration over the interval in question yields a system of integral equations subject to the original boundary conditions (which can frequently be incorporated into the integral equations).

Section 4.2 The theory of linear integral equations [as in Courant-Hilbert (1953)] leads to approximation methods not based on numerical quadrature. Some of these procedures are numerical, however, in the sense that large-scale computations are required for their implementation [see Kantorovich and Krylov (1958)].

CHAPTER 5

EIGENVALUE PROBLEMS

5.1 *Introduction; Sturm-Liouville Problems*

It is easily shown that a linear boundary-value problem may have nonunique solutions. This occurs in fact if and only if the corresponding homogeneous boundary-value problem has a nontrivial solution (see Theorem 1.2.3). If the coefficients of the equation and/or of the boundary conditions depend upon a parameter, it is frequently of interest to determine the value or values of the parameter for which such nontrivial solutions exist. These special parameter values are called eigenvalues and the corresponding nontrivial solutions are called eigenfunctions. A particularly simple and standard example is furnished by the homogeneous problem

$$y'' + \lambda y = 0; \qquad y(a) = y(b) = 0.$$

For each of the parameter values (eigenvalues)

$$\lambda = \lambda_n \equiv [n\pi/(b - a)]^2, \qquad n = 1, 2, \ldots$$

there exists a corresponding nontrivial solution (eigenfunction)

$$y(x) = y_n(x) \equiv c_n \sin \lambda_n^{1/2}(x - a), \qquad n = 1, 2, \ldots .$$

We note that the nth eigenfunction is nonunique to within an arbitrary constant factor c_n.

A fairly general class of eigen-problems, which includes many of the cases that occur in applied mathematics, is the Sturm-Liouville problems:

$$\begin{aligned} &\text{(a)} \quad Ly + \lambda r(x)y \equiv (p(x)y')' - q(x)y + \lambda r(x)y = 0, \\ &\text{(b)} \quad a_0 y(a) - a_1 p(a)y'(a) = 0, \qquad b_0 y(b) + b_1 p(b)y'(b) = 0. \end{aligned} \tag{5.1.1}$$

Here $p(x) > 0$, $r(x) > 0$, and $q(x) \geq 0$ while $p'(x)$, $q(x)$, and $r(x)$ are continuous on $[a, b]$. The constants a_ν and b_ν are nonnegative and at least one of each pair does not vanish. It is known that for such problems there exists an infinite sequence of nonnegative eigenvalues (see Problem 1.1)

$$0 \leq \lambda_1 < \lambda_2 < \lambda_3 \cdots. \tag{5.1.2a}$$

In addition there exist corresponding eigenfunctions, $y_n(x)$, which are twice continuously differentiable and satisfy the orthogonality relations:

$$\int_a^b y_n(x) y_m(x) r(x)\, dx = \delta_{nm}, \qquad n, m = 1, 2, \ldots. \tag{5.1.2b}$$

The normalization condition, (5.1.2b) with $n = m$, serves to make the eigenfunctions unique. It is also known that the nth eigenfunction has $n - 1$ distinct zeros in $a < x < b$. A proof of these results based on initial-value problems is contained in Coddington and Levinson (1955), pp. 189–190, 211–213.

We may relate the solution of (5.1.1) to an initial-value problem (just as in Section 2.2 for boundary-value problems). For any fixed λ we consider

$$\begin{aligned} &\text{(a)} \quad Lu + \lambda r(x) u = 0; \\ &\text{(b)} \quad a_0 u(a) - a_1 p(a) u'(a) = 0, \qquad c_0 u(a) - c_1 p(a) u'(a) = 1. \end{aligned} \tag{5.1.3}$$

Here c_0 and c_1 are any constants such that $(a_1 c_0 - a_0 c_1) \neq 0$. Then the two initial conditions in Equations (5.1.3b) are linearly independent and a unique nontrivial solution of the initial-value problem (5.1.3) exists. We denote this solution by $u(\lambda; x)$ and consider the (in general) transcendental equation

$$\phi(\lambda) \equiv b_0 u(\lambda; b) + b_1 p(b) u'(\lambda; b) = 0. \tag{5.1.4}$$

Clearly each eigenvalue λ_n in (5.1.2a) must satisfy this equation. Also every root, λ^*, of this equation is an eigenvalue of (5.1.1) and the corresponding solution $u(\lambda^*; x)$ of (5.1.3) is a corresponding eigenfunction of (5.1.1). We shall show, in Theorem 5.2.1, that the roots of (5.1.4) are simple. Note that the present analysis differs from the corresponding discussion of Section 1.2 only in that now a parameter in the equation must be adjusted and the adjoined initial condition remains fixed while previously the added initial condition was varied to satisfy the second boundary condition.

Of course the present considerations apply to eigenvalue problems more general than those in (5.1.1), for example, to problems in which the eigenvalue parameter λ enters into all of the coefficients of the equation and in the boundary conditions perhaps in a nonlinear way. Extensions to homogeneous systems of, say, m second-order equations with m parameters are also clearly suggested. We briefly discuss nonlinear eigenvalue problems in Section 5.5, that is, nonlinear boundary-value problems in which a parameter must be determined so that a solution exists (trivial or not).

To approximate the eigenvalues and eigenfunctions for problems of the form (5.1.1), and various generalizations of these problems, we may apply numerical methods which are exactly analogous to those used in Chapters 2, 3, and 4. But the proofs of convergence and estimates of the errors are now not always as easy to obtain as they were for the boundary-value problems. As with the boundary-value problems, the initial-value methods are more generally applicable and can easily yield higher-order-accurate approximations. The application of integral equation methods, in Section 5.4, automatically leads us to consider eigenvalue problems for integral equations which may not be associated with any particular Sturm-Liouville (or other) differential equation.

There are very important approximation methods for linear eigenvalue problems that are based on *variational principles.* These include some relevant numerical methods. But we do not discuss them here because the development of the required background should be done more carefully than can be done in our allotted space [see Collatz (1966), pp. 202–222].

Problems

5.1.1 (a) Show that the eigenvalues of (5.1.1) must be *nonnegative.* [HINT: Multiplying Equation (5.1.1a) by $y(x)$ and integrating, we get (since $r(x) > 0$ and $y(x) \not\equiv 0$)

$$\lambda = -\int_a^b y(x)Ly(x)\,dx \Big/ \int_a^b r(x)y^2(x)\,dx.$$

Use partial integration and the boundary conditions (5.1.1b) to show that the numerator is nonnegative since $p(x) > 0$, $q(x) \geq 0$, $a_0a_1 \geq 0$, and $b_0b_1 \geq 0$.]

(b) Show that the eigenvalues are *positive* if $a_0^2 + b_0^2 \neq 0$.

5.1.2 If $\lambda_n \neq \lambda_m$ are eigenvalues with corresponding eigenfunctions $y_n(x)$ and $y_m(x)$ of the problem (5.1.1), show that (5.1.2b) holds (for $n \neq m$). [HINT: Use partial integration in

$$\int_a^b (y_nLy_m - y_mLy_n)\,dx + (\lambda_m - \lambda_n)\int_a^b y_ny_mr(x)\,dx = 0.]$$

5.1.3 Use initial-value problems as in (5.1.3) to find the eigenvalues and eigenfunctions for the problem

$$y'' + \lambda y = 0, \qquad y'(a) = 0, \qquad y(b) = 0.$$

For example, require $y'(a) = 0$, $y(a) = 1$ and determine λ such that $y(b) = 0$.

5.2 Initial-Value Methods for Eigenvalue Problems

We consider the Sturm-Liouville problem (5.1.1), which has been reduced to finding the roots of Equation (5.1.4) and corresponding solutions of the initial-value problem (5.1.3). To approximate the solution of the initial-value problem (5.1.3) we first replace it by an equivalent first-order system, such as

$$u'(x) = \frac{v(x)}{p(x)}, \qquad u(a) = \frac{a_1}{a_1c_0 - a_0c_1};$$
$$v'(x) = [q(x) - \lambda r(x)]u(x), \qquad v(a) = \frac{a_0}{a_1c_0 - a_0c_1}. \tag{5.2.1}$$

The unique solution of this problem, for any λ, is denoted by

$$u(\lambda; x), \qquad v(\lambda; x);$$

and the equation (5.1.4) can be written as

$$\phi(\lambda) \equiv b_0u(\lambda; b) + b_1p(b)v(\lambda; b) = 0. \tag{5.2.2}$$

Now on some net, say a uniform net, for convenience, $x_j = jh + a$, $h = (b - a)/J$, we determine an approximate solution of (5.2.1) by one of the numerical procedures of Section 1.3. We denote this numerical solution for any fixed λ by

$$U_j(\lambda), \qquad V_j(\lambda); \qquad j = 0, 1, 2, \ldots.$$

If, as we assume, the numerical scheme is stable and has order of accuracy r and the solution of (5.2.1) is sufficiently smooth, then:

$$|U_j(\lambda) - u(\lambda; x_j)| \leq Mh^r, \qquad |V_j(\lambda) - v(\lambda; x_j)| \leq Mh^r. \tag{5.2.3}$$

Here the constant M is a bound on certain higher-order derivatives of u or v and thus depends upon the parameter λ; thus we write $M = M(\lambda)$. To approximate $\phi(\lambda)$ we use the numerical solution and define

$$\Phi(\lambda) \equiv b_0U_J(\lambda) + b_1p(b)V_J(\lambda). \tag{5.2.4}$$

From (5.2.2) and (5.2.3) it follows that, with $B \equiv b_0 + b_1 > 0$,

$$|\Phi(\lambda) - \phi(\lambda)| \leq BM(\lambda)h^r. \tag{5.2.5}$$

It is clear that, just as in Section 2.2, we can expect at best to approximate any eigenfunction to an accuracy of $\mathcal{O}(h^r)$. In fact we note that since the right-hand side of the system (5.2.1) is linear in λ, it follows by the remarks after (1.1.3) (or Theorem 1.1.3), that $u(\lambda; x)$ and $v(\lambda; x)$ are Lipschitz-continuous in λ. Then clearly for any λ and μ

$$\begin{aligned} |U_j(\lambda) - u(\mu; x_j)| &\le |U_j(\lambda) - u(\lambda; x_j)| + |u(\lambda; x_j) - u(\mu; x_j)| \\ &\le M(\lambda)h^r + K|\lambda - \mu|, \end{aligned} \tag{5.2.6a}$$

where K is the appropriate Lipschitz constant. A similar result applies for $v(\mu; x)$; that is,

$$|V_j(\lambda) - v(\mu; x_j)| \le M(\lambda)h^r + K|\lambda - \mu|. \tag{5.2.6b}$$

(This result is the analog of Lemma 2.2.1.) Thus, if $\mu = \lambda_n$ is an eigenvalue of (5.1.1) and $|\lambda - \lambda_n| = \mathcal{O}(h^r)$, then we actually obtain $\mathcal{O}(h^r)$ approximations to the eigenfunction $y_n(x) = u(\lambda_n; x)$, and its first derivative, $y_n'(x) = v(\lambda_n; x)/p(x)$.

To devise an iteration scheme for computing a root of (5.2.2) we first examine the derivative $d\phi(\lambda)/d\lambda \equiv \dot{\phi}(\lambda)$ at any root $\lambda = \lambda_n$. We have

THEOREM 5.2.1. *The roots* $\lambda = \lambda_n$ *of Equation* (5.2.2) *are simple; that is,* $\dot{\phi}(\lambda_n) \ne 0$, $n = 1, 2, \ldots$.

Proof. It follows from (5.2.1) and Theorem 1.1.3 that $\xi(\lambda; x) \equiv \partial u(\lambda; x)/\partial\lambda$ and $\eta(\lambda; x) \equiv \partial v(\lambda; x)/\partial\lambda$ exist, are continuous, and form the solution of the variational problem

$$\begin{aligned} \xi' &= p^{-1}(x)\eta, \qquad \xi(a) = 0; \\ \eta' &= [q(x) - \lambda r(x)]\xi - r(x)u(\lambda; x), \qquad \eta(a) = 0. \end{aligned} \tag{5.2.7}$$

Setting $\lambda = \lambda_n$, an eigenvalue of (5.1.1) and hence a root of Equation (5.2.2), we find that ξ satisfies

$$L\xi + \lambda_n r(x)\xi = -r(x)y_n(x), \qquad a_0\xi(a) - a_1 p(a)\xi'(a) = 0.$$

Now suppose that $\dot{\phi}(\lambda_n) = b_0\xi(b) + b_1 p(b)\xi'(b) = 0$. Then ξ is the solution of a linear *boundary*-value problem whose corresponding homogeneous problem has the nontrivial solution $y_n(x)$. Thus by the complete Alternative Theorem the inhomogeneous term, $-r(x)y_n(x)$, must be orthogonal to $y_n(x)$ (since L is self-adjoint) [see Courant and Hilbert (2) pp. 355–356]. This orthogonality condition now states that

$$\int_a^b r(x)y_n^2(x)\,dx = 0.$$

However this is impossible since $y_n(x) \not\equiv 0$ and $r(x) > 0$ [or see for instance (5.1.2b)]. Thus it follows that $\dot{\phi}(\lambda_n) \ne 0$. ∎

We now proceed to show that, at least in principle, every root of Equation (5.2.2) can be determined by iteration. For this purpose we may employ a different parameter, m_n, for each root and we write Equation (5.2.2), for each $n = 1, 2, \ldots$, as

$$\lambda = g_n(\lambda) \equiv \lambda - m_n\phi(\lambda). \tag{5.2.8a}$$

Then we consider the obvious functional iteration schemes, $\lambda_n^{(0)}$ = arbitrary and

$$\lambda_n^{(\nu+1)} = g_n(\lambda_n^{(\nu)}), \qquad \nu = 0, 1, 2, \ldots. \tag{5.2.8b}$$

For appropriate choices of m_n and $\lambda_n^{(0)}$ the sequence $\{\lambda_n^{(\nu)}\}$ will converge to the nth eigenvalue λ_n. This is essentially the content of (compare with Theorem 2.2.1)

THEOREM 5.2.2. *For each $n = 1, 2, \ldots$ there are constants $\rho_n > 0$, γ_n and Γ_n with $\gamma_n\Gamma_n > 0$ such that for any $\lambda_n^{(0)}$ in*

$$|\lambda_n - \lambda_n^{(0)}| \le (1 - K_n)\rho_n$$

and any m_n in

$$\begin{aligned} 0 < m_n < \frac{2}{\Gamma_n} \quad & \text{if} \quad \Gamma_n > 0, \\ \frac{2}{\Gamma} < m_n < 0 \quad & \text{if} \quad \Gamma_n < 0, \end{aligned} \tag{5.2.9a}$$

the iterates (5.2.8b) *converge to the eigenvalue λ_n. With the choice $m_n = 2/(\Gamma_n + \gamma_n)$ the iterates satisfy*

$$|\lambda_n^{(\nu)} - \lambda_n| \le \left[\frac{1 - (\gamma_n/\Gamma_n)}{1 + (\gamma_n/\Gamma_n)}\right]^\nu \frac{|\phi(\lambda_n^{(0)})|}{|\gamma_n|}, \qquad \nu = 1, 2, \ldots.$$

The magnitudes of γ_n and Γ_n are given by

$$\begin{aligned} |\gamma_n| &= \min_{|\lambda_n - \lambda| \le \rho_n} |b_0\xi(\lambda; b) + b_1p(b)\eta(\lambda; b)|, \\ |\Gamma_n| &= \max_{|\lambda_n - \lambda| \le \rho_n} |b_0\xi(\lambda; b) + b_1p(b)\eta(\lambda; b)|, \end{aligned} \tag{5.2.9b}$$

where ξ, η is the solution of (5.2.7) *and sign $\gamma_n \equiv$ sign $\Gamma_n \equiv$ sign $\dot\phi(\lambda_n)$. The constant K_n is $K_n \equiv \min(|1 - m_n\gamma_n|, |1 - m_n\Gamma_n|)$.*

Proof. By Theorem 5.2.1 we know that $\dot\phi(\lambda_n) \ne 0$ for each $n = 1, 2, \ldots$. But since the solution ξ, η of (5.2.7) depends continuously on λ it follows that

$$\dot\phi(\lambda) = b_0\xi(\lambda; b) + b_1p(b)\eta(\lambda; b) \tag{5.2.10}$$

is also a continuous function of λ. Then there is a neighborhood of each root in which $\dot\phi(\lambda)$ is bounded away from zero, let us say

$$\dot\phi(\lambda) \ne 0 \quad \text{for} \quad \lambda \text{ in } |\lambda - \lambda_n| \le \rho_n; \qquad n = 1, 2, \ldots.$$

Now we define γ_n and Γ_n as follows [that is, as in Equation (5.2.9a)]:

$$\text{sign}\,\gamma_n \equiv \text{sign}\,\Gamma_n \equiv \text{sign}\,\dot{\phi}(\lambda_n),$$
$$|\gamma_n| \equiv \min_{|\lambda-\lambda_n|\le\rho_n} |\dot{\phi}(\lambda)|, \qquad |\Gamma_n| \equiv \max_{|\lambda-\lambda_n|\le\rho_n} |\dot{\phi}(\lambda)|.$$

Of course it is clear from (5.1.2a) and the continuity of $\dot{\phi}(\lambda)$ that $(-1)^n\dot{\phi}(\lambda_n)$ has a fixed sign; thus the pairs (γ_n, Γ_n) will alternate in sign.

From the mean-value theorem it follows that for any λ and μ with g_n as defined in (5.2.8a)

$$g_n(\lambda) - g_n(\mu) = (\lambda - \mu) - m_n[\phi(\lambda) - \phi(\mu)],$$
$$= [1 - m_n\dot{\phi}(\mu + \theta(\lambda - \mu))](\lambda - \mu), \qquad 0 < \theta < 1.$$

Now let us restrict λ and μ to within ρ_n of λ_n and take m_n as specified in (5.2.9a). Then clearly $m_n\dot{\phi}\,(\mu + \theta(\lambda - \mu)) > 0$ and in this ρ_n neighborhood of λ_n the function $g_n(\lambda)$ satisfies a Lipschitz condition with constant

$$K_n = \max\,(|1 - m_n\gamma_n|, \qquad |1 - m_n\Gamma_n|) < 1,$$

since

$$0 < |\gamma_n| \le |\Gamma_n| \qquad \text{and} \qquad 0 < |m_n| < 2/|\Gamma_n|.$$

(With the choice $m_n = 2/(\Gamma_n + \gamma_n)$ we get $K_n = |\Gamma_n - \gamma_n|/|\Gamma_n + \gamma_n|$.)

Now the hypothesis of Theorem 1.4.1 applies, and the proof is concluded by applying this theorem. ∎

Of course we cannot evaluate $\phi(\lambda)$ exactly but rather the approximation $\Phi(\lambda)$ in (5.2.4). Thus the sequence of numerical approximations to the eigenvalue λ_n is actually defined in terms of $\lambda_n^{(0)}$ by

$$\lambda_n^{(\nu+1)} = \lambda_n^{(\nu)} - m_n\Phi(\lambda_n^{(\nu)}), \qquad \nu = 0, 1, \ldots. \tag{5.2.11}$$

But if $\lambda_n^{(0)}$ is sufficiently close to λ_n we can obtain, by this procedure, approximations to the nth eigenvalue, its corresponding eigenvector and the derivative of this eigenvector which are accurate to $\mathcal{O}(h^r)$. These results are from the following.

THEOREM 5.2.3. *Let* $|\lambda_n^{(0)} - \lambda_n| \le \rho_{n,0} \equiv \rho_n - M_nh^r$, *where* ρ_n *and* m_n *are as defined in Theorem 5.2.2 and*

$$M_n \equiv |m_n|B \max_{|\lambda-\lambda_n|\le\rho_n} M(\lambda).$$

Let $\lambda_n^{(\nu)}$ *be defined by* (5.2.11), *where* $U_j(\lambda_n^{(\nu)})$ *and* $V_j(\lambda_n^{(\nu)})$ *are numerical solutions of* (5.2.1) *using a stable scheme with order of accuracy r on the net* $x_j = a + jh$.

Then for some eigenfunction $y_n(x)$ of (5.1.1) *belonging to the eigenvalue* λ_n:

$$\left.\begin{aligned}&\text{(a)}\quad |\lambda_n^{(\nu)} - \lambda_n| \le \mathcal{O}(h^r) + \mathcal{O}(K_n^\nu),\\ &\text{(b)}\quad |U_j(\lambda_n^{(\nu)}) - y_n(x_j)| \le \mathcal{O}(h^r) + \mathcal{O}(K_n^\nu),\\ &\text{(c)}\quad |V_j(\lambda_n^{(\nu)}) - p(x_j)y_n'(x_j)| \le \mathcal{O}(h^r) + \mathcal{O}(K_n^\nu),\end{aligned}\right\}\begin{aligned}&\nu = 1, 2, \ldots,\\ &j = 1, 2, \ldots, J,\end{aligned} \tag{5.2.12}$$

where $0 < K_n < 1$ *is as defined in Theorem* 5.2.2.

Proof. We first note that by (5.2.5) and (5.2.8a) the iteration scheme (5.2.11) is of the form

$$\lambda_n^{(\nu+1)} = g_n(\lambda_n^{(\nu)}) + \delta_n^{(\nu)},$$

where

$$|\delta_n^{(\nu)}| \le M_n h^r.$$

But from the hypothesis and Theorem 5.2.2 it follows that Theorem 1.4.2 is applicable. Then from conclusion (b) of that theorem we get (5.2.12a).

Since the eigenfunction of (5.1.1) corresponding to an eigenvalue λ_n is nonunique to within an arbitrary scalar factor, we can take $y_n(x)$ such that

$$y_n(a) = u(\lambda_n; a), \qquad y_n'(a) = p^{-1}(a)v(\lambda_n; a),$$

where $u(\lambda_n; x)$, $v(\lambda_n; x)$ is the solution of (5.2.1) with $\lambda = \lambda_n$. Then clearly $y_n(x) \equiv u(\lambda_n; x)$, $y_n'(x) = p^{-1}(x)v(\lambda_n; x)$ and using (5.2.12a) in (5.2.6) with $\lambda = \lambda_n^{(\nu)}$ and $\mu = \lambda_n$ we obtain (5.2.12b–c). ∎

This result is of course quite similar to Theorem 2.2.2. Also, since K_n is independent of h, we can define an integer $\nu^* = \nu(h, r, K_n)$ such that

$$K_n^{\nu^*} \le h^r.$$

Then the error bounds in (5.2.12) are all $\mathcal{O}(h^r)$ for $\nu \ge \nu^*$.

While the above results furnish a theoretical justification for the initial-value method applied to Sturm-Liouville eigenvalue problems, they do not give practical estimates for the important parameters m_n or initial guesses $\lambda_n^{(0)}$. In practice these could be obtained by computing $\phi(\lambda)$ [really $\Phi(\lambda)$] to locate, roughly, sign changes and estimates of the slope $\dot{\phi}(\lambda)$ near these sign changes. If (as is most likely in such computations) a sequence of eigenvalues is desired, we can employ the value $m_{n+1} = -m_n$ as a reasonable (first) estimate for m_{n+1}.

Of course higher-order iteration schemes would be preferable, particularly when many eigenvalues are to be computed, and Newton's method is a reasonable choice. Thus in place of (5.2.8) we would use, given $\lambda_n^{(0)}$,

$$\lambda_n^{(\nu+1)} = \lambda_n^{(\nu)} - \frac{\phi(\lambda_n^{(\nu)})}{\dot{\phi}(\lambda_n^{(\nu)})}, \qquad \nu = 0, 1, 2, \ldots. \tag{5.2.13}$$

The derivative $\dot{\phi}(\lambda)$ is given by (5.2.10), in terms of the solution of the variational problem (5.2.7). Thus while solving the initial-value problem (5.2.1) numerically to compute $\Phi(\lambda_n^{(\nu)})$, the approximation to $\phi(\lambda_n^{(\nu)})$, we also solve (5.2.7) numerically to compute an approximation to $\dot{\phi}(\lambda_n^{(\nu)})$. It is quite clear in this case that very little extra computation is required to solve the variational problem, as all the coefficients must be evaluated previously in order to solve (5.2.1). Thus Newton's method is quite efficient for such problems.

Problems

5.2.1 Calculate the first seven eigenvalues of the problem

$$y'' + \lambda y = 0, \qquad y'(0) = y(2) = 0,$$

using shooting with: (a) functional iteration and (b) Newton's method. [See following problem for part (a).]

5.2.2 Show in detail how Theorem 5.2.2 applies in the above when the initial conditions used are

$$u'(0) = 0, \qquad u(0) = 1.$$

Verify in particular that the iterations (5.2.8) converge for the nth eigenvalue, provided that

$$0 < |m_n| < \frac{\sqrt{(2n-1)\pi}}{2}, \qquad (-1)^n m_n > 0, \qquad n = 1, 2, \ldots;$$

and the initial guess $\lambda_n^{(0)}$ is such that

$$|\sqrt{\lambda_n} - \sqrt{\lambda_n^{(0)}}| < \pi/4.$$

[Try using the value $m_n = (-1)^n\sqrt{(2n-1)\pi}/2$ in the calculations of part (a) in Problem 5.2.1.]

5.2.3 The nth positive zero, k_n, of the Bessel function $J_0(x)$ is the square root of the nth eigenvalue of

$$\frac{1}{x}(xy')' + k^2 y = 0, \qquad y'(0) = y(1) = 0.$$

Compute the first four such roots by the shooting method and compare them to the first four zeros of the solution of the initial-value problem

$$\frac{1}{x}(xJ_0')' + J_0 = 0; \qquad J(0) = 1, \qquad J_0'(0) = 0.$$

5.2.4 Show that Newton's method, as formulated in (5.2.13), for finding the eigenvalues of the problem

$$(*) \qquad y'' + \lambda^2 y = 0, \qquad y(0) = y(1) = 0$$

can be equivalent to using Newton's method for computing the roots of

$$\sin \lambda = 0$$

or of

$$\frac{\sin \lambda}{\lambda} = 0.$$

[HINT: Consider the initial-value problem

$$u' = \lambda v, \qquad u(0) = 0; \qquad v' = -\lambda u, \qquad v(0) = 1;$$

and the more obvious system equivalent to (*) suggested by (5.2.1).]

5.3 Finite-Difference Methods for Eigenvalue Problems

To study difference methods for eigen-problems we shall consider a slightly-less-general problem than that treated in the previous section. More general problems will then be covered in the exercises at the end of the section. Some of the present analysis in fact easily extends to partial differential equations. We consider first the problem

$$\begin{aligned} &\text{(a)}\quad Ly + \lambda y \equiv (p(x)y')' - q(x)y + \lambda y = 0; \\ &\text{(b)}\quad y(a) = 0, \qquad y(b) = 0; \end{aligned} \tag{5.3.1}$$

where $p(x) > 0$, $p'(x)$ and $q(x)$ are continuous, and $q(x) \geq 0$. This is a special case of (5.1.1) and so the eigenvalues and eigenvectors have the properties stated in and after (5.1.2).

Now we employ the uniform net

$$x_j = a + jh, \qquad j = 0, 1, \ldots, J + 1; \qquad h \equiv \frac{(b - a)}{J + 1},$$

and replace (5.3.1) by some finite-difference equations of the form

$$\begin{aligned} &\text{(a)}\quad L_h u_j + \Lambda u_j = 0, \qquad j = 1, 2, \ldots, J; \\ &\text{(b)}\quad u_0 = 0, \qquad u_{J+1} = 0. \end{aligned} \tag{5.3.2}$$

Here L_h is a "difference approximation" of the linear differential operator L, which for the present we take to be

$$L_h u_j \equiv \frac{1}{h}\left\{p\left(x_j + \frac{h}{2}\right)\left[\frac{u_{j+1} - u_j}{h}\right] - p\left(x_j - \frac{h}{2}\right)\left[\frac{u_j - u_{j-1}}{h}\right]\right\} - q(x_j)u_j. \tag{5.3.3a}$$

This can be written as

$$h^2 L_h u_j \equiv a_j u_{j-1} + b_j u_j + c_j u_{j+1}; \tag{5.3.3b}$$

$$a_j \equiv p\left(x_j - \frac{h}{2}\right), \qquad c_j \equiv p\left(x_j + \frac{h}{2}\right), \qquad b_j = -[a_j + c_j + h^2 q(x_j)]. \tag{5.3.3c}$$

The net function $\{u_j\}$ is intended to be an approximation, on the net, to some eigenfunction of (5.3.1), and the scalar Λ in (5.3.2) is intended to be an approximation to some corresponding eigenvalue λ.

Let us formulate the system (5.3.2) in vector form. We introduce the J-dimensional column vector $\mathbf{u}$ and Jth order square matrix A by

$$\mathbf{u} \equiv \begin{pmatrix} u_1 \\ u_2 \\ \vdots \\ u_J \end{pmatrix}; \tag{5.3.4a}$$

$$\begin{aligned} A \equiv (a_{i,j}), \qquad a_{j,j-1} &= -a_j, \qquad a_{j,j} = -b_j, \\ a_{j,j+1} = -c_j, \qquad a_{i,j} &= 0 \quad \text{if} \quad |i - j| > 1. \end{aligned} \tag{5.3.4b}$$

Then multiplying Equation (5.3.2a) by $(-h^2)$ and using (5.3.3) and (5.3.4) we obtain

$$A\mathbf{u} - h^2 \Lambda \mathbf{u} = 0. \tag{5.3.5}$$

Thus we find that our difference problem (5.3.2) is just an eigenvalue-eigenvector problem for the matrix A. But from Equations (5.3.3c) we note that $c_j = a_{j+1}$ for $j = 1, 2, \ldots, J - 1$, and so from (5.3.4b) we have $a_{j,j+1} = a_{j,j-1}$. Thus we conclude that A is a *symmetric* tridiagonal matrix. It is also rather easy to deduce that A is *positive definite* but since we do not use this fact directly it is posed as Problem 5.3.5.

There are very effective procedures for calculating the eigenvalues and eigenvectors of symmetric tridiagonal matrices. In particular we advocate using the Sturm sequence property of the principal minors of the matrix

$$(A - \mu I)$$

to locate the eigenvalues and then using the method of bisection to determine them accurately [see Wilkinson, pp. 299–302]. If many eigenvalues are to be determined a more rapidly converging iteration scheme may be employed. After accurate approximations to the required eigenvalues are obtained, the corresponding eigenvectors can be computed quite effectively by "inverse iteration"; that is, with $\mathbf{u}_0$ arbitrary and μ the approximation to an eigenvalue $h^2\Lambda$, we define a sequence of vectors $\{\mathbf{u}_\nu\}$ by

$$(A - \mu I)\mathbf{u}_{\nu+1} = \mathbf{u}_\nu, \qquad \nu = 0, 1, \ldots.$$

Of course the matrix $A - \mu I$ is near-singular and so one must take some care in solving these systems, that is, using Gauss elimination with maximal pivots and *not* the simple factorization (3.1.7). But in practice, only two or three iterations are required to determine the eigenvectors accurately [see Wilkinson, pp. 321–323].

Let us consider now the possible accuracy of the determination of any particular eigenvalue of (5.3.1). We first note that there are only J eigenvalues of the system (5.3.5). Thus, there is a problem of identifying what exact eigenvalue, λ, is being approximated by what approximate eigenvalue, Λ. Clearly, for any fixed J there are denumerably many exact eigenvalues which cannot be approximated well by any of the Λ. These points will be clarified in our error estimates.

First however we must define the error in "approximating" L by L_h. For any sufficiently smooth function, $\phi(x)$, say in the present case with four continuous derivatives, we define at the points of the net the local truncation errors

$$\tau_j\{\phi\} \equiv L_h\phi(x_j) - L\phi(x_j), \qquad j = 1, 2, \ldots, J. \tag{5.3.6a}$$

It follows that if $p'''(x)$ is continuous, then with L_h as defined in (5.3.3a)

$$\tau_j\{\phi\} = \mathcal{O}(h^2). \tag{5.3.6b}$$

The verification of this fact is contained in Problem 5.3.1.

Now let λ be some fixed eigenvalue of (5.3.1) with corresponding eigenfunction $y(x)$. From the definition (5.3.6a) and (5.3.1) we then have at the points of the net

$$\begin{aligned} &\text{(a)}\quad L_h y(x_j) + \lambda y(x_j) = \tau_j\{y\}, \qquad j = 1, 2, \ldots, J;\\ &\text{(b)}\quad y(x_0) = 0, \qquad y(x_{J+1}) = 0. \end{aligned} \tag{5.3.7}$$

Using the matrix A defined by (5.3.4b) and (5.3.3c), the above system can be written in vector form as

$$A\mathbf{y} - h^2\lambda\mathbf{y} = -h^2\boldsymbol{\tau}\{y\}. \tag{5.3.8}$$

Here we have introduced the J-dimensional vectors

$$\mathbf{y} \equiv \begin{pmatrix} y(x_1) \\ y(x_2) \\ \vdots \\ y(x_J) \end{pmatrix}, \qquad \boldsymbol{\tau}\{y\} \equiv \begin{pmatrix} \tau_1\{y\} \\ \tau_2\{y\} \\ \vdots \\ \tau_J\{y\} \end{pmatrix}.$$

Finally, let us recall the norms for any J-dimensional vector $\mathbf{v}$ with components v_j:

$$\|\mathbf{v}\| \equiv (\mathbf{v}, \mathbf{v})^{1/2} \equiv \left(\sum_{j=1}^{J} v_j^2\right)^{1/2}, \qquad \|\mathbf{v}\|_\infty \equiv \max_{1 \le j \le J} |v_j|. \tag{5.3.9}$$

For fixed λ, either the matrix $(A - h^2\lambda I)$ is nonsingular or else $h^2\lambda$ is an eigenvalue of A. In the former case we find from (5.3.8) that

$$\mathbf{y} = -h^2(A - h^2\lambda I)^{-1}\boldsymbol{\tau}\{y\},$$

and taking norms implies

$$\|\mathbf{y}\| \le h^2\|(A - h^2\lambda I)^{-1}\| \cdot \|\tau\{y\}\|. \tag{5.3.10}$$

Since A is symmetric, so is $(A - h^2\lambda I)^{-1}$, and the natural matrix norm above is the spectral norm. That is, in terms of the eigenvalues $h^2\Lambda_j$ of A,

$$\|(A - h^2\lambda I)^{-1}\| = \max_{1 \le j \le J} \left(\frac{1}{h^2|\Lambda_j - \lambda|}\right).$$

Using this result we obtain, from (5.3.10),

$$\min_{1 \le j \le J} |\Lambda_j - \lambda| \le \frac{\|\boldsymbol{\tau}\{y\}\|}{\|\mathbf{y}\|}.$$

Here we have assumed that the net points x_j are not all at nodes of the eigenfunction $y(x)$. This merely requires that h be sufficiently small, since the nth eigenfunction has at most $n - 1$ internal nodes. If $h^2\lambda$ is an eigenvalue of A the relation above holds trivially. Thus we have deduced in general the following.

THEOREM 5.3.1. *For each fixed eigenvalue* λ *of* (5.3.1) *with corresponding eigenfunction* $y(x)$, *there exists an eigenvalue, say* $h^2\Lambda$, *of* A *such that for* h *sufficiently small*

$$|\Lambda - \lambda| \le \frac{\|\boldsymbol{\tau}\{y\}\|}{\|\mathbf{y}\|}. \quad \blacksquare \tag{5.3.11}$$

From this result we can obtain estimates of the error in the maximum norm $\|\boldsymbol{\tau}\{y\}\|_\infty$. For this purpose, we use the normalized eigenfunction, that is, $\int_a^b y^2(x)\,dx = 1$. Then since $y(x_0) = y(x_{J+1}) = 0$, we have, by the normalization,

$$\begin{aligned} h\|\mathbf{y}\|^2 &= \left\{\sum_{i=1}^{J} hy^2(x_j) + \frac{y^2(x_0) + y^2(x_{J+1})}{2}h - \int_{x_0}^{x_{J+1}} y^2(x)\,dx\right\} + 1 \\ &= 1 + \frac{b-a}{12} y''(\xi)h^2, \qquad \xi \in [a, b]. \end{aligned}$$

Here we have employed the error in the trapezoidal rule [see Isaacson and

Keller (1966), p. 339]. We also see that, since $(J + 1)h = b - a$, we have

$$h\|\boldsymbol{\tau}\|^2 = h \sum_{i=1}^{J} \tau_j^2\{y\} \leq (b - a)\|\boldsymbol{\tau}\{y\}\|_\infty^2.$$

Using the above results, we deduce from (5.3.11) that

$$|\Lambda - \lambda| \leq \sqrt{b - a}\, \|\boldsymbol{\tau}(y\}\|_\infty \Big/ \left(1 + \frac{b - a}{12} y''(\xi)h^2\right)^{1/2}. \qquad (5.3.12)$$

Now (5.3.6b) implies that

$$|\Lambda - \lambda| \leq \mathcal{O}(h^2). \qquad (5.3.13)$$

Thus we find that as $h \to 0$ *any fixed eigenvalue*, λ, *of the problem* (5.3.1) *is approximated by some eigenvalue of the difference problem* (5.3.2) *with an error that is* $\mathcal{O}(h^2)$. Of course for any fixed h the bound (5.3.12) is still applicable. Then if λ is chosen as one of the very large eigenvalues, $|\Lambda - \lambda|$ must also be large for all Λ. But this is consistent with (5.3.12), since $\|\boldsymbol{\tau}\{y\}\|_\infty$ then becomes large. We recall that the higher eigenfunctions oscillate more rapidly in $[a, b]$ and thus in general will have derivatives of increasing magnitude. In the present case the fourth-order derivatives of $y(x)$ enter into the determination of the $\tau_j\{y\}$.

The procedures above can be extended to derive possibly higher-order-accurate approximations than the $\mathcal{O}(h^2)$ one in (5.3.13). In fact the only property of the matrix A that was used in deriving (5.3.11) and (5.3.12) is its symmetry. Thus we can state the more general result:

THEOREM 5.3.2. *Let the difference operator* L_h *in* (5.3.2) *be such that in the equivalent vector system* (5.3.5) *the coefficient matrix* A *is symmetric. Then for each eigenvalue* λ *of* (5.3.1) *and corresponding normalized eigenfunction* $y(x)$ *there exists an eigenvalue* $h^2\Lambda$ *of* A *such that* (5.3.11) *and* (5.3.12) *hold.* ∎

The above results can be generalized and extended in a number of important directions. Consider first the slightly more general eigenvalue problem

$$Ly + \lambda r(x)y = 0, \qquad y(a) = y(b) = 0. \qquad (5.3.14)$$

Here L is as defined in (5.3.1a) and $r(x) > 0$ is continuous on $[a, b]$. On the net $\{x_j\}$ we consider the more general difference approximation $u_0 = u_{J+1} = 0$;

$$L_h u_j + \Lambda M_h u_j = 0, \qquad j = 1, 2, \ldots, J. \qquad (5.3.15)$$

Here $L_h u_j$ could be as defined in (5.3.3a) and $M_h u_j$ is some other difference expression which is an approximation to $r(x_j)y(x_j)$ (see Problem 5.3.2). If

M_h is represented by a tridiagonal positive definite matrix then the Sturm-sequence and inverse-iteration methods previously mentioned can be used to find the eigenvalues and eigenvectors of the system (5.3.15) or (5.3.17a) [see Wilkinson, pp. 340–341]. The local truncation error for this approximation is now defined, for an eigenvector $y(x)$ belonging to the eigenvalue λ, as

$$\tau_j\{\lambda, y\} \equiv [L_h y(x_j) - Ly(x_j)] + \lambda[M_h y(x_j) - r(x_j)y(x_j)], \qquad 1 \le j \le J. \tag{5.3.16}$$

Now using (5.3.14) at the net points x_j we have

$$L_h y(x_j) + \lambda M_h y(x_j) = \tau_j\{\lambda, y\}, \qquad 1 \le j \le J.$$

This system and (5.3.15) can be written in vector form as

$$\begin{aligned} &\text{(a)} \quad A\mathbf{u} - h^2\Lambda B\mathbf{u} = 0; \\ &\text{(b)} \quad A\mathbf{y} - h^2\lambda B\mathbf{y} = h^2\boldsymbol{\tau}\{\lambda, y\}. \end{aligned} \tag{5.3.17}$$

Here $\mathbf{u}$, $\mathbf{y}$, and $\boldsymbol{\tau}$ are as previously defined and A and B are the matrices corresponding to the difference operators $-h^2L_h$ and M_h respectively. We now have the following.

THEOREM 5.3.3. *Let L_h and M_h in* (5.3.15) *be such that A is symmetric and B is symmetric-positive-definite. Then for each eigenvalue λ of* (5.3.14) *and corresponding normalized eigenfunction $y(x)$, there exists an eigenvalue $h^2\Lambda$ of $B^{-1}A$ such that*

$$|\Lambda - \lambda| \le \|B^{-1}\| \frac{\|\boldsymbol{\tau}\{\lambda, y\}\|}{\|\mathbf{y}\|}.$$

Proof. By the properties of A and B it is known that there exists a basis for the J-dimensional space, $\{\mathbf{e}_j\}$, such that

$$A\mathbf{e}_j = h^2\Lambda_j B\mathbf{e}_j, \qquad (B\mathbf{e}_j, \mathbf{e}_k) = \delta_{jk}; \qquad j, k = 1, 2, \ldots, J.$$

Now let $\mathbf{y}$ be expanded in these basis vectors, say

$$\mathbf{y} = \sum_{j=1}^{J} \xi_j \mathbf{e}_j.$$

Then using this representation in (5.3.17b), we form

$$\frac{h^4(B^{-1}\boldsymbol{\tau}, \boldsymbol{\tau})}{(B\mathbf{y}, \mathbf{y})} = \sum_{j=1}^{J} h^4(\Lambda_j - \lambda)^2 \frac{\xi_j^2}{\sum_{k=1}^{J} \xi_k^2}.$$

On the right we have a sum with nonnegative coefficients of sum unity and, hence, for some $\Lambda_j = \Lambda$ we have

$$|\Lambda - \lambda| \le \frac{(B^{-1}\boldsymbol{\tau}, \boldsymbol{\tau})^{1/2}}{(B\mathbf{y}, \mathbf{y})^{1/2}}.$$

But for any matrix M and vector $\mathbf{x}$ we have (in any norm)

$$\|M\| \geq \frac{|(M\mathbf{x}, \mathbf{x})|}{(\mathbf{x}, \mathbf{x})}.$$

Thus $(B^{-1}\boldsymbol{\tau}, \boldsymbol{\tau})^{1/2} \leq \|B^{-1}\|^{1/2} \cdot \|\boldsymbol{\tau}\|$ and the spectral norm of B^{-1} is implied here. Further, since B is symmetric-positive-definite, $\|B^{-1}\| = 1/\beta_1$, where β_1 is the least eigenvalue of B. It is also well known that, for any vector $\mathbf{x} \neq 0$,

$$\beta_1 \leq \frac{(B\mathbf{x}, \mathbf{x})}{(\mathbf{x}, \mathbf{x})},$$

and the theorem now follows. ∎

This more general result allows greater flexibility in devising difference approximations which have higher-order accuracy (see Problem 5.3.4).

Problems

5.3.1 Use Taylor's theorem to find an expression for

$$L\phi(x) - L_h\phi(x),$$

where L is as defined in (5.3.1a), L_h is as defined in (5.3.3a), and p, q, ϕ are as smooth as desired.

5.3.2 With L and L_h as above, find at least two difference operators M_h such that

$$[L\phi + \lambda r(x)\phi] - [L_h\phi + \lambda M_h\phi] = \mathcal{O}(h^2).$$

5.3.3 Find explicit expressions for the eigenvalues and eigenvectors of the difference scheme

$$u_{j-1} - 2u_j + u_{j+1} = h^2\Lambda u_j, \qquad 1 \leq j \leq N;$$
$$u_0 = u_{N+1} = 0, \qquad h = \pi/(N + 1).$$

Compare them with the eigenvalues and eigenfunctions of

$$y'' + \lambda y = 0, \qquad y(0) = y(\pi) = 0.$$

[HINT: Seek a solution of the difference equations in the form $u_j = \alpha^j$, and obtain two values $\alpha_\pm$ for which such solutions exist. Take a linear combination $u_j = A\alpha_+^j + B\alpha_-^j$ and determine the coefficients and Λ to satisfy the boundary conditions, $u_0 = u_{N+1} = 0$.]

5.3.4 (a) Devise a difference scheme for $y'' + \lambda y = 0$, $y(0) = y(1) = 0$ which yields $\mathcal{O}(h^4)$ approximations to the eigenvalues. Does this procedure necessarily yield such accuracy when applied to $y'' + \lambda r(x)y = 0$?

(b) Find the eigenvalues of the difference scheme and verify directly, with a comparison to $\lambda_n = n^2\pi^2$, that they are actually $\mathcal{O}(h^4)$. What about the eigenvectors?

5.3.5 For the matrix A as defined by (5.3.4b) and (5.3.3c), form the inner product $(A\mathbf{u}, \mathbf{u}) = \sum_i \sum_j a_{ij}u_iu_j$ and show that $(A\mathbf{u}, \mathbf{u}) > 0$ if $(\mathbf{u}, \mathbf{u}) > 0$; that is, show that A is positive-definite. [HINT: By proper arrangement of the sum show that

$$(A\mathbf{u}, \mathbf{u}) = \sum_{j=1}^{J} h^2(q_ju_j^2 + b_j(u_j - u_{j-1})^2) + c_Ju_J^2.]$$

5.3.6 Compute the first four eigenvalues of the example in Problem 5.2.3 by using finite differences. Vary the number of net points used and compare the results with those obtained by shooting with the same net spacing.

5.4 Eigenvalue Problems for Integral Equations

In Section 4.1 we showed how a boundary-value problem may be replaced by equivalent integral equations with the aid of various Green's functions. This procedure can also be used to convert eigenvalue problems for differential equations into eigenvalue problems for integral equations. Thus let $g(x, \xi)$ be the Green's function for the differential operator L in (5.1.1a) subject to the boundary conditions (5.1.1b). Then, treating the term $\lambda r(x)y(x)$ in (5.1.1a) as an inhomogeneous term, we see that any solution of (5.1.1) must satisfy the integral equation

$$y(x) = \lambda \int_a^b g(x, \xi)r(\xi)y(\xi)\, d\xi. \tag{5.4.1}$$

Conversely, if $y(x)$ is a nontrivial solution of (5.4.1) for some value of λ, we easily find by differentiation that this function must be an eigenfunction of (5.1.1) corresponding to the eigenvalue λ.

It is not difficult to show that the Green's function is symmetric, that is,

$$g(x, \xi) = g(\xi, x)$$

if the operator L and boundary conditions are self-adjoint. This is in fact the case for the problem at hand [see Courant and Hilbert (1953), p. 354]. Since $r(x) > 0$ on $[a, b]$ we can introduce a new variable and new kernel defined by

$$z(x) \equiv \sqrt{r(x)}\, y(x), \qquad k(x, \xi) \equiv \sqrt{r(x)}\, g(x, \xi)\sqrt{r(\xi)},$$

and, on multiplying Equation (5.4.1) by $\sqrt{r(x)}$, we obtain the *symmetric integral equation*

$$z(x) = \lambda \int_a^b k(x, \xi)z(\xi)\, d\xi. \tag{5.4.2}$$

Of course, the term "symmetric" applies to the kernel which satisfies, by virtue of the symmetry of the Green's function,

$$k(x, \xi) = k(\xi, x). \tag{5.4.3}$$

We shall now examine some numerical methods for solving general symmetric integral-equation problems of the form (5.4.2), not only those that arise from differential-equation problems. To insure that we include the latter problems we simply assume that the symmetric kernel, $k(x, y)$, is continuous in $a \le x, y \le b$. Under these conditions it is known that all the eigenvalues of (5.4.2) are real and denumerable in number, and that the corresponding eigenfunctions are continuous and orthogonal [see Courant and Hilbert (1953), pp. 122–132, and Problems 5.4.1 and 5.4.2]. It is obvious from Equation (5.4.2) that $\lambda = 0$ cannot be an eigenvalue, since the eigenfunctions are nontrivial by definition.

The numerical methods to be employed are essentially those of Section 4.2. Thus we introduce the arbitrarily-spaced net points ξ_j, $j = 1, 2, \ldots, J$ such that

$$a \le \xi_1 < \xi_2 < \cdots < \xi_J \le b.$$

These points are the nodes for a quadrature formula of the form

$$Q_J\{f(\xi)\} \equiv \sum_{j=1}^{J} \alpha_j f(\xi_j), \tag{5.4.4a}$$

which is to approximate an integral of the form

$$Q\{f(\xi)\} \equiv \int_a^b f(\xi)\, d\xi. \tag{5.4.4b}$$

Again we require that the quadrature scheme satisfy

$$\begin{aligned} &\text{(a)} \quad \alpha_j > 0, \qquad j = 1, 2, \ldots, J \\ &\text{(b)} \quad \lim_{J\to\infty} E_J\{f(\xi)\} \equiv \lim_{J\to\infty} [Q\{f(\xi)\} - Q_J\{(\xi)\}] = 0, \end{aligned} \tag{5.4.5}$$

for all functions $f(\xi)$ continuous on $[a, b]$.

To approximate the eigenvalues λ, and corresponding eigenfunctions $z(x)$, of (5.4.2), we seek nontrivial net functions $\{u_j\}$ and parameters, Λ, which satisfy the algebraic system

$$u_i = \Lambda \sum_{j=1}^{J} \alpha_j k(x_i, \xi_j) u_j, \qquad i = 1, 2, \ldots, J. \tag{5.4.6}$$

This is clearly a matrix eigenvalue problem, but in its present form the appropriate matrix is not necessarily symmetric. However, the system is easily symmetrized, in exact analogy with the treatment of (5.4.1), since the quadrature coefficients α_j are required to be positive. Thus we introduce the quantities

$$v_j \equiv \sqrt{\alpha_j}\, u_j, \qquad b_{ij} \equiv \sqrt{\alpha_i}\, k(x_i, x_j)\sqrt{\alpha_j}, \qquad i, j = 1, 2, \ldots, J \tag{5.4.7}$$

and (5.4.6) becomes, on multiplication by $\sqrt{\alpha_i}$,

$$v_i = \Lambda \sum_{j=1}^{J} b_{ij} v_j, \qquad i = 1, 2, \ldots, J. \tag{5.4.8a}$$

In matrix notation this can be written as

$$\mathbf{v} = \Lambda B \mathbf{v}, \tag{5.4.8b}$$

where the vector $\mathbf{v}$ and J-order matrix B are defined by

$$\mathbf{v} \equiv \begin{pmatrix} v_1 \\ v_2 \\ \vdots \\ v_J \end{pmatrix}, \qquad B \equiv (b_{ij}). \tag{5.4.9}$$

It is quite clear from the symmetry of the kernel, shown in Equation (5.4.3), that $b_{ij} = b_{ji}$ and so B is symmetric.

The computational problem is thus reduced to finding the eigenvalues, Λ^{-1}, and eigenvectors, $\mathbf{v}$, of the symmetric matrix B. Of course this matrix, in contrast to A in (5.3.4b), does not have any particularly simple structure (other than symmetry) to facilitate these computations. But there are procedures, by now standard, for reducing symmetric matrices to the tridiagonal form by means of a sequence of orthogonal transformations. In particular, the scheme devised by Householder is quite efficient and relatively accurate [see Wilkinson (1965), pp. 290–293]. The procedure of Section 5.3 can then be used to compute the eigenvalues and eigenvectors of the equivalent tridiagonal matrix. By transforming these eigenvectors with the inverses of the above orthogonal matrices, the eigenvectors of B are finally obtained (*ibid.*, p. 333).

We turn now to the problem of estimating the accuracy of the approximate eigenvalues, Λ. Our results are quite similar to the estimates obtained in Section 5.3. The basic result can be stated as follows.

THEOREM 5.4.1. *Let λ be any fixed eigenvalue of the integral equation* (5.4.2) *and $z(x)$ be a corresponding normalized eigenfunction, that is, $\int_a^b z^2(x)\,dx = 1$. Then for J sufficiently large there exists an eigenvalue Λ^{-1} of the matrix B in* (5.4.9) *such that*

$$|\Lambda^{-1} - \lambda^{-1}|^2 \leq \frac{\sum_{i=1}^{J} \alpha_i E_J^2\{k(x_i, \xi) z(\xi)\}}{1 + E_J\{z^2(\xi)\}}. \tag{5.4.10}$$

Proof. From the definition of the quadrature error, $E_J\{\cdot\}$, in (5.4.5b), we can write Equation (5.4.2) at each point $x = x_i$ as

$$z(x_i) = \lambda \sum_{j=1}^{J} \alpha_j k(x_i, \xi_j) z(\xi_j) + \lambda E_J\{k(x_i, \xi) z(\xi)\}, \qquad i = 1, 2, \ldots, J.$$

Multiplying through by $\lambda^{-1}\sqrt{\alpha_i}$ and introducing the quantities

$$w_i \equiv \sqrt{\alpha_i}\, z(x_i), \qquad \tau_i \equiv \sqrt{\alpha_i}\, E_J\{k(x_i, \xi) z(\xi)\},$$

we obtain in vector form the system

$$(B - \lambda^{-1} I)\mathbf{w} = -\boldsymbol{\tau}.$$

Now by the argument that led to Theorem 5.3.1 we conclude that for some eigenvalue Λ^{-1} of the symmetric matrix B

$$|\Lambda^{-1} - \lambda^{-1}| \leq \frac{\|\boldsymbol{\tau}\|}{\|\mathbf{w}\|}.$$

Finally, the normalization of $z(x)$ implies

$$\|\mathbf{w}\|^2 = \sum_{i=1}^{J} \alpha_i z^2(x_i) = 1 + E_J\{z^2(\xi)\},$$

and the theorem follows. ▮

We thus find that any fixed eigenvalue of the symmetric integral equation (5.4.2) can be approximated to an accuracy proportional to the error in the quadrature formula employed. Since the quadrature scheme is to satisfy (5.4.5b), then (5.4.10) implies, as $J \to \infty$,

$$|\Lambda^{-1} - \lambda^{-1}| \leq [\sqrt{b - a} + 0(1)] \max_{1 \leq i \leq J} |E_J\{k(x_i, \xi) z(\xi)\}|. \qquad (5.4.11)$$

But we must recall that the integrands, $k(x_i, \xi)z(\xi)$, may not have the smoothness properties required for the validity of the usual error expressions for standard quadrature formulae. For instance, if, as might seem reasonable, we use a J-point Gaussian quadrature scheme, then the familiar error estimate is valid only if the integrand has $2J$ continuous derivatives. Of course, as we said before, such higher-order-accurate schemes can still furnish accurate approximations.

Problems

5.4.1 The kernel $k(x, \xi)$ in Equation (5.4.2) is said to be *positive-definite* if

$$\int_a^b \int_a^b k(x, \xi)\phi(x)\phi(\xi)\, dx\, d\xi > 0$$

for all continuous nonvanishing functions on $[a, b]$. Prove that all eigenvalues of Equation (5.4.2) are *positive* if the kernel is positive-definite.

5.4.2 Prove that with $a_0^2 + b_0^2 \neq 0$ in Equation (5.1.1b) the kernel in Equation (5.4.1) is positive-definite when symmetrized, that is, that $k(x, \xi) \equiv g(x, \xi)\sqrt{r(x)r(\xi)}$ is positive-definite. [HINT: Since $r(x) > 0$ it suffices to show that, for all continuous $\psi(x)$ on $[a, b]$,

$$\int_a^b \int_a^b g(x, \xi)\psi(x)\psi(\xi)\, dx\, d\xi > 0.$$

But $\int_a^b g(x, \xi)\psi(\xi)\, d\xi \equiv y(x)$ must be the solution of $Ly(x) = -\psi(x)$ subject to the boundary conditions (5.1.1b). Now proceed as in Problem 5.1.1.]

5.5 Generalized Eigenvalue Problems

We discuss here a class of problems which embraces all of those previously studied. These are boundary-value problems, nonlinear in general, which contain two types of parameters (or rather of parameter sets). The first set, which we denote by an m-vector $\boldsymbol{\lambda} \equiv (\lambda_1, \lambda_2, \ldots, \lambda_m)^T$, correspond to an eigenvalue in that they are to be determined so that the boundary-value problem has a solution (trivial or not in the nonlinear case). The second set of parameters, denoted by a q-vector, $\boldsymbol{\sigma} \equiv (\sigma_1, \sigma_2, \ldots, \sigma_q)^T$, represent given data on which the solution and eigenvalue depend. (This dependence is usually sought for some specified set of $\boldsymbol{\sigma}$ values.) The boundary-value problem is now formulated as

$$\mathbf{y}' = \mathbf{f}(x, \mathbf{y}; \boldsymbol{\lambda}, \boldsymbol{\sigma}), \qquad a < x < b, \tag{5.5.1a}$$

$$E\mathbf{y}(a) + F\mathbf{y}(b) = \boldsymbol{\gamma}. \tag{5.5.1b}$$

Here $\mathbf{y}$ and $\mathbf{f}$ are n-vectors, E and F are matrices with $(m + n)$ rows and n columns and $\boldsymbol{\gamma}$ is an $(n + m)$-vector.

We have made a slight concession to simplicity in the rather special linear boundary conditions (5.5.1b). With little extra effort we could allow E, F, and $\boldsymbol{\gamma}$ to depend upon $\boldsymbol{\lambda}$ and $\boldsymbol{\sigma}$. In fact, it would be almost as easy to impose very general (nonlinear) boundary conditions of the form

$$\mathbf{g}(\mathbf{y}(a), \mathbf{y}(b), \boldsymbol{\lambda}, \boldsymbol{\sigma}) = 0,$$

where $\mathbf{g}$ is an $(n + m)$-vector function of the indicated $(2n + m + q)$ arguments. This generalization is posed as Problem 5.5.1. Standard eigenvalue problems of the form (5.1.1) can be put into the form (5.5.1) by adjoining some normalization condition which makes the eigenfunction unique.

It should be observed that we include the possibility $m = 0$, in which case there is no eigenvalue to be determined. Also the parameter $\boldsymbol{\sigma}$ may have been *artificially introduced* into the problem to facilitate its numerical solution by means of a continuity procedure. We shall just proceed formally in this section as detailed proofs would not really clarify matters. But all of our discussion can be made quite rigorous.

An obvious approach to the study of the boundary-value problem (5.5.1) stems from a consideration of the related initial-value problem

$$\mathbf{u}' = \mathbf{f}(x, \mathbf{u}; \boldsymbol{\lambda}, \boldsymbol{\sigma}), \tag{5.5.2a}$$

$$\mathbf{u}(a) = \mathbf{s}. \tag{5.5.2b}$$

Assuming modest smoothness conditions on $\mathbf{f}$ with respect to x and $\mathbf{u}$ for all $\boldsymbol{\lambda}$ and $\boldsymbol{\sigma}$ in appropriate sets, we can be assured that this initial-value problem has a unique solution, say

$$\mathbf{u} \equiv \mathbf{u}(\mathbf{s}, \boldsymbol{\lambda}, \boldsymbol{\sigma}; x). \tag{5.5.3}$$

If this solution exists on $a \leq x \leq b$ we define the $(n + m)$-vector function

$$\boldsymbol{\phi}(\mathbf{s}, \boldsymbol{\lambda}, \boldsymbol{\sigma}) \equiv E\mathbf{u}(\mathbf{s}, \boldsymbol{\lambda}, \boldsymbol{\sigma}; a) + F\mathbf{u}(\mathbf{s}, \boldsymbol{\lambda}, \boldsymbol{\sigma}; b) - \boldsymbol{\gamma}, \tag{5.5.4a}$$

and then consider the system of equations

$$\boldsymbol{\phi}(\mathbf{s}, \boldsymbol{\lambda}, \boldsymbol{\sigma}) = 0. \tag{5.5.4b}$$

For a fixed value of $\boldsymbol{\sigma}$ this represents $(n + m)$ equations in as many unknowns $(\mathbf{s}, \boldsymbol{\lambda})$. Let $(\mathbf{s}_0, \boldsymbol{\lambda}_0)$ be a root corresponding to the fixed parameter value $\boldsymbol{\sigma} = \boldsymbol{\sigma}_0$. Then it is clear that

$$\mathbf{y}_0(x) \equiv \mathbf{u}(\mathbf{s}_0, \boldsymbol{\lambda}_0, \boldsymbol{\sigma}_0; x)$$

is a solution of the boundary-value problem (5.5.1) corresponding to the eigenvalue $\boldsymbol{\lambda} = \boldsymbol{\lambda}_0$ for the parameter value $\boldsymbol{\sigma} = \boldsymbol{\sigma}_0$.

Conversely, if the problem (5.5.1) with $\boldsymbol{\sigma} = \boldsymbol{\sigma}_0$ has an eigenvalue and corresponding solution, then the equation (5.5.4) has some root which we may call $(\mathbf{s}_0, \boldsymbol{\lambda}_0)$ when $\boldsymbol{\sigma} = \boldsymbol{\sigma}_0$. If the function $\mathbf{f}(x, \mathbf{u}; \boldsymbol{\lambda}, \boldsymbol{\sigma})$ is, for example, continuous in x and continuously differentiable with respect to $\mathbf{u}$, $\boldsymbol{\lambda}$, and $\boldsymbol{\sigma}$ in some open $n + m + q + 1$-dimensional domain containing $\mathbf{y}_0(x)$, $\boldsymbol{\lambda}_0$, $\boldsymbol{\sigma}_0$, $a \leq x \leq b$, then it is easy to prove that the initial-value problem (5.5.2) will have a unique solution which exists on $a \leq x \leq b$ for all initial data $\mathbf{s}$ sufficiently close to $\mathbf{s}_0 \equiv \mathbf{y}_0(a)$, provided that $(\boldsymbol{\lambda}, \boldsymbol{\sigma})$ is also close to $(\boldsymbol{\lambda}_0, \boldsymbol{\sigma}_0)$. This is the basic type of result which justifies the use of the shooting method in attempts to solve problems of the form (5.5.1) (or, more accurately, in attempts to compute accurate approximations to the solutions). Obviously, if we can somehow guess at approximations $(\mathbf{s}^{(0)}, \boldsymbol{\lambda}^{(0)})$ close to $(\mathbf{s}_0, \boldsymbol{\lambda}_0)$, then an iterative procedure applied to the systems (5.5.4) with $\boldsymbol{\sigma} = \boldsymbol{\sigma}_0$ may converge to the desired root.

Let us formulate the application of Newton's method for computing a root of

$$\boldsymbol{\phi}(\mathbf{s}, \boldsymbol{\lambda}, \boldsymbol{\sigma}_0) = 0.$$

Given the initial guess $(\mathbf{s}^{(0)}, \boldsymbol{\lambda}^{(0)})$ we define the sequence $\{\mathbf{s}^{(\nu)}, \boldsymbol{\lambda}^{(\nu)}\}$ by

$$\mathbf{s}^{(\nu+1)} = \mathbf{s}^{(\nu)} + \Delta\mathbf{s}^{(\nu)}, \qquad \boldsymbol{\lambda}^{(\nu+1)} = \boldsymbol{\lambda}^{(\nu)} + \Delta\boldsymbol{\lambda}^{(\nu)}, \qquad \nu = 0, 1, 2, \ldots, \tag{5.5.5a}$$

where $\Delta\mathbf{s}^{(\nu)}$, $\Delta\boldsymbol{\lambda}^{(\nu)}$ are determined by the linear system

$$\frac{\partial\boldsymbol{\phi}(\cdot)}{\partial\mathbf{s}}\,\Delta\mathbf{s}^{(\nu)} + \frac{\partial\boldsymbol{\phi}(\cdot)}{\partial\boldsymbol{\lambda}}\,\Delta\boldsymbol{\lambda}^{(\nu)} = -\boldsymbol{\phi}(\mathbf{s}^{(\nu)}, \boldsymbol{\lambda}^{(\nu)}, \boldsymbol{\sigma}_0), \qquad \nu = 0, 1, 2, \ldots. \tag{5.5.5b}$$

The argument in $\boldsymbol{\phi}(\cdot)$ is always that of the right-hand side. Each system in (5.5.5b) is of order $(n + m)$ and $\partial\boldsymbol{\phi}/\partial\mathbf{s}$ is $(n + m) \times n$ while $\partial\boldsymbol{\phi}/\partial\boldsymbol{\lambda}$ is $(n + m) \times m$. These coefficient matrices can be obtained in terms of the solutions of appropriate variational problems. That is, we define the $n \times n$ matrix

$$\frac{\partial\mathbf{u}(\mathbf{s}, \boldsymbol{\lambda}, \boldsymbol{\sigma}; x)}{\partial\mathbf{s}} \equiv W(\mathbf{s}, \boldsymbol{\lambda}, \boldsymbol{\sigma}; x) \tag{5.5.6a}$$

and the $n \times m$ matrix

$$\frac{\partial\mathbf{u}(\mathbf{s}, \boldsymbol{\lambda}, \boldsymbol{\sigma}; x)}{\partial\boldsymbol{\lambda}} \equiv V(\mathbf{s}, \boldsymbol{\lambda}, \boldsymbol{\sigma}; x). \tag{5.5.6b}$$

Formally differentiating in the initial-value problem (5.5.2), we obtain the variational problems

$$W' = A(x; \mathbf{s}, \boldsymbol{\lambda}, \boldsymbol{\sigma})W, \qquad W(a) = I, \tag{5.5.7a}$$

$$V' = A(x; \mathbf{s}, \boldsymbol{\lambda}, \boldsymbol{\sigma})V + G(x; \mathbf{s}, \boldsymbol{\lambda}, \boldsymbol{\sigma}), \qquad V(a) = 0, \tag{5.5.7b}$$

where the $n \times n$ matrix A and $n \times m$ matrix G are

$$\begin{aligned} A(x; \mathbf{s}, \boldsymbol{\lambda}, \boldsymbol{\sigma}) &\equiv \frac{\partial\mathbf{f}}{\partial\mathbf{u}}\,(x, \mathbf{u}(\mathbf{s}, \boldsymbol{\lambda}, \boldsymbol{\sigma}; x); \boldsymbol{\lambda}, \boldsymbol{\sigma}), \\ G(x; \mathbf{s}, \boldsymbol{\lambda}, \boldsymbol{\sigma}) &\equiv \frac{\partial\mathbf{f}}{\partial\boldsymbol{\lambda}}\,(x, \mathbf{u}(\mathbf{s}, \boldsymbol{\lambda}, \boldsymbol{\sigma}; x); \boldsymbol{\lambda}, \boldsymbol{\sigma}). \end{aligned} \tag{5.5.8}$$

Now it follows from differentiating in (5.5.4a) and using (5.5.6) and (5.5.7) that

$$\frac{\partial\boldsymbol{\phi}(\mathbf{s}, \boldsymbol{\lambda}, \boldsymbol{\sigma})}{\partial\mathbf{s}} = E + FW(\mathbf{s}, \boldsymbol{\lambda}, \boldsymbol{\sigma}; b), \qquad \frac{\partial\boldsymbol{\phi}(\mathbf{s}, \boldsymbol{\lambda}, \boldsymbol{\sigma})}{\partial\boldsymbol{\lambda}} = FV(\mathbf{s}, \boldsymbol{\lambda}, \boldsymbol{\sigma}; b). \tag{5.5.9a}$$

Thus introducing the $(n + m)$-order matrix Q by

$$Q(\mathbf{s}, \boldsymbol{\lambda}, \boldsymbol{\sigma}) \equiv [E + FW(\mathbf{s}, \boldsymbol{\lambda}, \boldsymbol{\sigma}; b), FV(\mathbf{s}, \boldsymbol{\lambda}, \boldsymbol{\sigma}; b)], \tag{5.5.9b}$$

the system (5.5.5*b*) can be written as

$$Q(\mathbf{s}^{(\nu)}, \boldsymbol{\lambda}^{(\nu)}, \boldsymbol{\sigma}_0)\begin{pmatrix}\Delta\mathbf{s}^{(\nu)}\\ \Delta\boldsymbol{\lambda}^{(\nu)}\end{pmatrix} = -\boldsymbol{\phi}(\mathbf{s}^{(\nu)}, \boldsymbol{\lambda}^{(\nu)}, \boldsymbol{\sigma}_0), \qquad \nu = 0, 1, 2, \ldots. \tag{5.5.10}$$

In brief, to apply Newton's method we integrate the nonlinear initial-value problem (5.5.2) with $(\mathbf{s}, \boldsymbol{\lambda}, \boldsymbol{\sigma}) = (\mathbf{s}^{(\nu)}, \boldsymbol{\lambda}^{(\nu)}, \boldsymbol{\sigma}_0)$. This solution is used to evaluate the matrices A and G in (5.5.8) as well as $\boldsymbol{\phi}(\mathbf{s}^{(\nu)}, \boldsymbol{\lambda}^{(\nu)}, \boldsymbol{\sigma}_0)$ in (5.5.4a). Then the systems (5.5.7) are solved [these are $(n + m)$ linear initial-value problems for first-order systems of n equations] and used to evaluate $Q(\mathbf{s}^{(\nu)}, \boldsymbol{\lambda}^{(\nu)}, \boldsymbol{\sigma}_0)$ as in (5.5.9b). Finally the linear algebraic system (5.5.10), of order $(n + m)$, is solved to yield the corrections $\Delta\mathbf{s}^{(\nu)}$ and $\Delta\boldsymbol{\lambda}^{(\nu)}$ from which $\mathbf{s}^{(\nu+1)}$ and $\boldsymbol{\lambda}^{(\nu+1)}$ are computed by (5.5.5a). For efficiency in storage and computing time the systems in (5.5.2) and (5.5.7) should be integrated simultaneously as one large system. We point out that in many problems, especially those motivated by physical applications, the quantities W and V in (5.5.6) are of independent interest.

In order to validate the application of Newton's method we would have to show (at least) that the matrix $Q(\mathbf{s}, \boldsymbol{\lambda}, \boldsymbol{\sigma})$ is nonsingular at each point $(\mathbf{s}^{(\nu)}, \boldsymbol{\lambda}^{(\nu)}, \boldsymbol{\sigma}_0)$. This can be done under appropriate conditions, and in fact the set-up above can actually be used to prove existence and (local) uniqueness of solutions to the problem (5.5.1). Roughly, the idea is to determine an initial guess $(\mathbf{s}^{(0)}, \boldsymbol{\lambda}^{(0)})$ such that $Q(\mathbf{s}^{(0)}, \boldsymbol{\lambda}^{(0)}, \boldsymbol{\sigma}_0)$ is nonsingular, and

$$\|Q^{-1}(\mathbf{s}^{(0)}, \boldsymbol{\lambda}^{(0)}, \boldsymbol{\sigma}_0)\| \le K_0, \qquad |\boldsymbol{\phi}(\mathbf{s}^{(0)}, \boldsymbol{\lambda}^{(0)}, \boldsymbol{\sigma}_0)| \le \eta/K_0. \tag{5.5.11a}$$

Further, the function $\mathbf{f}$ is assumed so smooth that

$$\|Q(\mathbf{s}, \boldsymbol{\lambda}, \boldsymbol{\sigma}_0) - Q(\mathbf{s}', \boldsymbol{\lambda}', \boldsymbol{\sigma}_0)\| \le K_1\left|\begin{pmatrix}\mathbf{s}\\ \boldsymbol{\lambda}\end{pmatrix} - \begin{pmatrix}\mathbf{s}'\\ \boldsymbol{\lambda}'\end{pmatrix}\right|, \tag{5.5.11b}$$

for all $(\mathbf{s}, \boldsymbol{\lambda})^T$ and $(\mathbf{s}', \boldsymbol{\lambda}')^T$ within a distance ρ of $(\mathbf{s}^{(0)}, \boldsymbol{\lambda}^{(0)})^T$. Finally, if the above constants satisfy

$$K_0K_1\rho < 1, \qquad \eta \le (1 - K_0K_1\rho)\rho, \tag{5.5.11c}$$

then $\boldsymbol{\phi}(\mathbf{s}, \boldsymbol{\lambda}, \boldsymbol{\sigma}_0) = 0$ has a unique root within ρ of $(\mathbf{s}^{(0)}, \boldsymbol{\lambda}^{(0)})$. This final result follows by contracting maps and is, in a slightly different notation, Theorem 1.4.4 [in Problem 1.4.5]. In fact by strengthening (5.5.11c) to require that

$$K_0K_1\rho < \tfrac{2}{3}, \qquad \eta \le (1 - \tfrac{3}{2}K_0K_1\rho)\rho, \tag{5.5.11d}$$

it follows from Theorem 1.4.5 [in Problem 1.4.7] that the Newton iterates (5.5.5) converge quadratically to the root.

Of course if a stable, accurate-of-order-p numerical method is used to solve the initial-value problems (5.5.2) and (5.5.7) then we can show that for sufficiently fine net spacing h the numerical determination of a root of (5.5.4) is within $\mathcal{O}(h^p)$ of an exact root. Then a solution of the generalized eigenvalue problem (5.5.1) is determined, along with an eigenvalue, to within an error that is $\mathcal{O}(h^p)$. Given the above-mentioned existence proof, our results about the shooting method follow somewhat as in the proof of Theorem 2.3.1, but are in fact very much more general. [For example, $A + B$ in Section 2.3 need not be nonsingular; $Q(\mathbf{s}) \equiv A + BW(\mathbf{s}, b)$ should satisfy conditions similar to those in (5.5.11a–c).]

5.5.1 Poincaré Continuation; Continuity Methods

Suppose that the generalized eigenvalue problem (5.5.1) has a solution for the parameter value $\boldsymbol{\sigma} = \boldsymbol{\sigma}_0$. Then under reasonable smoothness assumptions we may expect that a solution exists for $\boldsymbol{\sigma}$ near $\boldsymbol{\sigma}_0$ and that in fact the two solutions should be close, in some sense. This is frequently, but not always, the case. When it is true, an obvious continuity procedure is suggested for computing solutions over an entire domain of $\boldsymbol{\sigma}$ values. (In fact, as has been previously suggested, the parameter $\boldsymbol{\sigma}$ may have been introduced into the problem in order to apply some sort of continuity technique; see Problems 5.5.4–5.5.6.) The theoretical justification for the basic assumption is, as we show, but a slight extension of the Poincaré continuation procedure which is well known in the study of periodic solutions of differential equations [see Coddington and Levinson (1955), pp. 348–350].

Let the solution of (5.5.1) with $\boldsymbol{\sigma} = \boldsymbol{\sigma}_0$ be denoted by $\mathbf{y} = \mathbf{y}_0(x)$, $\boldsymbol{\lambda} = \boldsymbol{\lambda}_0$. Then with the choice $\mathbf{s} = \mathbf{s}_0 \equiv \mathbf{y}_0(a)$ we have, using (5.5.4),

$$\boldsymbol{\phi}(\mathbf{s}_0, \boldsymbol{\lambda}_0, \boldsymbol{\sigma}_0) = 0.$$

Under the previously-mentioned differentiability conditions on $\mathbf{f}(x, \mathbf{u}; \boldsymbol{\lambda}, \boldsymbol{\sigma})$ we observe from (5.5.9) that the Jacobian of $\boldsymbol{\phi}$ with respect to the $(n + m)$ variables $(\mathbf{s}, \boldsymbol{\lambda})$ is

$$\det \frac{\partial \boldsymbol{\phi}(\mathbf{s}, \boldsymbol{\lambda}, \boldsymbol{\sigma})}{\partial(\mathbf{s}, \boldsymbol{\lambda})} = \det Q(\mathbf{s}, \boldsymbol{\lambda}, \boldsymbol{\sigma}).$$

Let us assume now that $Q(\mathbf{s}_0, \boldsymbol{\lambda}_0, \boldsymbol{\sigma}_0)$ is nonsingular. [Note that this is *not* the assumption made above, Equation (5.5.11a), but would follow from (5.5.11a–c) since then $Q(\mathbf{s}, \boldsymbol{\lambda}, \boldsymbol{\sigma}_0)$ is nonsingular in some sphere including $(\mathbf{s}_0, \boldsymbol{\lambda}_0)$ and $(\mathbf{s}^{(0)}, \boldsymbol{\lambda}^{(0)})$.] Then, since $\boldsymbol{\phi}(\mathbf{s}, \boldsymbol{\lambda}, \boldsymbol{\sigma})$ is continuous in $\boldsymbol{\sigma}$, we may apply the implicit-function theorem to conclude that there exist an $\varepsilon > 0$

and unique continuous functions

$$\mathbf{s}(\boldsymbol{\sigma}), \qquad \boldsymbol{\lambda}(\boldsymbol{\sigma}), \tag{5.5.12a}$$

such that

$$\mathbf{s}(\boldsymbol{\sigma}_0) = \mathbf{s}_0, \qquad \boldsymbol{\lambda}(\boldsymbol{\sigma}_0) = \boldsymbol{\lambda}_0, \tag{5.5.12b}$$

and

$$\boldsymbol{\phi}(\mathbf{s}(\boldsymbol{\sigma}), \boldsymbol{\lambda}(\boldsymbol{\sigma}), \boldsymbol{\sigma}) = 0, \tag{5.5.12c}$$

for all $\boldsymbol{\sigma}$ in the sphere $N_\varepsilon(\boldsymbol{\sigma}_0) \equiv \{\boldsymbol{\sigma} \mid |\boldsymbol{\sigma} - \boldsymbol{\sigma}_0| < \varepsilon\}$. Finally, recalling (5.5.2)–(5.5.4), we find that a family of solutions to the generalized eigenvalue problem (5.5.1) is given by

$$\mathbf{y}(\boldsymbol{\sigma}; x) = \mathbf{u}(\mathbf{s}(\boldsymbol{\sigma}), \boldsymbol{\lambda}(\boldsymbol{\sigma}), \boldsymbol{\sigma}; x) \tag{5.5.13a}$$

with corresponding eigenvalue

$$\boldsymbol{\lambda} = \boldsymbol{\lambda}(\boldsymbol{\sigma}) \tag{5.5.13b}$$

for all $\boldsymbol{\sigma} \in N_\varepsilon(\boldsymbol{\sigma}_0)$.

When this continuation theorem is valid it is clear that the solution for a given value of $\boldsymbol{\sigma}$ will be a close approximation to the solution for the parameter values $\boldsymbol{\sigma} \pm \Delta\boldsymbol{\sigma}$ if $|\Delta\boldsymbol{\sigma}|$ is sufficiently small. Thus in whatever iteration scheme is employed to solve (5.5.4b), a sequence of close initial estimates of roots for a sequence of $\boldsymbol{\sigma}$ values can be generated as soon as one solution is known for a given value of $\boldsymbol{\sigma}$. This clarifies one form of continuity method in which $\boldsymbol{\sigma}$ is introduced into the problem in such a way, for example, that for $\boldsymbol{\sigma} = 0$ the resulting problem is easily solved (perhaps with an explicit solution). Starting values are thus furnished and one seeks to solve on a sequence of $\boldsymbol{\sigma}$ values whose final value is such that (5.5.1) becomes the problem whose solution was originally required. The need for introducing such continuity parameters may only become apparent after other attempts have proven fruitless.

If solutions of (5.5.1) are to be sought for a sequence of $\boldsymbol{\sigma}$ values then it would seem likely that even "better" initial guesses could be furnished by some sort of extrapolation procedure. This is of course justified if it is known that the functions in (5.5.12a) have more smoothness properties than just continuity. But the implicit-function theorem endows the "root" $(\mathbf{s}(\boldsymbol{\sigma}), \boldsymbol{\lambda}(\boldsymbol{\sigma}))$ with the same continuity and differentiability properties in $\boldsymbol{\sigma}$ as those enjoyed by $\boldsymbol{\phi}(\mathbf{s}, \boldsymbol{\lambda}, \boldsymbol{\sigma})$ as a function of $\boldsymbol{\sigma}$, $\mathbf{s}$, and $\boldsymbol{\lambda}$. Thus, for instance, with the continuously-differentiable $\mathbf{f}$ we have assumed, it follows that $\mathbf{s}(\boldsymbol{\sigma})$ and $\boldsymbol{\lambda}(\boldsymbol{\sigma})$ are continuously differentiable on $N_\varepsilon(\boldsymbol{\sigma}_0)$. Now suppose that a solution is known for some $\boldsymbol{\sigma} \in N_\varepsilon(\boldsymbol{\sigma}_0)$ and $\Delta\boldsymbol{\sigma}$ is such that $\boldsymbol{\sigma} \pm \Delta\boldsymbol{\sigma} \in N_\varepsilon(\boldsymbol{\sigma}_0)$. Then reasonable approximations to the roots at these new parameter values are given by the first two terms in the Taylor expansions

$$\begin{aligned} \mathbf{s}(\boldsymbol{\sigma} \pm \Delta\boldsymbol{\sigma}) &\doteq \mathbf{s}(\boldsymbol{\sigma}) \pm \frac{\partial \mathbf{s}(\boldsymbol{\sigma})}{\partial \boldsymbol{\sigma}} \Delta\boldsymbol{\sigma} \equiv \mathbf{s}^{(0)}(\boldsymbol{\sigma} \pm \Delta\boldsymbol{\sigma}), \\ \boldsymbol{\lambda}(\boldsymbol{\sigma} \pm \Delta\boldsymbol{\sigma}) &\doteq \boldsymbol{\lambda}(\boldsymbol{\sigma}) \pm \frac{\partial \boldsymbol{\lambda}(\boldsymbol{\sigma})}{\partial \boldsymbol{\sigma}} \Delta\boldsymbol{\sigma} \equiv \boldsymbol{\lambda}^{(0)}(\boldsymbol{\sigma} \pm \Delta\boldsymbol{\sigma}). \end{aligned} \tag{5.5.14}$$

In the case of a scalar parameter (or if $\Delta\boldsymbol{\sigma}$ has only one nonzero component) a rather obvious approach to the estimates in (5.5.14) is obtained by approximating the required derivatives by difference quotients. The resulting formulas are exactly those obtained by using linear extrapolation from two solutions. Of course this procedure is not as accurate as that in (5.5.14) and, perhaps more important, requires a knowledge of two solutions for close values of $\boldsymbol{\sigma}$. However, as we shall show, it is quite efficient to get very accurate approximations to the matrices $\partial\mathbf{s}/\partial\boldsymbol{\sigma}$ and $\partial\boldsymbol{\lambda}/\partial\boldsymbol{\sigma}$ using only one solution. Then larger steps, $\Delta\boldsymbol{\sigma}$, can be employed or (equivalently) more accurate initial guesses are obtained for smaller $|\Delta\boldsymbol{\sigma}|$.

To obtain the derivatives occurring in (5.5.14) we observe that the family of solutions (5.5.13) employed in (5.5.4) yields the result (5.5.12c) which is an identity in $\boldsymbol{\sigma}$ on $N_\varepsilon(\boldsymbol{\sigma}_0)$. Differentiating this identity with respect to $\boldsymbol{\sigma}$ gives us the system

$$\frac{\partial \boldsymbol{\phi}(\cdot)}{\partial \mathbf{s}} \frac{\partial \mathbf{s}}{\partial \boldsymbol{\sigma}} + \frac{\partial \boldsymbol{\phi}(\cdot)}{\partial \boldsymbol{\lambda}} \frac{\partial \boldsymbol{\lambda}}{\partial \boldsymbol{\sigma}} = -\frac{\partial \boldsymbol{\phi}(\cdot)}{\partial \boldsymbol{\sigma}},$$

where $(\cdot) \equiv (\mathbf{s}(\boldsymbol{\sigma}), \boldsymbol{\lambda}(\boldsymbol{\sigma}), \boldsymbol{\sigma})$. Recalling (5.5.9), this system can be written as

$$Q(\mathbf{s}(\boldsymbol{\sigma}), \boldsymbol{\lambda}(\boldsymbol{\sigma}), \boldsymbol{\sigma}) \begin{pmatrix} \partial \mathbf{s}(\boldsymbol{\sigma})/\partial\boldsymbol{\sigma} \\ \partial \boldsymbol{\lambda}(\boldsymbol{\sigma})/\partial\boldsymbol{\sigma} \end{pmatrix} = -FZ(\boldsymbol{\sigma}; b). \tag{5.5.15}$$

Here we have used (5.5.4a) and (5.5.2) to write

$$\frac{\partial \boldsymbol{\phi}(\cdot)}{\partial \boldsymbol{\sigma}} = FZ(\boldsymbol{\sigma}; b), \tag{5.5.16a}$$

where $Z(\boldsymbol{\sigma}; x) = \partial \mathbf{u}(\mathbf{s}(\boldsymbol{\sigma}), \boldsymbol{\lambda}(\boldsymbol{\sigma}), \boldsymbol{\sigma}; x)/\partial\boldsymbol{\sigma}$ is the n-rowed-by-q-columned matrix solution of the variational system

$$Z' = A(x; \mathbf{s}(\boldsymbol{\sigma}), \boldsymbol{\lambda}(\boldsymbol{\sigma}), \boldsymbol{\sigma})Z + H(x; \boldsymbol{\sigma}), \qquad Z(a) = 0. \tag{5.5.16b}$$

The $(n + m)$th-order matrix A is defined in (5.5.8) and the $n \times q$ matrix H is

$$H(x; \boldsymbol{\sigma}); \equiv \frac{\partial \mathbf{f}}{\partial \boldsymbol{\sigma}} (x, \mathbf{u}(\mathbf{s}(\boldsymbol{\sigma}), \boldsymbol{\lambda}(\boldsymbol{\sigma}), \boldsymbol{\sigma}; x); \boldsymbol{\lambda}(\boldsymbol{\sigma}), \boldsymbol{\sigma}). \tag{5.5.16c}$$

We recall that the nonsingularity of $Q(\mathbf{s}(\boldsymbol{\sigma}), \boldsymbol{\lambda}(\boldsymbol{\sigma}), \boldsymbol{\sigma})$ for a given $\boldsymbol{\sigma}$ value is our sufficient condition for Poincaré continuation, in which case (5.5.15) has a unique solution.

In summary we advocate the continuity method using the initial estimates in (5.5.14). The required derivatives are obtained by solving the system (5.5.15). This is done, for a given value of $\boldsymbol{\sigma}$, only *after* a sufficiently-accurate solution as in (5.5.12) or (5.5.13) has been computed. To obtain the coefficient matrix, Q, and the inhomogeneous term, $-FZ$, we must solve the three variational initial-value systems (5.5.7a), (5.5.7b), and (5.5.16b) only once using the accurate solution to evaluate the matrices in (5.5.8) and (5.5.16c). It should be recalled that if Newton's method is being employed, then a procedure for evaluating the matrix Q is already required and the only additional complication is in solving for $Z(\boldsymbol{\sigma}; b)$. But again, as with W and V, the components of Z may be of independent physical interest.

Many problems of the form (5.5.1) are such that the above procedures can be greatly simplified. For instance, the boundary conditions (5.5.1b) may require that $y_1(a) = y_2(a) = \cdots = y_r(a) = 0$ for some $r < n$. Then in (5.5.2b) we take $s_1 = s_2 = \cdots = s_r = 0$ and the system (5.5.4) reduces to $m + n - r$ equations in the as many unknowns $\boldsymbol{\lambda}$, $s_{r+1}, \ldots, s_n$. All subsequent calculations are correspondingly reduced.

The parallel shooting techniques of Section 2.4 can be applied, in an obvious manner, to the generalized eigenvalue problems. The finite-difference methods, as in Section 3.3, can also be employed, but their theoretical justification is considerably more complicated.

Problems

5.5.1 Consider the generalized eigenvalue problem posed by (5.5.1a) and

$$\mathbf{g}(\mathbf{y}(a), \mathbf{y}(b), \boldsymbol{\lambda}, \boldsymbol{\sigma}) = 0. \tag{*}$$

Determine the corresponding transcendental system that results from using the initial-value problem (5.5.2) to solve this boundary-value problem. Determine the linear variational problems whose solutions yield the coefficient matrix for Newton's method in this case. [We assume that $\mathbf{g}(\mathbf{u}, \mathbf{v}, \boldsymbol{\lambda}, \boldsymbol{\sigma})$ has continuous derivatives $\partial\mathbf{g}/\partial\mathbf{u}$ and $\partial\mathbf{g}/\partial\mathbf{v}$ for all arguments.]

5.5.2 Determine a sufficient condition for Poincaré continuation in a neighborhood, $|\boldsymbol{\sigma} - \boldsymbol{\sigma}_0| < \varepsilon$, of a parameter value $\boldsymbol{\sigma}_0$ for which (5.5.1a) and (*) have a solution. Find the system which replaces (5.5.15) for the determination of $\partial\mathbf{s}(\boldsymbol{\sigma}_0)/\partial\boldsymbol{\sigma}$ and $\partial\boldsymbol{\lambda}(\boldsymbol{\sigma}_0)/\partial\boldsymbol{\sigma}$. How is the inhomogeneous term computed?

5.5.3 Let $\boldsymbol{\lambda}$ and $\boldsymbol{\sigma}$ in Equation (5.5.1a) be scalars (that is one-dimensional), and let Equation (5.5.1b) reduce to

$$y_1(a) = \cdots = y_n(a) = 0, \qquad y_1(b) = 0.$$

Formulate the initial-value procedure, Newton's method and accurate continuity method for this generalized eigenvalue problem. [Note that there is no initial parameter **s** to be introduced, just as in the Sturm-Liouville case treated in Section 5.2.]

5.5.4 The boundary-value problem

$$\text{(a)}\quad y'' + \frac{e^y}{2} = 0, \qquad y'(0) = 0, \qquad y(1) = 0$$

has *two* positive solutions. Consider the related boundary-value problem

$$\text{(b)}\quad z'' + (1 - \sigma)\frac{\pi^2}{4}z + \sigma\frac{e^z}{2} = 0, \qquad z'(0) = z(1) = 0,$$

which for $\sigma = 0$ has a one-parameter family of solutions

$$z(0, x) = a \cos \frac{\pi x}{2}.$$

Does the Poincaré continuation result hold for problem (b) in the neighborhood of $\sigma = 0$? What about the simpler problem

$$\text{(c)}\quad z'' + \sigma\frac{e^z}{2} = 0, \qquad z'(0) = z(1) = 0.$$

Try using the continuity method on (b) and (c) to get from $\sigma = 0$ to $\sigma = 1$, and compute both positive solutions of (a) in this way.

5.5.5 Consider the boundary-value problem

$$\mathbf{y}' = \mathbf{f}(x, \mathbf{y}), \qquad A\mathbf{y}(a) + B\mathbf{y}(b) = \boldsymbol{\alpha}, \tag{5.5.17}$$

where $\mathbf{f}$ and $\partial\mathbf{f}/\partial\mathbf{y}$ are bounded and continuous for $x \in [a, b]$, $|\mathbf{y}| < \infty$, and $A + B$ is nonsingular. This problem can be imbedded in the one-parameter family of problems

$$\mathbf{z}' = \sigma\mathbf{f}(x, \mathbf{z}), \qquad A\mathbf{z}(a) + B\mathbf{z}(b) = \boldsymbol{\alpha}. \tag{5.5.18}$$

(a) Show by Poincaré continuation that problem (5.5.18) has a solution $\mathbf{z}(x, \sigma)$ for each σ in some interval $0 \le \sigma \le \varepsilon$.

(b) If $\|\partial\mathbf{f}/\partial\mathbf{y}\| \le K$, show that in the above interval we may take ε satisfying

$$\varepsilon < \frac{1}{K|b - a|} \log\left(1 + \frac{1}{\|(A + B)^{-1}B\|}\right).$$

[HINT: Use Theorem 1.2.6.] Note that (5.5.18) is almost equivalent to scaling the independent variable in (5.5.17) by σ. This is actually the case for autonomous systems. Then our continuity procedure consists in stretching the interval to the desired length.

5.5.6 Suppose that $(A + B)$ in Problem 5.5.5 is singular but that for some matrix P† with positive eigenvalues $(A + BP)$ is nonsingular. Show that, with the real matrix†

$$M \equiv \frac{1}{b - a} \log P,$$

the one-parameter family of problems

$$\mathbf{z}' = \sigma \mathbf{f}(x, \mathbf{z}) + (1 - \sigma)M\mathbf{z}, \qquad A\mathbf{z}(a) + B\mathbf{z}(b) = \boldsymbol{\alpha} \qquad (5.5.19)$$

has a solution $\mathbf{z}(x, \sigma)$ for each σ in some interval $0 \leq \sigma \leq \varepsilon$. Note that part (a) of Problem 5.5.5 results if $P \equiv I$ in the above.

SUPPLEMENTARY REFERENCES AND NOTES

Section 5.1. Thorough treatments of Sturm-Liouville eigenvalue problems are given in Ince (1944) and Coddington and Levinson (1955). The latter also studies much more general eigenvalue problems. The elegant and powerful variational formulation of self-adjoint eigenvalue problems is described in Collatz (1960), Kantorovich and Krylov (1958), and Courant and Hilbert (1937). A theory of eigenvalue problems for linear first-order systems is contained in Atkinson (1964).

Section 5.3 Variational methods play a large role in the study of difference methods for Sturm-Liouville eigenvalue problems. Farrington, Gregory, and Taub (1957) use them to get higher-order-accurate difference equations which are automatically symmetric. Then by Theorem 5.3.2 the eigenvalues are also higher-order-accurate approximations. Weinberger (1962) obtains upper and lower bounds on the eigenvalues by constructing special difference equations, and Birkhoff et al. (1966) improve this technique to obtain more accurate bounds as well as estimates for the accuracy of the eigenvector approximation. The error in difference approximations to the eigenvectors is also studied by Gary (1965).

Section 5.4 One of the basic methods for studying Sturm-Liouville eigenvalue problems is based on replacing them by equivalent integral equations and then developing the Fredholm Theory [see Courant and Hilbert (1953)]. The error in "difference" approximations to the eigenvalues of integral equations is briefly discussed in H. Keller (1965). A thorough study of such methods is contained in an excellent paper of H. Wielandt (1956).

† The condition on P need only be that $\log P$ exist. For convenience in calculations, we have required the logarithm to be real. For a definition of $\log P$, see Coddington and Levinson (1955), pp. 65–66.

Section 5.5 It may be possible to continue a solution even though det $Q(\mathbf{s}_0, \boldsymbol{\lambda}_0, \boldsymbol{\sigma}_0) = 0$ (that is, when the implicit function theorem fails). Continuation of periodic solutions of autonomous differential equations is an example of this situation [see Coddington and Levinson (1955), pp. 352–353]. A rather complicated example containing most of the exceptional cases which is solved by shooting with Aitkens' δ^2-method (rather than Newton's method, which we usually advocate) is contained in Keller and Wolfe (1965). A brief account of several different numerical studies of this same problem is given in Keller and Reiss (1965).

CHAPTER 6

PRACTICAL EXAMPLES AND COMPUTATIONAL EXERCISES

Introduction

We present here details of some problems that were solved by the methods of the previous chapters or by very similar procedures. All of the problems are of independent interest and were originally studied for purposes other than to serve as illustrations for this monograph. In fact our theorems on existence, uniqueness, and convergence do not generally apply here (usually because of the presence of some type of singularity). But as the computations show, the behavior of the numerical procedures is just as if the theory were valid. We could have presented more general theoretical results to cover some of these and many other cases. However, it is likely that many, if not most, problems to be met in practice will be of this type in that they do not fit some relevant theory exactly. One of the main tasks confronting applied mathematicians in general is to judge correctly which approximation techniques are valid in the absence of complete theoretical justification. This is perhaps most necessary in the application of numerical methods since they are so easily applied in this developing age of digital computers. Our examples are intended to indicate judgments of this type as well as to illustrate modifications in the methods of the text. Some computations are suggested in each section and it would be instructive to try to duplicate the results in the text.

6.1 Shooting; Lubrication Theory

This problem in the theory of lubrication concerns the flow of a viscous compressible fluid through a very narrow gap and was treated by J. D. Cole, H. B. Keller, and P. Saffman [1967]. The programming of the numerical work was done by W. H. Mitchell and all the calculations reported here were performed in about 50 seconds on an I.B.M. 7094 in the W. H. Booth Computing Center at the California Institute of Technology.

The pressure distribution in the lubricant (that is, viscous fluid) between a cylindrical bearing and a plane surface results in a vertical thrust on the bearing. Thus thrust and the details of the pressure distribution are of interest in the theory of lubrication. Under the usual assumptions of this theory, for a compressible viscous isothermal film, the pressure $p(\phi)$ is found to satisfy the first-order ordinary differential equation

$$\frac{d}{d\phi}\left(\frac{p(\phi)}{p_0}\right) = \beta \cos^2 \phi - \alpha\left(\frac{p_0}{p(\phi)}\right) \cos^4 \phi, \qquad -\frac{\pi}{2} < \phi < \frac{\pi}{2}. \tag{6.1.1}$$

Here ϕ is defined by

$$x = (2Rh)^{1/2} \tan \phi$$

where, as shown in Figure 6.1.1, R is the radius of the cylinder and h is the gap width. The parameters α and β are defined by

$$\alpha \equiv \frac{12\mu F}{p_0\rho_0}\left(\frac{2R}{h^5}\right)^{1/2}, \qquad \beta \equiv \frac{6\mu U}{p_0}\left(\frac{2R}{h^3}\right)^{1/2}, \tag{6.1.2}$$

where ω is the angular speed of the cylinder, $U \equiv R\omega$, μ is the coefficient of viscosity of the lubricant, p_0 and ρ_0 are the pressure and density of the lubricant far from the gap (that is, at $|x| = \infty$), and F is the mass flux of lubricant through the gap per unit length of the cylinder. We have assumed that

$$p\left(-\frac{\pi}{2}\right) = p\left(\frac{\pi}{2}\right) = p_0, \tag{6.1.3}$$

so that the lubricant is driven through the gap solely by the rotation of the cylinder and not by any external pressure gradients.

In general, β and p_0 are known, and it is required to find the pressure distribution, $p(\phi)$, and the mass flux, α, such that the boundary-value problem (6.1.1, 6.1.3) is satisfied. Then, writing the vertical thrust on the bearing as $T = \sqrt{2Rh}\, p_0\tau$, we have, to within higher-order terms in h/R,

$$\tau = \int_{-\pi/2}^{\pi/2} \left[\frac{p(\phi)}{p_0} - 1\right] \sec^2 \phi \, d\phi. \tag{6.1.4}$$

The problem thus formulated may be termed a nonlinear eigenvalue problem. For $\beta \ll 1$ and $\beta \gg 1$, approximate solutions can be obtained by ordinary perturbation and singular perturbation techniques, respectively. In the intermediate range of parameter values, numerical solutions are required.

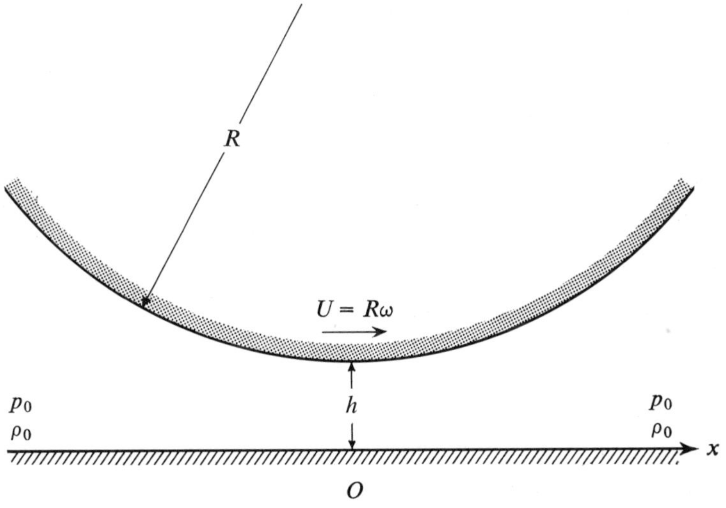

FIGURE 6.1.1 Sketch of the gap between a rotating cylinder and fixed plane

To facilitate comparisons with some of this analytical work it is convenient to introduce new variables, with $p_1 \equiv p(0)$, as follows:

$$\theta \equiv \phi - \frac{\pi}{2}, \qquad y(\theta) \equiv \frac{p(\phi)}{p_0},$$
$$\varepsilon \equiv \left(\frac{p_1}{p_0}\right)\beta^{-1}, \qquad \lambda \equiv \left(\frac{p_0}{p_1}\right)\alpha\beta^{-1}. \tag{6.1.5}$$

It is clear that the solution of (6.1.1) and (6.1.3) may be extended periodically, with period π, to $0 \le \phi \le \pi$, so that the problem becomes

$$\varepsilon\frac{dy}{d\theta} = \sin^2\theta - \lambda\frac{\sin^4\theta}{y}, \qquad -\frac{\pi}{2} < \theta < \frac{\pi}{2}, \tag{6.1.6}$$

and

$$y\left(\frac{\pi}{2}\right) = y\left(-\frac{\pi}{2}\right) = 1. \tag{6.1.7}$$

The boundary conditions (6.1.3) now serve to determine p_0/p_1, since

$$y(0) = \frac{p_0}{p_1}\,(=y(\pi)). \tag{6.1.8}$$

We shall solve the nonlinear eigenvalue problem (6.1.6–7) by the simple shooting technique using Newton's method. Thus we consider the initial-value problem

$$\begin{aligned}
&\text{(a)} \quad \varepsilon \frac{du}{d\theta} = \sin^2 \theta - \lambda \frac{\sin^4 \theta}{u}, \\
&\text{(b)} \quad u\left(\frac{\pi}{2}\right) = 1
\end{aligned} \tag{6.1.9}$$

on the interval $-\pi/2 \leq \theta \leq \pi/2$. If $u = u(\lambda, \theta)$ is the solution of (6.1.9) for a fixed value of ε, and we can find $\lambda = \lambda(\varepsilon)$ such that

$$\phi(\lambda) \equiv u\left(\lambda, -\frac{\pi}{2}\right) - 1 = 0, \tag{6.1.10}$$

then clearly $y(\theta) \equiv u(\lambda, \theta)$ is a solution of (6.1.6–7) with the corresponding pair of parameter values ε, $\lambda(\varepsilon)$. Given some initial estimate λ_0 of the root of (6.1.10), we define the sequence $\{\lambda_\nu\}$ by Newton's method

$$\lambda_{\nu+1} = \lambda_\nu - \frac{\phi(\lambda_\nu)}{[d\phi(\lambda_\nu)/d\lambda]}, \qquad \nu = 0, 1, 2, \ldots . \tag{6.1.11}$$

If the solution $u(\lambda, \theta)$ of (6.1.9) is continuously differentiable with respect to λ, then, with

$$v(\lambda, \theta) \equiv \frac{\partial u(\lambda, \theta)}{\partial \lambda}, \tag{6.1.12}$$

we obtain the variational problem

$$\begin{aligned}
&\text{(a)} \quad \varepsilon \frac{dv}{d\theta} = \left(\frac{\lambda v}{u} - 1\right) \frac{\sin^4 \theta}{u}, \\
&\text{(b)} \quad v\left(\frac{\pi}{2}\right) = 0.
\end{aligned} \tag{6.1.13}$$

Now clearly, from (6.1.10) and (6.1.12),

$$\frac{d\phi(\lambda)}{d\lambda} = v\left(\lambda, -\frac{\pi}{2}\right),$$

and so the Newton iterates become simply

$$\lambda_{\nu+1} = \lambda_\nu + \frac{1 - u(\lambda_\nu, -\pi/2)}{v(\lambda_\nu, -\pi/2)}, \qquad \nu = 0, 1, 2, \ldots . \tag{6.1.14}$$

In the calculations we use the net

$$\theta_j = \pi/2 - j\Delta\theta$$

with spacings $\Delta\theta = \pi/102$ for $\varepsilon \geq 1/10$, and

$$\Delta\theta = \pi/502$$

for $\varepsilon \leq 1/10$. On these nets we solve the problems (6.1.9) and (6.1.13) as a first-order system of two equations using the Runge-Kutta scheme (1.3.14) to start (that is, to compute at θ_0, θ_1, θ_2, and θ_3) and the modified Adams method (1.3.16) to compute on $\theta_4 \geq \theta_j \geq -\pi/2$. Very little experimentation was required to find that the integration should be performed in the backward manner already indicated by (6.1.9b). (Theoretical considerations also suggested this as being more stable.)

For ε "large" the perturbation solution in powers of $1/\varepsilon$ implies that $\lambda \approx 4/3$. The calculations were started with $\varepsilon = 2$, using $\lambda = \lambda_0 = 1$ in the numerical integration of (6.1.9) and (6.1.13), and the sequence (6.1.14) was terminated when

$$|\lambda_\nu - \lambda_{\nu-1}| < 5 \times 10^{-6}.$$

This first run required $\nu = 4$ iterations, and all subsequent cases used only $\nu = 3$ or $\nu = 2$ iterations. When convergence was obtained for a given value of ε, the converged value, say $\lambda(\varepsilon)$ (or rather a rounded approximation to it), is used as the initial estimate, λ_0, for the next, slightly smaller, value of ε. Some of the sequences of Newton iterates obtained in this way are shown in Table 6.1.1, p. 158 (only half the ε values used in $1/10 \leq \varepsilon \leq 1$ are shown in this table).

To check the accuracy of the numerical work we compare some of the numerical results with corresponding results of the singular perturbation approximation. In particular this analytical procedure gives

$$\lambda(\varepsilon) = 1 + 2\varepsilon^2 - 16\varepsilon^4 + \cdots, \tag{6.1.15}$$

and with a numerical integration of some auxiliary differential equations (to determine the approximate coefficients) we get

$$y(0) \doteq 20.63\varepsilon^2 - 600\varepsilon^4 + \cdots. \tag{6.1.16}$$

In Table 6.1.2 (p. 158) the numerical solutions are compared with these approximations.

Of course the singular perturbation formulae become more accurate as $\varepsilon \to 0$. On the other hand, it is to be expected that the numerical calculations

TABLE 6.1.1

Some Newton iterates for determination by shooting of the parameter values $\lambda = \lambda(\varepsilon)$ in the nonlinear eigenvalue problem (6.1.6) *and* (6.1.7).

	ε	λ_0	λ_1	λ_2	λ_3	λ_4
$\Delta\theta = \pi/102$	2	1.000 0	1.291 5953	1.307 8512	1.307 8921	1.307 8921
	1	1.307 9	1.293 2455	1.293 2779	1.293 2779	
	$\frac{1}{2}$	1.258 1	1.215 9251	1.216 0673	1.216 0673	
	$\frac{1}{3}$	1.175 6	1.141 0717	1.141 1758	1.141 1758	
	$\frac{1}{4}$	1.114 0	1.092 9940	1.093 0389	1.093 0389	
	$\frac{1}{5}$	1.077 0	1.064 6403	1.064 6550	1.064 6550	
	$\frac{1}{6}$	1.055 0	1.047 2529	1.047 2579		
	$\frac{1}{7}$	1.041 0	1.035 9506	1.035 9524		
	$\frac{1}{8}$	1.031 7	1.028 2207	1.028 2215		
	$\frac{1}{9}$	1.025 2	1.022 7130	1.022 7133		
	$\frac{1}{10}$	1.020 5	1.018 6566	1.018 6567		
$\Delta\theta = \pi/502$	$\frac{1}{10}$	1.000 0	1.018 6417	1.018 6568	1.018 6568	
	$\frac{1}{20}$	1.018 7	1.004 9022	1.004 9048		
	$\frac{1}{30}$	1.004 9	1.002 2029	1.002 2029		
	$\frac{1}{40}$	1.002 2	1.001 2438	1.001 2438		
	$\frac{1}{50}$	1.001 2	1.000 7975	1.000 7975		
	$\frac{1}{60}$	1.000 8	1.000 5543	1.000 5543		
	$\frac{1}{70}$	1.000 6	1.000 4075	1.000 4075		
	$\frac{1}{80}$	1.000 4	1.000 3121	1.000 3121		
	$\frac{1}{90}$	1.000 3	1.000 2466	1.000 2466		
	$\frac{1}{100}$	1.000 2	1.000 1998	1.000 1998		

TABLE 6.1.2

Comparison of singular perturbation approximations (6.1.15) *and* (6.1.16) *with corresponding results from the numerical calculations.*

		$\varepsilon = \frac{1}{5}$	$\varepsilon = \frac{1}{10}$	$\varepsilon = \frac{1}{20}$	$\varepsilon = \frac{1}{100}$
λ	Singular Perturbation	1.0540 0000	1.0184 0000	1.0049 0000	1.0001 9984
	Numerical Calculations	1.0646 5511	1.0186 5686	1.0049 0484	1.0001 9988
$y(0)$	Singular Perturbation	−.1348 000	.1463 0000	.0478 2500	.0020 5700
	Numerical Calculation	.4129 7201	.1616 4435	.0481 1537	.0020 5708

become less accurate (for fixed net spacing) as $\varepsilon \to 0$. Thus we conclude from the comparison in Table 6.1.2 that our numerical results are quite accurate.

In Figure 6.1.2 we present some graphs of solutions of the nonlinear eigenvalue problem (6.1.6–7) for several values of ε.

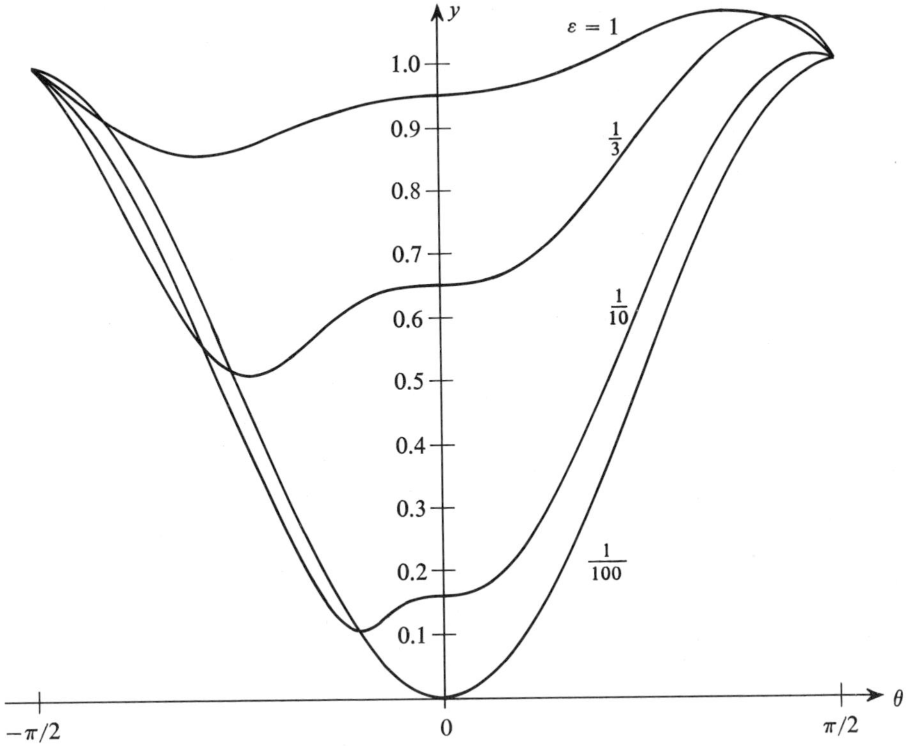

FIGURE 6.1.2

The thrust is approximated by using Simpson's rule and the numerical values $y(\theta_j)$ in the reduced form of (6.1.4), which is

$$\tau = \frac{1}{y(0)} \int_{-\pi/2}^{\pi/2} \left(\frac{y(\theta) - y(0)}{\sin^2 \theta} \right) d\theta. \tag{6.1.17}$$

The strange numbers of net points used were specially chosen so that this numerical integration could be done without the need for end-corrections. The singularity of the integrand at $\theta = 0$ is easily treated by simply eliminating the two panels over $-\Delta\theta \leq \theta \leq \Delta\theta$ in the quadrature formula. In this particular case the accuracy of Simpson's rule is maintained, since for the exact solution we find that

$$\frac{dy(0)}{d\theta} = \frac{d^2y(0)}{d\theta^2} = \frac{d^4y(0)}{dy^4} = \frac{d^5y(0)}{d\theta^5} = 0, \qquad \frac{d^3y(0)}{d\theta^3} = 2\varepsilon.$$

The computed value of $_Ty(0)$ from (6.1.17), using the above procedure with $\varepsilon = 10^{-2}$, was

$$_Ty(0) = 2.993.$$

From the singular perturbation procedure a crude approximation to the thrust is obtained as

$$_Ty(0) \approx \pi(1 - 10\varepsilon). \tag{6.1.18}$$

With $\varepsilon = 10^{-2}$, this gives

$$_Ty(0) \approx 2.827,$$

which is within 6% of the above numerical value. For smaller ε the formula (6.1.18) is expected to improve rapidly; it agrees best with the computed values of thrust for the smaller values of ε.

6.1.1 *Computing Exercise; Forced Flow*

If the lubricant is forced through the gap by an external pressure gradient, for example

$$p_0 = p\left(-\frac{\pi}{2}\right) \neq p\left(\frac{\pi}{2}\right) = p_2,$$

then the function $y(\theta)$ defined in (6.1.5) will be discontinuous at $\theta = 0$. The boundary conditions (6.1.7) still apply, but the differential equation (6.1.6) now holds only in the two intervals $-\pi/2 < \theta < 0$ and $0 < \theta < \pi/2$. The discontinuity condition at $\theta = 0$ becomes

$$y(0_-) = Ry(0^+), \qquad R \equiv \frac{p_2}{p_0}. \tag{6.1.19}$$

Solve the forced-flow case numerically by integrating (6.1.9) and (6.1.13) from $\theta = \pi/2$ to $\theta = 0_+$. Then apply the jump conditions

$$\begin{aligned} &\text{(a)} \quad u(0_-) = Ru(0_+), \\ &\text{(b)} \quad v(0_-) = Rv(0_+) \end{aligned} \tag{6.1.20}$$

and continue the integration from $\theta = 0_-$ to $\theta = -\pi/2$. Finally use (6.1.14) to find $\lambda = \lambda(\varepsilon, R)$ by Newton's method. [How is Equation (6.1.20b) derived?]

We note that for $R = 1$ the solution reduces to that in the case previously treated. Thus values of $\lambda(\varepsilon, 1)$ are given by the final entry in each row of Table 6.1.1. Using continuity in R, these furnish initial guesses at $\lambda(\varepsilon, 1 \pm \Delta R)$. This procedure can be continued.

A more efficient procedure than the obvious continuity method just suggested can be given (see Section 5.5.1). It is based on the fact that quite accurate approximations to $\lambda(\varepsilon, R \pm \Delta R)$ can be obtained from the linear approximation (that is, the first two terms in the Taylor expansion)

$$\lambda(\varepsilon, R \pm \Delta R) \doteq \lambda(\varepsilon, R) \pm \Delta R \frac{\partial \lambda}{\partial R}(\varepsilon, R). \tag{6.1.21}$$

The parameter $\lambda(\varepsilon, R)$ is of course determined such that the function $u = u(\varepsilon, R; \theta)$ satisfies the differential equation (6.1.9a) on $(0, \pi/2)$ and $(-\pi/2, 0)$ and the boundary conditions (6.1.9b), (6.1.20a), and (6.1.10). We write this latter condition now as

$$u\left(\lambda(\varepsilon, R), R, -\frac{\pi}{2}\right) - 1 = 0.$$

Differentiating with respect to R, we find that

$$\frac{\partial \lambda}{\partial R} = -\left(\frac{\partial u}{\partial R}\Big/\frac{\partial u}{\partial \lambda}\right)_{\theta = -\pi/2}.$$

Thus introducing the variational problem for $w \equiv \partial u/\partial R$,

$$\text{(a)} \quad \varepsilon \frac{dw}{d\theta} = \left(\frac{\lambda w}{u} - 1\right)\frac{\sin^4 w}{u}, \qquad \theta \in (0, \pi/2), \qquad \theta \in (-\pi/2, 0),$$

$$\text{(b)} \quad w\left(\frac{\pi}{2}\right) = 0, \tag{6.1.22}$$

$$\text{(c)} \quad w(0_-) = Rw(0_+) + u(0_+),$$

we recall that $v = \partial u/\partial \lambda$ in (6.1.13). Hence, we have

$$\frac{\partial \lambda}{\partial R} = -\frac{w(-\pi/2)}{v(-\pi/2)}. \tag{6.1.23}$$

After λ, $u(\theta)$ and $v(\theta)$ have been determined for a given (ε, R) (that is, after the iterations have converged) *one integration* of the linear problem (6.1.22) will yield $\partial\lambda/\partial R$ by means of (6.1.23). Compare the step sizes ΔR that can be taken with this procedure with those using ordinary continuity methods.

Note that we could just as well consider the accurate continuity method with respect to the parameter ε and use

$$\lambda(\varepsilon \pm \Delta\varepsilon, R) \doteq \lambda(\varepsilon, R) \pm \Delta\varepsilon \frac{\partial\lambda(\varepsilon, R)}{\partial\varepsilon}. \tag{6.1.24}$$

Work out the detailed formulation for determining the derivative $\partial\lambda/\partial\varepsilon$. Try computing with these initial guesses.

Compare all the above with the general treatment of Section 5.5.1, using the notation $\boldsymbol{\sigma} = \binom{\varepsilon}{R}$ for the parameters.

6.2 *Finite Differences; Biophysics*

A class of problems concerning the diffusion of, say, oxygen into a cell in which an enzyme-catalyzed reaction occurs has been formulated and studied by means of singular perturbation theory by J. D. Murray. We present here a difference method for one particular such problem. The programming of the numerical work was done by J. Steadman, and all the calculations reported here were performed in about 20 seconds on a Control Data 6600 at the A.E.C. Computing and Applied Mathematics Center of the Courant Institute of Mathematical Sciences at New York University.

The diffusion-kinetics equation governing the steady concentration C of some substrate in an enzyme-catalyzed reaction has the general form

$$\nabla(D \nabla C) = g(C).$$

Here D is the molecular-diffusion coefficient of the substrate in the medium containing, say, uniformly-distributed bacteria and $g(C)$ is proportional to the reaction rate of the enzyme-substrate reaction. We consider the case with constant diffusion coefficient, D_0, in a spherical cell with the Michaelis–Menten-theory reaction rate. In dimensionless variables the diffusion-kinetics equation can now be written as

$$Ly \equiv (x^2y')' = x^2f(y), \qquad 0 < x < 1, \tag{6.2.1}$$

where

$$x \equiv \frac{r}{R}, \quad y(x) \equiv \frac{C(r)}{C_0}, \quad \varepsilon \equiv \frac{D_0C_0}{(nqR^2)}, \quad f(y) \equiv \varepsilon^{-1}\frac{y(x)}{y(x) + k}, \quad k \equiv \frac{k_m}{C_0}.$$

Here R is the radius of the cell, C_0 is the constant concentration of the substrate in $r > R$, k_m is the Michaelis constant, q is the maximum rate at which each bacterium can operate, and n is the number of bacteria. Typical ranges for both dimensionless parameters, ε and k, are, in some cases, 10^{-3} to 10^{-1}.

Assuming the cell membrane to have infinite permeability, it follows that

$$y(1) = 1. \tag{6.2.2a}$$

Further, from the assumed continuity and symmetry of $y(x)$ with respect to $x = 0$, we must have

$$y'(0) = 0. \tag{6.2.2b}$$

Equations (6.2.1) and (6.2.2) form a nonlinear second-order two-point boundary-value problem for which we seek *positive* solutions for various values of ε and k.

For small values of ε a singular perturbation approximation to the solution has been given by J. D. Murray. For larger parameter values, specifically when $6\varepsilon k > 1$, an iteration scheme with $y^{(0)}(x) \equiv 0$ and

$$Ly^{(\nu+1)} = x^2 f(y^{(\nu)}), \qquad \frac{d}{dx} y^{(\nu+1)}(0) = 0, \qquad y^{(\nu+1)}(1) = 1, \qquad \nu = 0, 1, \ldots, \tag{6.2.3a}$$

can be shown to converge to a positive solution $y(x)$ in the alternating manner

$$0 \equiv y^{(0)}(x) \le y^{(2)}(x) \le \cdots \le y(x) \le \cdots \le y^{(3)}(x) \le y^{(1)}(x) \equiv 1. \tag{6.2.3b}$$

Less-precise upper and lower bounds on the exact solution can be derived for the case of arbitrary (small) parameter values. The uniqueness of *positive* solutions is also easily demonstrated. We do not present any of these details here but shall show how accurate *finite-difference* approximations can be obtained and shall illustrate some of the typical difficulties that can arise.

With the net spacing $h = 1/(J + 1)$ and net points

$$x_j = jh,$$

we define the difference operator, L_h, which is to approximate L in (6.2.1), by

$$h^2 L_h v_j \equiv x_{j-1/2}^2 v_{j-1} - [x_{j-1/2}^2 + x_{j+1/2}^2] v_j + x_{j+1/2}^2 v_{j+1}. \tag{6.2.4}$$

Now let u_j be the numerical approximation to $y(x_j)$ and require that, in place of (6.2.1),

$$L_h u_j = x_j^2 f(u_j), \qquad j = 0, 1, 2, \ldots, J. \tag{6.2.5}$$

The boundary conditions (6.2.2a–b) are replaced by, respectively,

$$\begin{aligned} &\text{(a)}\quad u_{J+1} = 1, \\ &\text{(b)}\quad u_1 - u_{-1} = 0. \end{aligned} \tag{6.2.6}$$

Here and in (6.2.5), for $j = 0$, we have introduced the notation u_{-1} to represent an approximation to the extension of the solution $y(x)$ to $y(-h)$. Using (6.2.6) in (6.2.5), we can eliminate u_{-1} and u_{J+1} to obtain the $J + 1$ difference equations

$$\begin{aligned}
\phi_0(\mathbf{u}) &\equiv u_0 - u_1 = 0; \\
\phi_j(\mathbf{u}) &= [-x_{j-1/2}^2 u_{j-1} + (x_{j-1/2}^2 + x_{j+1/2}^2)u_j - x_{j+1/2}^2 u_{j+1}] \\
&\qquad + h^2 x_j^2 f(u_j) = 0, \qquad 1 \le j < J; \qquad (6.2.7) \\
\phi_J(\mathbf{u}) &\equiv [-x_{J-1/2}^2 u_{J-1} + (x_{J-1/2}^2 + x_{J+1/2}^2)u_J] \\
&\qquad - x_{J+1/2}^2 + h^2 x_J^2 f(u_J) = 0.
\end{aligned}$$

To solve these nonlinear difference equations Newton's method is employed. Thus, as in (3.2.9), the Jacobian matrix of $\boldsymbol{\phi}(\mathbf{u})$ is

$$A(\mathbf{u}) \equiv \frac{\partial \boldsymbol{\phi}(\mathbf{u})}{\partial \mathbf{u}} = \begin{pmatrix} B_0 & C_0 & & \cdots & 0 \\ A_1 & B_1 & C_1 & \cdots & \vdots \\ \vdots & & & & \\ & \cdots & A_{J-1} & B_{J-1} & C_{J-1} \\ 0 & & \cdots & A_J & B_J \end{pmatrix}, \qquad (6.2.8a)$$

where explicitly

$$\begin{aligned}
B_0(\mathbf{u}) &\equiv \frac{\partial \phi_0}{\partial u_0} = 1, \qquad C_0 \equiv \frac{\partial \phi_0}{\partial u_1} = -1, \\
A_j(\mathbf{u}) &\equiv \frac{\partial \phi_j}{\partial u_{j-1}} = -x_{j-1/2}^2, \qquad 1 \le j \le J, \\
B_j(\mathbf{u}) &\equiv \frac{\partial \phi_j}{\partial u_j} = (x_{j-1/2}^2 + x_{j+1/2}^2) + h^2 x_j^2 \frac{\varepsilon^{-1} k}{(u_j + k)^2}, \qquad 1 \le j \le J, \qquad (6.2.8b) \\
C_j(\mathbf{u}) &\equiv \frac{\partial \phi_j}{\partial u_{j+1}} = -x_{j+1/2}^2, \qquad 1 \le j \le J - 1.
\end{aligned}$$

Then the iterates $\mathbf{u}^{(\nu)} \equiv (u_0^{(\nu)}, u_1^{(\nu)}, \ldots, u_J^{(\nu)})^T$ are computed from

$$\mathbf{u}^{(\nu+1)} = \mathbf{u}^{(\nu)} + \Delta\mathbf{u}^{(\nu)}, \qquad \nu = 0, 1, 2, \ldots, \qquad (6.2.9a)$$

where each $\Delta\mathbf{u}^{(\nu)}$ is the solution of the corresponding linear system

$$A(\mathbf{u}^{(\nu)})\, \Delta\mathbf{u}^{(\nu)} = -\boldsymbol{\phi}(\mathbf{u}^{(\nu)}), \qquad \nu = 0, 1, 2, \ldots. \qquad (6.2.9b)$$

These linear systems are each of order $J + 1$ but have the simple tridiagonal form discussed in Section 3.1. Thus they are easily solved using the simple recursions derived there [see Equations (3.1.6–7)]. It is of interest to note that while only $B_j(\mathbf{u})$ actually varies with $\mathbf{u}$, the factorization of $A(\mathbf{u}^{(\nu)})$ must be done anew for each iteration. To start the iterations we use a simple approximation suggested by the analytical bounds alluded to above, namely

$$u_j^{(0)} = (1 - \varepsilon k)x_j^2 + \varepsilon k; \qquad j = 0, 1, \ldots, J + 1. \tag{6.2.10}$$

It is usually necessary, in order for Newton's method to converge to a desired solution, that the initial iterate, $u_j^{(0)}$, be "sufficiently close" to this solution. We were rather lucky that on the first attempt, using $\varepsilon = k = 0.1$ and (6.2.10) with $h = 10^{-2}$, the procedure (6.2.9) converged in only three iterations. The details are illustrated in Figure 6.2.1, where the initial guess ($\nu = 0$) and the first three iterates $u_j^{(\nu)}$ are plotted.

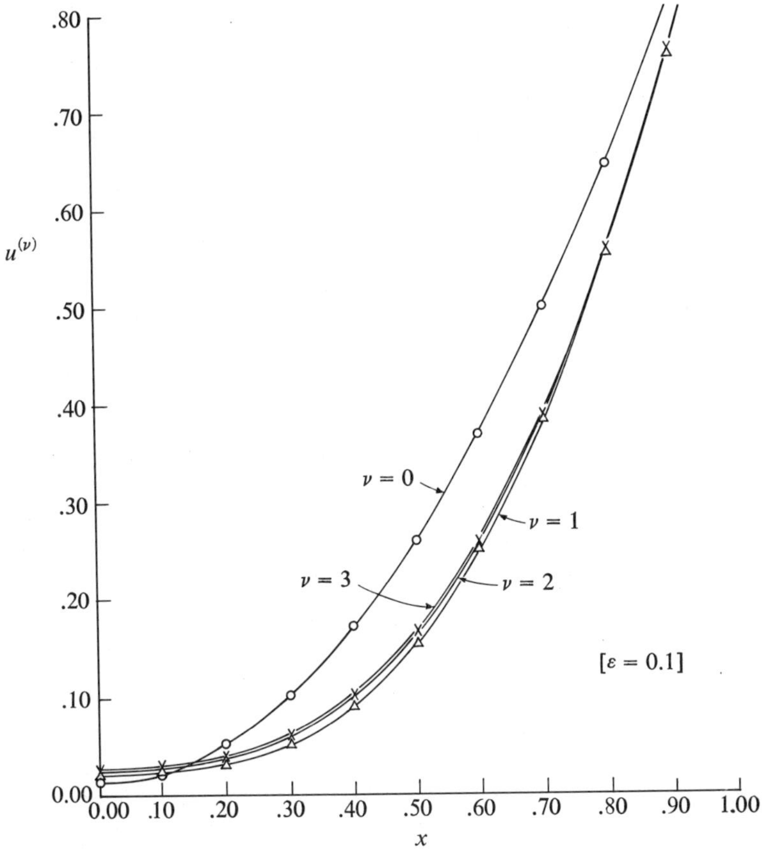

FIGURE 6.2.1

Using the same net, $k = 0.1$, and reducing ε to $\varepsilon = 0.05$, the initial iterate (6.2.10) again resulted in the convergence of Newton's method. Now, however, it required 15 iterations and the "solution" was not positive on $0 < x \leq 1$. These iterates are shown in Figure 6.2.2. It is clear that we have found a solution which is not physical. (Note that the slope of the solution is discontinuous at $u = -0.1$, where $f(u)$ has an infinite jump discontinuity. The corresponding solution of (6.2.1) does not have a second derivative at these points.) The desired positive solution for $\varepsilon = .05$, obtained as described below, is shown dashed in Figure 6.2.2.

The difficulty in the above case is of course due to the fact that the initial guess was too crude. But assuming (as we could in fact prove) that the

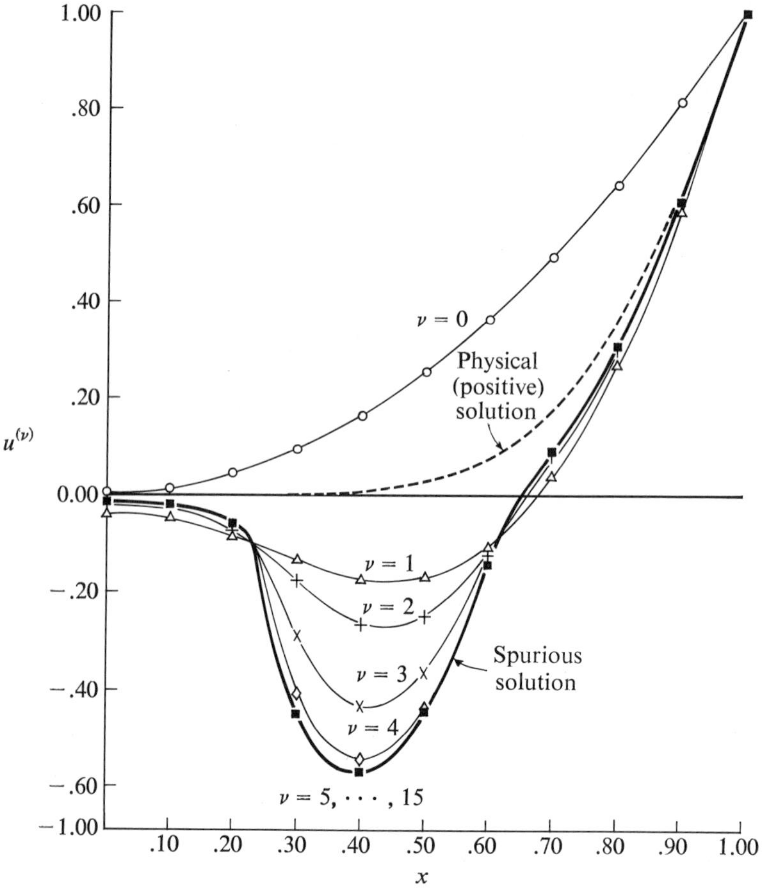

FIGURE 6.2.2

desired positive solution depends continuously on the parameter ε, we can employ a form of continuity method to get close initial estimates. Thus we use the converged solution for ε as the initial guess at the solution for $\varepsilon - \Delta\varepsilon$. In this way there was no difficulty starting with (6.2.10) for $\varepsilon = k = 0.1$ and continuing, with k fixed, as described for 19 values of ε in the decreasing sequence $\varepsilon = 10^{-1}(.01)10^{-2}(10^{-3})10^{-3}$. Some of these solutions are shown in Figure 6.2.3.

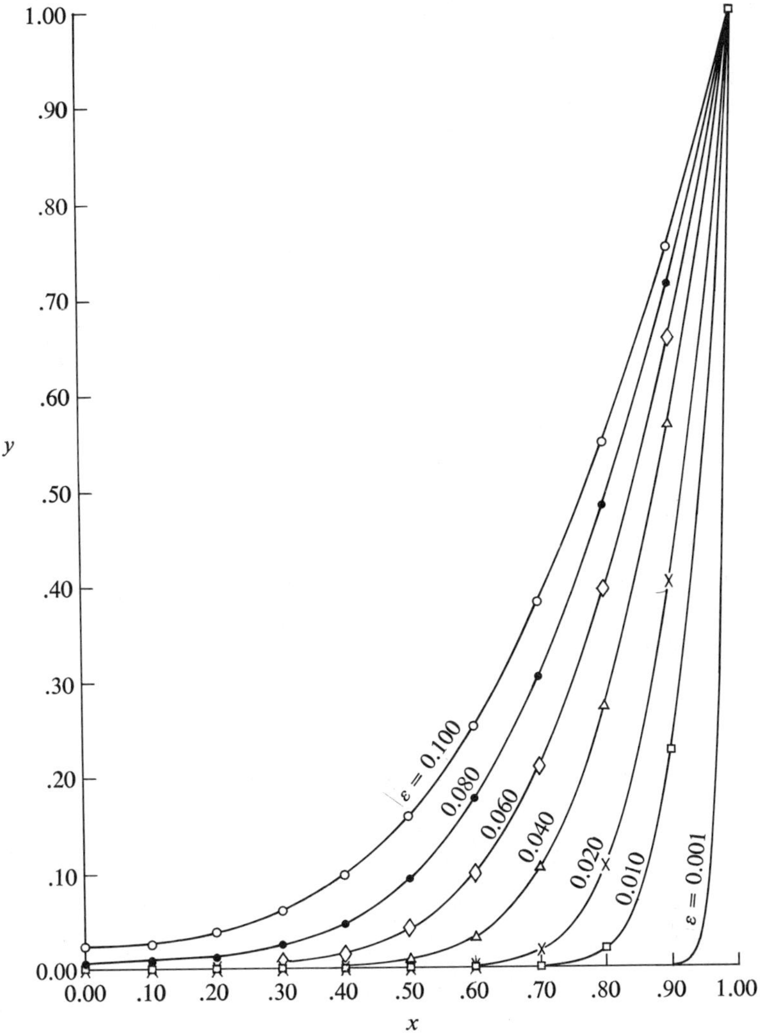

FIGURE 6.2.3

This sequence of calculations was done with the net spacing $h = 10^{-3}$, so that there were 1001 net points on $0 \leq x \leq 1$ [that is, $J + 1 = 1000$ nonlinear algebraic equations in the system (6.2.7)]. The convergence test for Newton's method required that

$$\delta_\nu \equiv h^{-2} \sum_{j=0}^{J} |\phi_j(\mathbf{u}^{(\nu)})| = \sum_{j=0}^{J} |L_h u_j^{(\nu)} - x_j^2 f(u_j^{(\nu)})| \leq 10^{-6}. \tag{6.2.11}$$

A summary of the convergence properties is shown in Table 6.2.1. Since the factor h^{-2} was (inadvertently) included in this test we are assured that the final solution satisfies each difference equation to within 10^{-12} and on the average to within 10^{-15}, when $h = 10^{-3}$. The quantity

$$\Delta_\nu = \sum_{j=0}^{J} |\Delta u_j^{(\nu)}| \tag{6.2.12}$$

was also computed, and the final value is listed in the last column in Table 6.2.1. (This is a measure of the deviation in the numerical results from the exact solution of the difference equations.) The quadratic nature of the convergence of Newton's method in this case is clearly shown in the table. It is apparent that the last iterate did not significantly alter the results in at least five cases (that is, for $\varepsilon = .010, .009, .008, .007$, and $.002$). In fact our test was so severe when $h = 10^{-3}$ that there were not enough significant digits remaining to obtain the full benefit of the last iteration in almost all cases. This is also borne out by the entries in the last column, Δ_{final}.

6.2.1 $h \to 0$ Extrapolation

The machine code for the numerical scheme (6.2.7–9) was used to compute $h \to 0$ extrapolated solutions. This was done by using the Newton scheme to solve the difference equations for the two net spacings $h = \frac{1}{20}$ and $h = \frac{1}{40}$. Then at each net point of the cruder net we formed, in an obvious notation (see Section 3.1.1),

$$\tilde{u}(x_j) = \frac{4}{3} u_{2j}\left(\frac{h}{2}\right) - \frac{1}{3} u_j(h), \qquad x_j = jh, \qquad j = 0, 1, \ldots, 20. \tag{6.2.13}$$

Some results of these calculations are shown in Table 6.2.2. In the columns headed "$h = \frac{1}{20}$" and "$h = \frac{1}{1000}$" we list corresponding difference solutions, at the points $x_j = 0$ and $x_j = \frac{1}{2}$, for the indicated values of ε. The column headed "$\tilde{u}(x)$" contains the values computed by means of (6.2.13) for the appropriate values of x and ε.

The convergence properties of Newton's method for all three net spacings ($h = \frac{1}{20}, \frac{1}{40}, \frac{1}{1000}$) was the same. Thus the time to compute $\tilde{u}(x_j)$ as in (6.2.13) with $h = \frac{1}{20}$ would be about the same as that required to compute

TABLE 6.2.1

Convergence of Newton's method in solving the 1000 *difference equations* (6.2.7) *with* $h = 10^{-3}$ *to approximate solutions of the boundary-value problem* (6.2.1–2) *with* $k = 0.1$. *The quantity* δ_ν *measures the error in satisfying the difference equations by the* ν*th iterate* [*see* (6.2.11)] *and* Δ_{final} *is the last value of* Δ_ν *computed* [*see* (6.2.12)].

ε	δ_0	δ_1	δ_2	δ_3	δ_4	δ_5	Δ_{final}
.100	8.19×10^2	3.30×10	8.18×10^{-1}	1.08×10^{-3}	9.27×10^{-7}		3.75×10^{-9}
.090	2.91×10^2	9.89	9.39×10^{-2}	1.64×10^{-5}	9.80×10^{-7}		5.72×10^{-9}
.080	3.54×10^2	1.39×10	1.44×10^{-1}	2.64×10^{-5}	9.14×10^{-7}		8.95×10^{-10}
.070	4.41×10^2	1.99×10	2.29×10^{-1}	4.67×10^{-5}	8.64×10^{-7}		1.02×10^{-9}
.060	5.66×10^2	3.00×10	4.05×10^{-1}	1.04×10^{-4}	7.42×10^{-7}		4.37×10^{-10}
.050	7.54×10^2	4.86×10	8.20×10^{-1}	3.13×10^{-4}	6.91×10^{-7}		8.81×10^{-10}
.040	1.06×10^3	8.71×10	2.01	1.38×10^{-3}	6.05×10^{-7}		7.54×10^{-11}
.030	1.64×10^3	1.84×10^2	6.55	1.05×10^{-2}	5.71×10^{-7}		7.93×10^{-10}
.020	2.93×10^3	5.29×10^2	3.56×10	2.09×10^{-1}	7.90×10^{-6}	4.83×10^{-7}	1.48×10^{-10}
.010	7.46×10^3	3.47×10^3	6.68×10^2	3.87×10	1.47×10^{-1}	2.41×10^{-6}	1.81×10^{-10}
						$(2.68 \times 10^{-7} = \delta_6)$	
.009	1.23×10^3	3.96×10	1.17×10^{-1}	1.49×10^{-6}	2.73×10^{-7}		1.08×10^{-10}
.008	1.47×10^3	5.33×10	1.95×10^{-1}	3.25×10^{-6}	2.62×10^{-7}		6.08×10^{-11}
.007	1.79×10^3	7.45×10	3.50×10^{-1}	9.02×10^{-6}	2.50×10^{-7}		3.25×10^{-11}
.006	2.24×10^3	1.10×10^2	6.86×10^{-1}	3.07×10^{-5}	2.58×10^{-7}		1.11×10^{-11}
.005	2.92×10^3	1.74×10^2	1.52	1.34×10^{-4}	1.94×10^{-7}		6.10×10^{-11}
.004	4.03×10^3	3.03×10^2	4.03	8.12×10^{-4}	2.25×10^{-7}		5.03×10^{-11}
.003	6.05×10^3	6.24×10^2	1.41×10	8.31×10^{-3}	1.74×10^{-7}		8.44×10^{-12}
.002	1.06×10^4	1.73×10^3	8.14×10	2.17×10^{-1}	1.70×10^{-6}	1.30×10^{-7}	4.89×10^{-12}
.001	2.61×10^4	1.05×10^4	1.59×10^3	5.24×10	6.15×10^{-2}	1.67×10^{-7}	1.91×10^{-11}

TABLE 6.2.2

Comparison of $h \to 0$ extrapolated solution (using $h = \frac{1}{20}$ and $h = \frac{1}{40}$) and difference solution for the net spacings $h = \frac{1}{20}$ and $h = \frac{1}{1000}$. The comparisons are of the computed approximations to $y(x)$ at $x = 0$ and $x = \frac{1}{2}$.

	$x_j = 0$			$x_j = \frac{1}{2}$		
ε	$h = \frac{1}{20}$	$\tilde{u}(0)$	$h = \frac{1}{1000}$	$h = \frac{1}{20}$	$\tilde{u}(\frac{1}{2})$	$h = \frac{1}{1000}$
.100	2.47141×10^{-2}	2.28706×10^{-2}	2.27927×10^{-2}	1.63074×10^{-1}	1.62561×10^{-1}	1.62562×10^{-1}
.090	1.37060×10^{-2}	1.24441×10^{-2}	1.23952×10^{-2}	1.28596×10^{-1}	1.28120×10^{-1}	1.28120×10^{-1}
.080	6.94581×10^{-3}	6.15949×10^{-3}	6.13261×10^{-3}	9.60633×10^{-2}	9.56128×10^{-2}	9.56133×10^{-2}
.070	3.14332×10^{-3}	2.70368×10^{-3}	2.69121×10^{-3}	6.66093×10^{-2}	6.61678×10^{-2}	6.61683×10^{-2}
.060	1.21684×10^{-3}	1.00338×10^{-3}	9.98898×10^{-4}	4.15850×10^{-2}	4.11370×10^{-2}	4.11375×10^{-2}
.050	3.73485×10^{-4}	2.89092×10^{-4}	2.88133×10^{-4}	2.23036×10^{-2}	2.18556×10^{-2}	2.18560×10^{-2}
.040	7.90739×10^{-5}	5.51098×10^{-5}	5.51652×10^{-5}	9.50409×10^{-3}	9.11223×10^{-3}	9.11220×10^{-3}
.030	8.68991×10^{-6}	4.94543×10^{-6}	5.03606×10^{-6}	2.76392×10^{-3}	2.51597×10^{-3}	2.51591×10^{-3}
.020	2.44811×10^{-7}	8.21931×10^{-8}	9.29283×10^{-8}	3.76343×10^{-4}	2.97021×10^{-4}	2.97518×10^{-4}
.010	1.35987×10^{-10}	-1.32918×10^{-11}	1.12845×10^{-11}	5.97694×10^{-6}	2.44531×10^{-6}	2.62288×10^{-6}
.009	3.70678×10^{-11}	-5.53370×10^{-12}	2.12627×10^{-12}	2.92525×10^{-6}	9.82325×10^{-7}	1.10258×10^{-6}
.008	8.24765×10^{-12}	-1.63822×10^{-12}	2.95151×10^{-13}	1.28161×10^{-6}	3.23194×10^{-7}	3.96498×10^{-7}
.007	1.40995×10^{-12}	-3.43248×10^{-13}	2.71460×10^{-14}	4.86301×10^{-7}	7.67188×10^{-8}	1.15575×10^{-7}
.006	1.69239×10^{-13}	-4.75580×10^{-14}	1.40153×10^{-15}	1.52150×10^{-7}	8.11170×10^{-9}	2.51026×10^{-8}
.005	1.23842×10^{-14}	-3.82330×10^{-15}	3.07870×10^{-17}	3.63431×10^{-8}	-2.10557×10^{-9}	3.52988×10^{-9}
.004	4.35024×10^{-16}	-1.41489×10^{-16}	1.73200×10^{-19}	5.82349×10^{-9}	-9.78488×10^{-10}	2.48493×10^{-10}
.003	4.65226×10^{-18}	-1.54438×10^{-18}	8.62714×10^{-23}	5.88562×10^{-10}	-1.27689×10^{-10}	5.11736×10^{-12}
.002	5.34157×10^{-21}	-1.78023×10^{-21}	2.41798×10^{-28}	1.21321×10^{-11}	-3.85515×10^{-12}	7.66428×10^{-15}
.001	2.52302×10^{-26}	-8.41008×10^{-27}	6.53728×10^{-41}	1.56115×10^{-14}	-5.19796×10^{-15}	3.30634×10^{-21}

u_j for a spacing of $h = \frac{1}{60}$ and so is *less than* $\frac{1}{16}$ *the time* required for the calculations with $h = 10^{-3}$. It was found, as expected, that the agreement of all the different calculations was best near $x = 1$ and worst near $x = 0$ (in fact the differences were monotonic in x). A glance at Table 6.2.2 reveals that the $h \to 0$ extrapolated solution, $\tilde{u}(x_j)$, has at least three significant digits in agreement with the difference solution $u_j(\frac{1}{1000})$ in $\frac{1}{2} \leq x_j \leq 1$ for all $\varepsilon \geq 0.20$. At least one significant digit agrees at $x_j = 0$ for the same ε range. While the relative error in $\tilde{u}(x_j)$ is rather large for x_j near zero and ε small (say $\varepsilon \leq .03$), it should be noted that the absolute error is extremely small even down to $\varepsilon = .001$. Of course the negative values of $\tilde{u}(0)$ for $\varepsilon \leq 0.01$ are nonsense and are caused by the coarseness of the net spacing used in the extrapolation method. In fact the values of u_0 computed with $h = \frac{1}{1000}$ may not have any significant digits for $\varepsilon \leq .009$, say, but it is of interest to note that the difference scheme gives only positive values of u_j for all j and ε.

It is suggested, by the analysis in Section 3.1 and 3.2, that

$$|y(x_j) - \tilde{u}(x_j)| = \mathcal{O}(h^4) \qquad \text{and} \qquad |y(x_j) - u_j| = \mathcal{O}(h^2).$$

For $h = 10^{-3}$ we see that the error $\mathcal{O}(10^{-6})$ in the difference solution, u_j, is easily the order of magnitude of the solution for x_j near zero (if the higher derivatives of the solution are not very small). Thus, as seems to be the case, very accurate results are obtained over part of the interval [0, 1] and only order of magnitude results over the remainder (for small ε).

In conclusion it seems quite clear that we could easily obtain the same accuracy as in the $h = 10^{-3}$ case with much less computing effort (say using $h \to 0$ extrapolation with $h = 10^{-2}$ and $h = 10^{-2}/2$ in about one third the time).

6.2.2 *Computing Exercise; Nonlinear Diffusivity*

In many reactions the diffusion coefficient is a function of the substrate concentration. For the spherically-symmetric case treated above we need only replace (6.2.1) by

$$Ly \equiv (x^2 D(y)y')' = x^2 f(y), \qquad 0 < x < 1, \tag{6.2.14}$$

where $D(y)$ is the nonlinear diffusion coefficient. The difference operator (6.2.4) can now be replaced by

$$\begin{aligned} h^2 L_h v_j \equiv x_{j-1/2}^2 D_{j-1/2}(\mathbf{v}) v_{j-1} - [x_{j-1/2}^2 D_{j-1/2}(\mathbf{v}) + x_{j+1/2}^2 D_{j+1/2}(\mathbf{v})] v_j \\ + x_{j+1/2}^2 D_{j+1/2}(\mathbf{v}) v_{j+1}, \end{aligned} \tag{6.2.15a}$$

where

$$D_{j\pm 1/2}(\mathbf{v}) \equiv D\left(\frac{v_{j\pm 1} + v_j}{2}\right). \tag{6.2.15b}$$

The difference equations (6.2.5) and (6.2.6), using the above definition of L_h, can again be solved by Newton's method. In fact the linear system (6.2.9b) still has a tridiagonal coefficient matrix, but now the elements of this matrix involve derivatives of $D(\mathbf{u})$. For instance, we find from the derivative of the jth equation with respect to u_{j-1} that

$$A_j(\mathbf{u}) = -x_{j-1/2}^2 D_{j-1/2}(\mathbf{u}) + x_{j-1/2}^2 D'_{j-1/2}(\mathbf{u}) \cdot \frac{(u_j - u_{j-1})}{2}, \qquad 1 \le j \le J, \tag{6.2.16a}$$

where

$$D'_{j\pm 1/2}(\mathbf{u}) \equiv \left.\frac{dD(\xi)}{d\xi}\right|_{\xi=(u_{j\pm 1}+u_j)/2}. \tag{6.2.16b}$$

We leave the remaining details and the somewhat different treatment that results at x_0 to the reader.

A diffusion coefficient of particular interest is

$$D(y) \equiv 1 + \frac{\lambda}{(y + k_2)^2}. \tag{6.2.17}$$

Computations are of interest for various parameter values; try $\lambda = k_2 = 10^{-2}$ with the same ε and k values used above. Note that for $\lambda = 0$ the problem reduces to the one previously solved. Thus if there is difficulty in getting close initial guesses for the smaller ε values, the continuity procedure in λ can be employed, working in "small" steps from $\lambda = 0$ to $\lambda = 10^{-2}$. An alternative, of course, is to use continuity in ε as in the worked-out example, but with possibly smaller steps in ε. (It turns out that only one extra value, $\varepsilon = 0.015$, is required.)

Finally, it would seem to be quite simple to solve either the linear or non-linear diffusivity case by the shooting method. Try shooting in both directions for small ε and observe the striking difference.

APPENDIX

FUNCTION SPACE APPROXIMATION METHODS

We present here a very brief sketch of some approximation methods which are frequently as practical and effective as any of those methods previously studied. However, the theoretical justification of these methods is considerably more difficult and less well developed. These methods are expansion procedures, of which the power-series method in Section 2.4.1 is a (not so practical or typical) special case. More specifically, the solution is approximated by a linear combination of linearly-independent functions in an appropriate function space. The coefficients in the expansion are to be determined so that this combination minimizes some measure of the error in satisfying the boundary-value problem. There is tremendous variety in the choice of approximating functions and in the choice of "measure of error" in satisfying the problem. We proceed to indicate three procedures of this type.

The problems we consider are the most general nonlinear eigenvalue problems discussed in Section 5.5.

$$\mathbf{y}' = \mathbf{f}(x, \mathbf{y}; \boldsymbol{\lambda}, \boldsymbol{\sigma}), \qquad a < x < b; \tag{A.1}$$

$$\mathbf{g}(\mathbf{y}(a), \mathbf{y}(b); \boldsymbol{\lambda}, \boldsymbol{\sigma}) = 0. \tag{A.2}$$

Here $\mathbf{y}(x)$ and $\mathbf{f}$ are n-vectors, $\boldsymbol{\lambda}$ is an m-vector, $\boldsymbol{\sigma}$ is a q-vector, and $\mathbf{g}$ is an $(n + m)$-vector. For some fixed value of the parameter $\boldsymbol{\sigma}$ we seek a value of the "eigenvalue" $\boldsymbol{\lambda}$, and a function $\mathbf{y}(t) \equiv \mathbf{y}(t; \boldsymbol{\lambda}, \boldsymbol{\sigma})$ such that (A.1) and (A.2) are satisfied. These solutions are required for all $\boldsymbol{\sigma}$ in some parameter set. Of course, as special cases, the eigenvalue $\boldsymbol{\lambda}$ may be absent, in which case $m = 0$ and the parameter $\boldsymbol{\sigma}$ may not appear.

A.1 Galerkin's Method

The approximating functions are chosen from some Hilbert space $\mathscr{H}$ of functions that are, say, piecewise continuously differentiable on $[a, b]$.

Specifically let us assume that $\{\phi_j(x)\}$ is an orthonormal basis for $\mathscr{H}$, with

$$(\phi_j, \phi_k) \equiv \int_a^b \phi_j(x)\phi_k(x)w(x)\,dx = \delta_{ij}, \qquad i, j = 1, 2, \ldots. \tag{A.3}$$

Here $w(x)$ is the (positive) weight function defining the inner product on $\mathscr{H}$. Then we may define an Nth-order approximation to a solution of (A.1) and (A.2) as a combination of the form

$$\mathbf{u}_N(x) \equiv \sum_{j=1}^{N} \boldsymbol{\xi}_j \phi_j(x). \tag{A.4}$$

The N coefficient vectors $\boldsymbol{\xi}_j$ of dimension n are to be determined by requiring that

$$\boldsymbol{\gamma}_k(\boldsymbol{\xi}_1, \ldots, \boldsymbol{\xi}_N; \boldsymbol{\lambda}, \boldsymbol{\sigma}) \equiv \int_a^b [\mathbf{u}_N'(x) - \mathbf{f}(x, \mathbf{u}_N(x); \boldsymbol{\lambda}, \boldsymbol{\sigma})]\phi_k(x)w(x)\,dx = 0,$$
$$k = 1, 2, \ldots, N-1, \tag{A.5a}$$

and

$$\boldsymbol{\gamma}_N(\boldsymbol{\xi}_1, \ldots, \boldsymbol{\xi}_N; \boldsymbol{\lambda}, \boldsymbol{\sigma}) \equiv \mathbf{g}(\mathbf{u}_N(a), \mathbf{u}_N(b); \boldsymbol{\lambda}, \boldsymbol{\sigma}) = 0. \tag{A.5b}$$

Thus in Galerkin's method to "approximately satisfy the boundary value problem" means to satisfy the boundary conditions exactly and for the error in satisfying the equation to be orthogonal to the first $N - 1$ basis functions. That is, the measure of error to be made zero is the projection of the error in satisfying the equation on the subspace spanned by $\phi_1, \ldots, \phi_{N-1}$. Of course any function orthogonal to all of the basis functions vanishes and so in the limit as $N \to \infty$ the functions $\mathbf{u}_N(x)$ may very well converge to a solution. This convergence question is quite open in the indicated general case, but see Urabe [2].

The system (A.5) contains $(nN + m)$ equations in the as many unknowns $\boldsymbol{\xi}_1, \ldots, \boldsymbol{\xi}_N, \boldsymbol{\lambda}$. In some problems it is possible to pick the basis functions $\phi_j(x)$ so that n of the boundary conditions in (A.2) are identically satisfied. Then an additional orthogonality condition, from (A.5a) with $k = N$, can be imposed. If the differential equation and the boundary conditions are all linear, then the system (A.5) is linear in the components of the $\boldsymbol{\xi}_j$. If the original linear problem is also homogeneous, then $\boldsymbol{\xi}_j \equiv 0$, $j = 1, 2, \ldots, N$ is clearly a solution, and we have in fact an algebraic eigenvalue problem in which $\boldsymbol{\lambda}$ is to be determined so that nontrivial solutions exist. In the nonlinear case, Newton's method is again an excellent scheme for seeking accurate approximations to the roots of (A.5). Continuity techniques employing the parameters $\boldsymbol{\sigma}$, or even introducing such parameters, are also clearly suggested as in Section 5.5.1. Another alternative iteration scheme is suggested in the next subsection.

A.2 Collocation Methods

Now let the functions $\{\psi_j(x)\}$ form a complete set on some Banach space, $\mathscr{B}$, which includes $C^1(a, b)$. Further, let interpolation by linear combinations of these functions converge, together with the first derivatives, for functions in $C^1(a, b)$. This means that for each finite set

$$\{\psi_1(x), \psi_2(x), \ldots, \psi_N(x)\}$$

there are corresponding points $x_{j,N} \in [a, b]$ such that for any $\phi(x) \in C^1(a, b)$ there exist (unique) constants $a_{k,N}$ such that

$$\phi(x_{j,N}) = \sum_{k=1}^{N} a_{k,N}\psi_k(x_{j,N}), \qquad j = 1, 2, \ldots, N.$$

Further, for these combinations, it is required that:

$$\lim_{N\to\infty} \sum_{k=1}^{N} a_{k,N}\psi_k(x) = \phi(x),$$

$$\lim_{N\to\infty} \sum_{k=1}^{N} a_{k,N}\psi_k'(x) = \phi'(x).$$

In particular cases these conditions may be varied or relaxed somewhat.

Approximate solutions of (A.1–2) are now sought, for a given value of N, in the form

$$\mathbf{v}_N(x) \equiv \sum_{j=1}^{N} \boldsymbol{\eta}_j\psi_j(x). \tag{A.6}$$

The conditions for determining the coefficients $\boldsymbol{\eta}_j$ and the eigenvalues $\boldsymbol{\lambda}$ are that $\mathbf{v}_N(x)$ should satisfy the differential equation at $N - 1$ distinct points $x_{j,N-1} \in [a, b]$ and should satisfy the boundary conditions. Thus we obtain the $(nN + m)$ equations in as many unknowns

$$\boldsymbol{\gamma}_k(\boldsymbol{\eta}_1, \ldots, \boldsymbol{\eta}_N; \boldsymbol{\lambda}, \boldsymbol{\sigma}) \equiv \mathbf{v}_N'(x_{k,N-1}) - \mathbf{f}(x_{k,N-1}, \mathbf{v}_N)(x_{k,N-1}; \boldsymbol{\lambda}, \boldsymbol{\sigma}) = 0,$$
$$k = 1, 2, \ldots, N - 1; \tag{A.7a}$$

$$\boldsymbol{\gamma}_N(\boldsymbol{\eta}_1, \ldots, \boldsymbol{\eta}_N; \boldsymbol{\lambda}, \boldsymbol{\sigma}) \equiv \mathbf{g}(\mathbf{v}_N(a), \mathbf{v}_N(b); \boldsymbol{\lambda}, \boldsymbol{\sigma}) = 0. \tag{A.7b}$$

We have indicated in (A.7a) the use of the interpolation points corresponding to the first $N - 1$ basis functions. This may of course be altered, as an optimum choice of points for interpolation of any $\phi(x) \in C^1(a, b)$ need not be near optimum for interpolating $[\mathbf{v}_N'(x) - \mathbf{f}(x, \mathbf{v}_N(x); \boldsymbol{\lambda}, \boldsymbol{\sigma})]$ which may only be in $C(a, b)$. Again, if the functions $\psi_j(x)$ can be chosen so that n of the conditions in (A.7b) are identically satisfied, the condition in (A.7a) can be imposed at an additional point; that is, we could use the set $x_{k,N}$, $k = 1, 2, \ldots, N$. For linear problems this scheme, which we have called collocation, is but a generalization of Lanczos's (1957) selected-points method (in which the $\psi_j(x) \equiv x^{j-1}$ and the $x_{k,N}$ are the zeros or extrema of Chebyshev, Legendre, or other polynomials).

To solve (A.7), we can try the usual suggestions of Newton plus continuity. Another proposed iteration is based on a special case of collocation employed by Clenshaw (1966) [in which $n = 2$, $m = q = 1$, so that all of the features of the system (A.1–2) are included in this example]. The estimate $\boldsymbol{\lambda} = \boldsymbol{\lambda}^{(\nu)}$, say, of the eigenvalue is kept fixed, and Newton's method is employed on the $n(N - 1)$ equations in (A.7a) and some selected n of the $(n + m)$ equations in (A.7b) to determine the (converged) vectors $\boldsymbol{\eta}_1^{(\nu)}, \ldots, \boldsymbol{\eta}_N^{(\nu)}$. This stage corresponds to what is frequently called an "inner iteration" in related contexts. Upon the completion (that is, convergence) of the inner iterations, the function

$$\mathbf{v}_N^{(\nu)}(x) = \sum_{j=1}^{N} \boldsymbol{\eta}_j^{(\nu)} \psi_j(x)$$

is presumably an (accurate) approximation to the solution of *some* boundary-value problem for (A.1) with $\boldsymbol{\lambda} = \boldsymbol{\lambda}^{(\nu)}$. But it only satisfies n of the required $n + m$ boundary conditions (A.2).

The "outer iterations" are designed to change $\boldsymbol{\lambda}^{(\nu)}$ so that the remaining m conditions in (A.7b) are more nearly satisfied. For $m = 1$ some interpolation and false position procedures are straightforward. But quite generally we could again apply Newton's method to these m equations in the unknowns $\boldsymbol{\lambda}$. To do this rigorously we would have to determine $\partial \boldsymbol{\eta}_j^{(\nu)}/\partial \boldsymbol{\lambda}$ for $j = 1, 2, \ldots, N$, which is equivalent to the original application of Newton's method to all of (A.7). Of course other procedures, based on contracting maps, can be employed for the outer iterations.

A.3 Generalized Ritz Methods

Many boundary-value problems (for the determination of some equilibrium state of a physical system, for example) can be formulated in terms of variational problems. That is, some functional (representing for example the energy of the system) is to be minimized over an appropriate space of admissible functions, say $\mathscr{H}$, as in Section A.1. Or we may easily form some functional whose minimum value is attained for the solution of the boundary-value problem. As an *example*, consider the expression

$$I\{\mathbf{w}, \boldsymbol{\lambda}, \boldsymbol{\sigma}\} \equiv \int_a^b \|\mathbf{w}'(x) - \mathbf{f}(x, \mathbf{w}(x); \boldsymbol{\lambda}, \boldsymbol{\sigma})\|_I^2 \, dx + \|\mathbf{g}(\mathbf{w}(a), \mathbf{w}(b); \boldsymbol{\lambda}, \boldsymbol{\sigma})\|_{II}^2,$$

where $\|\cdot\|_I$ and $\|\cdot\|_{II}$ are some vector norms for n- and $(n + m)$-dimensional real vector spaces, respectively. Clearly $I\{\mathbf{w}, \boldsymbol{\lambda}, \boldsymbol{\sigma}\} \geq 0$ for all $\mathbf{w}(x) \in C^1(a, b)$ and $I\{\cdot\} = 0$ for a solution of (A.1–2).

For any functional $I\{\cdot\}$, using an approximation of the form

$$\mathbf{w}_N(x) = \sum_{j=1}^{N} \boldsymbol{\zeta}_j \phi_j(x), \tag{A.8}$$

a scalar function of the N coefficient vectors, $\boldsymbol{\zeta}_j$, and the eigenvalue parameters $\boldsymbol{\lambda}$, as well as $\boldsymbol{\sigma}$ is defined by

$$\Phi(\boldsymbol{\zeta}_1, \boldsymbol{\zeta}_2, \ldots, \boldsymbol{\zeta}_N, \boldsymbol{\lambda}, \boldsymbol{\sigma}) \equiv I\{\mathbf{w}_N(x), \boldsymbol{\lambda}, \boldsymbol{\sigma}\}. \tag{A.9}$$

The Ritz procedure is to minimize Φ with respect to the components ζ_{ij} of $\boldsymbol{\zeta}_j$ and the components λ_k of $\boldsymbol{\lambda}$. In general this leads to the system of $(nN + m)$ equations

$$\frac{\partial \Phi}{\partial \zeta_{ij}}(\boldsymbol{\zeta}_1, \ldots, \boldsymbol{\zeta}_N, \boldsymbol{\lambda}, \boldsymbol{\sigma}) = 0, \qquad i = 1, 2, \ldots, n, \qquad j = 1, 2, \ldots, N; \tag{A.10a}$$

$$\frac{\partial \Phi}{\partial \lambda_k}(\boldsymbol{\zeta}_1, \ldots, \boldsymbol{\zeta}_N, \boldsymbol{\lambda}, \boldsymbol{\sigma}) = 0, \qquad k = 1, 2, \ldots, m. \tag{A.10b}$$

For many important special cases that frequently occur in physical applications, the systems (A.10) simplify in various ways. The most familiar example occurs when the integrand in the functional $I\{\cdot\}$ is a homogeneous quadratic form in $\mathbf{w}$ and $\mathbf{w}'$ and the space $\mathscr{H}$ is such that the boundary conditions are automatically satisfied. In fact, under fairly common circumstances, the Ritz and Galerkin procedures are identical [see Kantorovich and Krylov (1958)].

Convergence of the Ritz method has been studied extensively for variational problems leading to linear boundary-value problems. An interesting exception, given by Ciarlet, Schultz, and Varga (1967), leads to higher-order-accurate approximations to the solution of various nonlinear problems of second and higher order.

For linear boundary-value problems that come from variational problems, the Ritz procedure can lead to finite-difference methods. The basic idea here is to employ "basis" functions $\phi_j(x)$ which are piecewise-linear and continuous, and vanish at all but one point (at which it takes on the value unity) of some net. See, for example, Courant (1943) or Friedrichs and Keller (1966).

BIBLIOGRAPHY

ANTOSIEWICZ, H., and W. GAUTSCHI
"Numerical methods in ordinary differential equations." In: *Survey of Numerical Analysis*, J. Todd, Ed. New York: McGraw-Hill, 1962, pp. 314–346.

ATKINSON, F. V.
Discrete and Continuous Boundary Problems. New York: Academic Press, 1964.

BABUŠKA, I., M. PRÁGER and E. VITÁSEK
Numerical Processes in Differential Equations. New York: Interscience, 1966.

BELLMAN, R., and R. KALABA
Quasilinearization and Nonlinear Boundary Value Problems. New York: Amer. Elsevier Publ. Co., 1965.

BERS, L., F. JOHN and M. SCHECHTER
Partial Differential Equations. New York: Interscience, 1964.

BIRKHOFF, G., and G-C. ROTA
Ordinary Differential Equations. Boston: Ginn & Co., 1962.

BIRKHOFF, G., C. DE BOOR, B. SWARTZ and B. WENDROFF
"Rayleigh-Ritz approximation by piecewise cubic polynomials." *SIAM Jour. Numer. Anal. 3* (1966), pp. 188–203.

CIARLET, P., M. SCHULTZ and R. VARGA
"Numerical methods of high-order accuracy for nonlinear boundary value problems." *Numer. Mathe., 9* (1967), pp. 394–430.

CLENSHAW, C. W.
"The solution of van der Pol's equation in Chebyshev series." In: *Numerical Solutions of Nonlinear Differential Equations*, D. Greenspan, Ed. New York: John Wiley & Sons, 1966, pp. 55–63.

CODDINGTON, E. A., and N. LEVINSON
Theory of Ordinary Differential Equations. New York: McGraw-Hill, 1955.

COLE, J. D., H. B. KELLER and P. G. SAFFMAN
"The flow of a viscous compressible fluid through a very narrow gap." *SIAM Jour. Appl. Math. 15* (1967), pp. 605–617.

COLLATZ, L.
The Numerical Treatment of Differential Equations, 3rd ed. Berlin: Springer, 1960.

Conti, R.
"Problemes lineaires pour les equations differentielles ordinaires." *Math. Nachrichten 23* (1961), pp. 161–178.

Conti, S. D.
"The numerical solution of linear boundary value problems." *SIAM Review 8* (1966), pp. 309–321.

Courant, R., and D. Hilbert
1. *Methoden der Mathematischen Physik*, Vol. II. New York: Interscience, 1937.
2. *Methods of Mathematical Physics*, Vol. I. New York: Interscience, 1953.

Courant, R.
"Variational methods for the solution of problems of equilibrium and vibrations." *Bull. Amer. Math. Soc. 49* (1943), pp. 1–23.

Dahlquist, G.
1. "Convergence and stability in the numerical integration of ordinary differential equations." *Math. Scand. 4* (1956), pp. 33–53.
2. "Stability and error bounds in the numerical integration of ordinary differential equations." *Trans. Roy. Inst. Tech.*, Stockholm, No. 130 (1959).

Davis, P. J. and P. Rabinowitz
Numerical Integration. Waltham, Mass.: Blaisdell Publishing Co., 1967.

Farrington, C. C., R. T. Gregory and A. H. Taub
"On the numerical solution of Sturm-Liouville differential equations." *M. O. C. 11* (1957), pp. 131–150.

Fox, L.
1. *The Numerical Solution of Two-Point Boundary Problems in Ordinary Differential Equations.* Fairlawn, N. J.: Oxford University Press, 1957.
2. "Some numerical experiments with eigenvalue problems in ordinary differential equations." In: *Boundary Problems in Differential Equations*, R. E. Langer, Ed. Madison: Univ. of Wisconsin Press, 1960, pp. 243–255.

Friedrichs, K. O., and H. B. Keller
"A finite difference scheme for generalized Neumann problems." In: *Numerical Solution of Partial Differential Equations*, J. Bramble, Ed. New York: Academic Press, 1966, pp. 1–19.

Gary, J.
"Computing eigenvalues of ordinary differential equations by finite differences." *M. O. C. 19* (1965), pp. 365–379.

Godunov, S.
"On the numerical solution of boundary value problems for systems of linear ordinary differential equations." *Uspehi Mat. Nauk. 16* (1961), pp. 171–174.

GOODMAN, T. R., and G. N. Lance
"The numerical integration of two-point boundary value problems." *M. O. C. 10* (1956), pp. 82–86.

HARTMAN, P.
Ordinary Differential Equations. New York: John Wiley & Sons, 1964.

HENRICI, P.
1. *Discrete Variable Methods in Ordinary Differential Equations.* New York: John Wiley & Sons, 1962.
2. *Error Propagation for Difference Methods.* New York: John Wiley & Sons, 1963.

INCE, E. L.
Ordinary Differential Equations. New York: Dover, 1944.

ISAACSON, E., and H. B. KELLER
Analysis of Numerical Methods. New York: John Wiley & Sons, 1966.

KALNINS, A.
"Analysis of shells of revolution subjected to symmetrical and nonsymmetrical loads." *Trans. A.S.M.E., Ser. E., Jour. Appl. Mech. 31* (1964), pp. 467–476.

KALABA, R.
"On nonlinear differential equations, the maximum operation and monotone convergence." *Jour. Math. Mech. 8* (1959), pp. 519–574.

KANTOROVICH, L. V., and G. P. AKILOV
Functional Analysis in Normed Spaces. New York: Macmillan, 1964.

KANTOROVICH, L. V., and V. I. KRYLOV
Approximate Methods of Higher Analysis. New York: Interscience, 1958.

KELLER, H. B., and E. L. REISS
"Computers in solid mechanics—a case history." *Amer. Math. Monthly 72*, Part II (1965), pp. 92–98.

KELLER, H. B., and A. W. WOLFE
"On the nonunique equilibrium states and buckling mechanism of spherical shells." *SIAM Jour. Appl. Math. 13* (1965), pp. 674–705.

KELLER, H.
1. "On the accuracy of finite difference approximations to the eigenvalues of differential and integral operators." *Numer. Math. 7* (1965), pp. 412–419.
2. "Existence theory for two point boundary value problems." *Bulletin A. M. S. 72* (1966), pp. 728–731.

LANCASTER, P.
"Error analysis for the Newton-Raphson Method." *Numer. Math. 9* (1966), pp. 55–68.

LANCZOS, C.
Applied Analysis. London: Pitman, 1957.

LASOTA, A., and Z. OPIAL
"On the existence of solutions of linear problems for ordinary differential equations." *Bull. Acad. Polon. Sci. 14* (1966), pp. 371–376.

LEES, M.
1. "A boundary value problem for nonlinear ordinary differential equations." *J. Math. and Mech. 10* (1961), pp. 423–430.
2. "Discrete methods for nonlinear two-point boundary value problems." In: *Numerical Solution of Partial Differential Equations*, J. H. Bramble, Ed. New York: Academic Press, 1966, pp. 59–72.

MORRISON, D. D., J. D. RILEY and J. F. ZANCANARO
"Multiple shooting method for two-point boundary value problems." *Comm. ACM 5* (1962), pp. 613–614.

MURRAY, J. D.
"A simple method for obtaining approximate solutions for a large class of diffusion-kinetic enzyme problems." *Math. Biosciences 2* (1968)

ORTEGA, J., and W. RHEINBOLDT
"On discretization and differentiation of operators with application to Newton's method." *SIAM Jour. Numer. Anal. 3* (1966), pp. 143–156.

ORTEGA, J., and M. ROCKOFF
"Nonlinear difference equations and Gauss-Seidel type iterative methods." *SIAM Jour. Numer. Anal. 3* (1966), pp. 497–513.

OSTROWSKI, A.
Solution of Equations and Systems of Equations. New York: Academic Press, 1960.

PEREYRA, V.
"On improving an approximate solution of a functional equation by deferred corrections." *Numer. Math. 8* (1966), pp. 376–391.

REISS, E., H. GREENBERG and H. KELLER
"Nonlinear deflections of shallow spherical shells." *J. Aero./Space Sci. 24* (1957), pp. 533–543.

RILEY, J., M. BENNETT and E. MCCORMICK
"Numerical integration of variational equations." *M.O.C. 21* (1967), pp. 12–17.

SYLVESTER, R., and F. MEYER
"Two-point boundary problems by quasilinearization." *J. Appl. Math. 13* (1965), pp. 586–602.

TRAUB, J. F.
Iterative Methods for the Solution of Equations. Engelwood Cliffs, N. J.: Prentice-Hall, 1964.

TROESCH, B. A.
"Intrinsic difficulties in the numerical solution of a boundary value problem." Space Tech. Labs., Tech. Note NN-142 (1960).

URABE, M.
1. "Convergence of numerical integration in solution of equations." *J. Sci. Hiroshima Univ. 19* (1956), pp. 479–489.
2. "Galerkin's procedure for nonlinear periodic systems and its extension to multipoint boundary value problems for general nonlinear systems." In: *Numerical Solutions of Nonlinear Differential Equations*, D. Greenspan, Ed. New York: John Wiley & Sons, 1966, pp. 297–327.

VARGA, R. S.
1. *Matrix Iterative Analysis.* Engelwood Cliffs, N. J.; Prentice-Hall, 1962.
2. "Hermite interpolation-type ritz methods for two point boundary value problems." In: *Numerical Solution of Partial Differential Equations*, J. H. Bramble, Ed. New York: Academic Press, 1965, pp. 365–373.

WEINBERGER, H. F.
Variational Methods for Eigenvalue Problems, Lecture Notes, University of Minnesota, Inst. of Tech., Dept. of Math., 1962.

WEINITSCHKE, H. J.
"On the stability problem for shallow spherical shells." *Jour. Math. Phys. 38* (1960), pp. 209–231.

WENDROFF, B.
Theoretical Numerical Analysis. New York: Academic Press, 1966.

WIELANDT, H.
"Error bounds for eigenvalues of symmetric integral equations." In *Proceedings of Symposia in Applied Mathematics*, Vol. VI, *Numerical Analysis.* Providence, R. I: American Math. Socy., 1956, pp. 261–282.

WILKINSON, J. H.
The Algebraic Eigenvalue Problem. Fairlawn, N. J.: Oxford University Press. 1965.

INDEX

A B C D E F G H I J 5 4 3 2 1 7 0 6 9 8

DA DUE